INTEGRATE
the benjamin cummings custom laboratory program for anatomy & physiology

Anatomy and Physiology I Lab
HLTH129
Lock Haven University
Health Sciences

Jeff
Hunsicker

Pearson Learning Solutions

New York   Boston   San Francisco
London   Toronto   Sydney   Tokyo   Singapore   Madrid
Mexico City   Munich   Paris   Cape Town   Hong Kong   Montreal

Senior Vice President, Editorial and Marketing: Patrick F. Boles
Senior Sponsoring Editor: Natalie Danner
Development Editor: Annette Fantasia
Editorial Assistant: Jill Johnson
Executive Marketing Manager: Nathan L. Wilbur
Operations Manager: Eric M. Kenney
Production Manager: Jennifer Berry
Art Director: Renée Sartell
Cover Designer: Kristen Kiley

Cover Art: Courtesy of DK Images and Prentice-Hall, Inc.

Pyrex, pHydrion, Chem3D Plus, Apple, Macintosh, Chemdraw, Hypercard, graphTool, Corning, Teflon, Mel-Temp, Rotaflow, Tygon, Spec20, and LambdaII UV/Vis are registered trademarks.

Chem3D Plus is a registered trademark of the Cambridge Soft Corp.

This special edition published in cooperation with Pearson Learning Solutions.

Printed in the United States of America.

Please visit our web site at *www.pearsoncustom.com*.

Attention bookstores: For permission to return unused stock, contact us at *pe-uscustomreturns@pearson.com*.

Pearson Learning Solutions, 501 Boylston Street, Suite 900, Boston, MA 02116
A Pearson Education Company
www.pearsoned.com

1 2 3 4 5 6 7 8 9 10 XXXX 14 13 12 11 10 09

ISBN 10: 0-558-28003-X
ISBN 13: 978-0-558-28003-1

Contents

The Language of Anatomy
Elaine N. Marieb 1

The Language of Anatomy: Additional Activities
Health Science Faculty: Ingram, Page, Preische and Streator 13

The Integumentary System
Elaine N. Marieb 15

Integumentary System: Additional Activities
Health Science Faculty: Ingram, Page, Preische and Streator 25

Overview of the Skeleton: Classification and Structure of Bones and Cartilages
Elaine N. Marieb 29

The Axial Skeleton
Elaine N. Marieb 41

Axial Skeleton: Additional Activities
Health Science Faculty: Ingram, Page, Preische and Streator 65

The Appendicular Skeleton
Elaine N. Marieb 67

Appendicular Skeleton: Additional Activities
Health Science Faculty: Ingram, Page, Preische and Streator 85

Articulations and Body Movements
Elaine N. Marieb 87

Articulations: Shoulder
Elaine N. Marieb 101

Articulations: Elbow
Elaine N. Marieb 103

Articulations: Ankle
Elaine N. Marieb 105

Articulations and Body Movement: Additional Activities
Health Science Faculty: Ingram, Page, Preische and Streator 107

Microscopic Anatomy, Organization, and Classification of Skeletal Muscle
Elaine N. Marieb 109

Muscle Physiology: Additional Activities 117
Health Science Faculty: Ingram, Page, Preische and Streator . . . .

Gross Anatomy of the Muscular System 119
Elaine N. Marieb . . . .

Gross Anatomy of Muscular System: Additional Activities 153
Health Science Faculty: Ingram, Page, Preishe and Streator . . . .

Histology of Nervous Tissue 155
Elaine N. Marieb . . . .

Neurophysiology: Additional Activities 167
Health Science Faculty: Ingram, Page, Preische and Streator . . . .

Gross Anatomy of the Brain and Cranial Nerves 169
Elaine N. Marieb . . . .

Spinal Cord, Spinal Nerves, and the Autonomic Nervous System 195
Elaine N. Marieb . . . .

Human Reflex Physiology 213
Elaine N. Marieb . . . .

The Special Senses 225
Elaine N. Marieb . . . .

Special Senses: Olfaction and Taste 253
Elaine N. Marieb . . . .

Special Senses: Vision 261
Elaine N. Marieb . . . .

The Language of Anatomy

M ost of us are naturally curious about our bodies. This fact is amply demonstrated by infants, who are fascinated with their own waving hands or their mother's nose. The study of the gross anatomy of the human body elaborates on this fascination. Unlike the infant, however, the student of anatomy must learn to observe and identify the dissectible body structures formally. The purpose of any gross-anatomy experience is to examine the three-dimensional relationships of body structures—a goal that can never completely be achieved by using illustrations and models, regardless of their excellence.

When beginning the study of any science, the student is often initially overcome by jargon unique to the subject. The study of anatomy is no exception. But without this specialized terminology, confusion is inevitable. For example, what do *over, on top of, superficial to, above,* and *behind* mean in reference to the human body? Anatomists have an accepted set of reference terms that are universally understood. These allow body structures to be located and identified with a minimum of words and a high degree of clarity. Thus it is not surprising that physicians' orders and progress notes, therapists' records, and nurses' notes use *anatomical terminology* to describe body parts, regions, positions, and activities. The ability to understand and use correct anatomical terminology is a skill that distinguishes health care personnel who are successful and comfortable in their chosen profession from those perpetually unsure of just what is expected of them.

This exercise presents some of the most important anatomical terminology used to describe the body and introduces you to basic concepts of **gross anatomy,** the study of body structures visible to the naked eye.

Anatomical Position

When anatomists or doctors refer to specific areas of the human body, they do so in accordance with a universally accepted standard position called the **anatomical position.** It is essential to understand this position because much of the body terminology employed in this book refers to this body positioning, regardless of the position the body happens to be in. In the anatomical position the human body is erect, with feet together, head and toes pointed forward, and arms hanging at the sides with palms facing forward (Figure 1).

• Assume the anatomical position, and notice that it is not particularly comfortable. The hands are held unnaturally forward rather than hanging partially cupped toward the thighs.

Objectives

1. To describe the anatomical position verbally or by demonstration.
2. To use proper anatomical terminology to describe body directions, planes, and surfaces.
3. To name the body cavities and indicate the important organs in each.

Materials

☐ Human torso model (dissectible)
☐ Human skeleton
☐ Demonstration: sectioned and labeled kidneys (three separate kidneys uncut or cut so that (a) entire, (b) transverse section, and (c) longitudinal sectional views are visible)

 See Appendix C, Exercise 1 for links to A.D.A.M. Interactive Anatomy.

Surface Anatomy

Body surfaces provide a wealth of visible landmarks for study of the body.

Anterior Body Landmarks

Note the following regions in Figure 2a:

Abdominal: Pertaining to the anterior body trunk region inferior to the ribs

Antebrachial: Pertaining to the forearm

Antecubital: Pertaining to the anterior surface of the elbow

Axillary: Pertaining to the armpit

Brachial: Pertaining to the arm

Buccal: Pertaining to the cheek

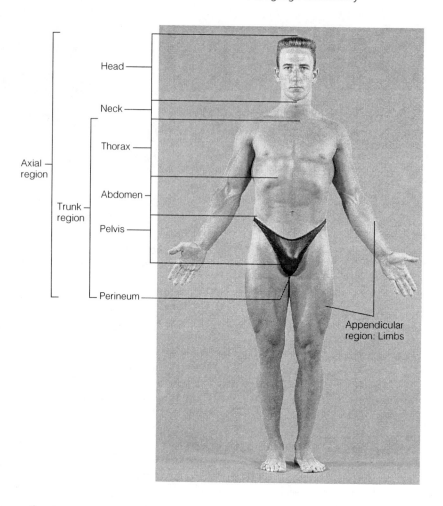

Figure 1   Anatomical position.

Carpal: Pertaining to the wrist

Cervical: Pertaining to the neck region

Coxal: Pertaining to the hip

Crural: Pertaining to the leg

Deltoid: Pertaining to the roundness of the shoulder caused by the underlying deltoid muscle

Digital: Pertaining to the fingers or toes

Femoral: Pertaining to the thigh

Frontal: Pertaining to the forehead

Hallux: Pertaining to the great toe

Inguinal: Pertaining to the groin

Mammary: Pertaining to the breast

Manus: Pertaining to the hand

Mental: Pertaining to the chin

Nasal: Pertaining to the nose

Oral: Pertaining to the mouth

Orbital: Pertaining to the bony eye socket (orbit)

Palmar: Pertaining to the palm of the hand

Patellar: Pertaining to the anterior knee (kneecap) region

Pedal: Pertaining to the foot

Pelvic: Pertaining to the pelvis region

Peroneal: Pertaining to the side of the leg

Pollex: Pertaining to the thumb

Pubic: Pertaining to the genital region

Sternal: Pertaining to the region of the breastbone

Tarsal: Pertaining to the ankle

Thoracic: Pertaining to the chest

Umbilical: Pertaining to the navel

Posterior Body Landmarks

Note the following body surface regions in Figure 2b:

Acromial: Pertaining to the point of the shoulder

Calcaneal: Pertaining to the heel of the foot

Cephalic: Pertaining to the head

Dorsum: Pertaining to the back

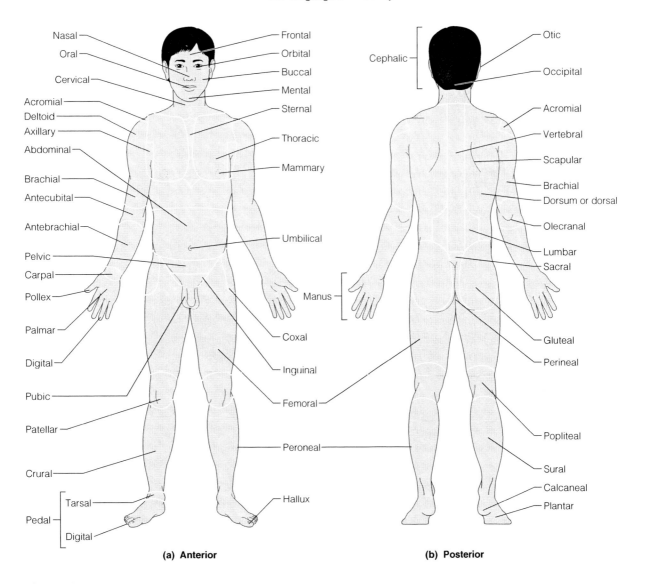

Nasal — Frontal
Oral — Orbital
Cervical — Buccal
— Mental
Acromial — Sternal
Deltoid
Axillary — Thoracic
Abdominal
— Mammary
Brachial
Antecubital
Antebrachial
— Umbilical
Pelvic
Carpal
Pollex
Manus
Palmar
Digital — Coxal
Pubic — Inguinal
Patellar — Femoral
Crural
Pedal — Tarsal
— Digital — Peroneal
— Hallux

Cephalic — Otic
— Occipital
— Acromial
— Vertebral
— Scapular
— Brachial
— Dorsum or dorsal
— Olecranal
— Lumbar
— Sacral
— Gluteal
— Perineal
— Popliteal
— Sural
— Calcaneal
— Plantar

(a) Anterior   (b) Posterior

Figure 2 Surface anatomy. (a) Anterior body landmarks. **(b)** Posterior body landmarks.

Gluteal: Pertaining to the buttocks or rump

Lumbar: Pertaining to the area of the back between the ribs and hips; the loin

Occipital: Pertaining to the posterior aspect of the head or base of the skull

Olecranal: Pertaining to the posterior aspect of the elbow

Otic: Pertaining to the ear

Perineal: Pertaining to the region between the anus and external genitalia

Plantar: Pertaining to the sole of the foot

Popliteal: Pertaining to the back of the knee

Sacral: Pertaining to the region between the hips (overlying the sacrum)

Scapular: Pertaining to the scapula or shoulder blade area

Sural: Pertaining to the calf or posterior surface of the leg

Vertebral: Pertaining to the area of the spinal column

Activity:
Locating Body Landmarks

Locate the anterior and posterior body landmarks on yourself, your lab partner, and a torso model before continuing. ■

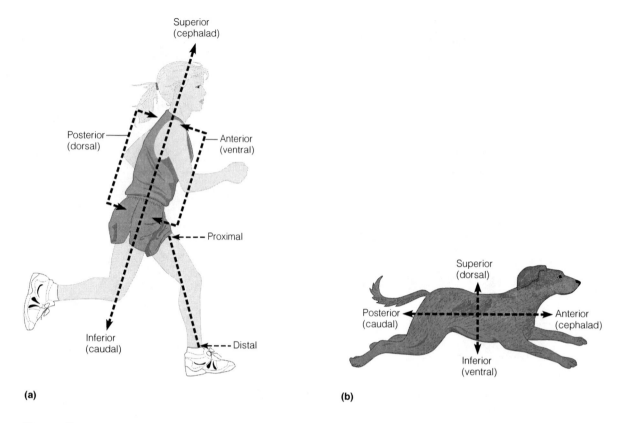

Figure 3 Anatomical terminology describing body orientation and direction.
(a) With reference to a human. **(b)** With reference to a four-legged animal.

Body Orientation and Direction

Study the terms below, referring to Figure 3. Notice that certain terms have a different meaning for a four-legged animal than they do for a human.

Superior/inferior (*above/below*): These terms refer to placement of a structure along the long axis of the body. Superior structures always appear above other structures, and inferior structures are always below other structures. For example, the nose is superior to the mouth, and the abdomen is inferior to the chest.

Anterior/posterior (*front/back*): In humans the most anterior structures are those that are most forward—the face, chest, and abdomen. Posterior structures are those toward the backside of the body. For instance, the spine is posterior to the heart.

Medial/lateral (*toward the midline/away from the midline or median plane*): The ear is lateral to the nose; the sternum (breastbone) is medial to the ribs.

The terms of position described above depend on an assumption of anatomical position. The next four term pairs are more absolute. Their applicability is not relative to a particular body position, and they consistently have the same meaning in all vertebrate animals.

Cephalad/caudal (*toward the head/toward the tail*): In humans these terms are used interchangeably with *superior* and *inferior.* But in four-legged animals they are synonymous with *anterior* and *posterior* respectively.

Dorsal/ventral (*backside/belly side*): These terms are used chiefly in discussing the comparative anatomy of animals, assuming the animal is standing. *Dorsum* is a Latin word meaning "back." Thus, *dorsal* refers to the animal's back or the *back*side of any other structures; e.g., the posterior surface of the human leg is its dorsal surface. The term *ventral* derives from the Latin term *venter,* meaning "belly," and always refers to the belly side of animals. In humans the terms *ventral* and *dorsal* are used interchangeably with the terms *anterior* and *posterior,* but in four-legged animals *ventral* and *dorsal* are synonymous with *inferior* and *superior* respectively.

Proximal/distal (*nearer the trunk or attached end/farther from the trunk or point of attachment*): These terms are used primarily to locate various areas of the body limbs. For example, the fingers are distal to the elbow; the knee is proximal to the toes.

Superficial/deep (*toward or at the body surface/away from the body surface or more internal*): These terms locate body organs according to their relative closeness to the body surface. For example, the lungs are deep to the rib cage, and the skin is superficial to the skeletal muscles.

4

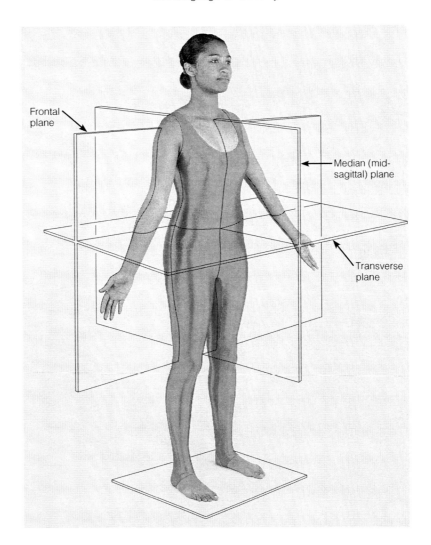

Figure 4 Planes of the body.

A c t i v i t y :
Practicing Using Correct Anatomical Terminology

Before continuing, use a human torso model, a skeleton, or your own body to specify the relationship between the following structures.

1. The wrist is _____ to the hand.

2. The trachea (windpipe) is _____ to the spine.

3. The brain is _____ to the spinal cord.

4. The kidneys are _____ to the liver.

5. The nose is _____ to the cheekbones. ∎

Body Planes and Sections

The body is three-dimensional, and in order to observe its internal structures, it is often helpful and necessary to make use of a **section,** or cut. When the section is made through the body wall or through an organ, it is made along an imaginary surface or line called a **plane.** Anatomists commonly refer to three planes (Figure 4) or sections that lie at right angles to one another.

Sagittal plane: A plane that runs longitudinally, dividing the body into right and left parts, is referred to as a sagittal plane. If it divides the body into equal parts, right down the median plane of the body, it is called a **median,** or **midsagittal, plane.** All other sagittal planes are referred to as **parasagittal planes.**

Frontal plane: Sometimes called a **coronal plane,** the frontal plane is a longitudinal plane that divides the body (or an organ) into anterior and posterior parts.

Transverse plane: A transverse plane runs horizontally, dividing the body into superior and inferior parts. When organs are sectioned along the transverse plane, the sections are commonly called **cross sections.**

As shown in Figure 5, a sagittal or frontal plane section of any nonspherical object, be it a banana or a body organ, provides quite a different view than a transverse section.

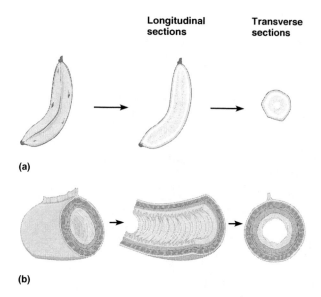

Longitudinal sections

Transverse sections

(a)

(b)

Figure 5 Comparison of longitudinal and transverse sections. Sections of **(a)** a banana and **(b)** the small intestine.

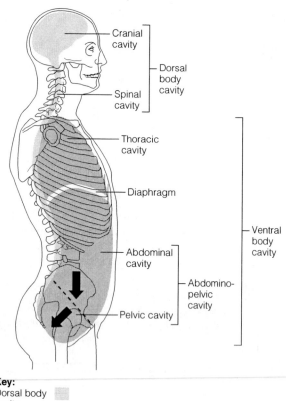

Cranial cavity

Dorsal body cavity

Spinal cavity

Thoracic cavity

Diaphragm

Abdominal cavity

Abdomino-pelvic cavity

Pelvic cavity

Ventral body cavity

Key:
Dorsal body cavity

Ventral body cavity

Figure 6 Body cavities. Arrows indicate the angle of the relationship between the abdominal and pelvic cavities.

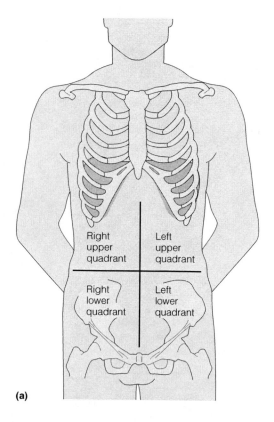

Right upper quadrant

Left upper quadrant

Right lower quadrant

Left lower quadrant

(a)

Figure 7 Abdominopelvic surface and cavity. **(a)** The four quadrants. *(continues on next page)*

Activity:
Observing Organ Specimens

Go to the demonstration area and observe the transversely and longitudinally cut organ specimens. Pay close attention to the different structural details in the samples. ■

Body Cavities

The axial portion of the body has two large cavities that provide different degrees of protection to the organs within them (Figure 6).

Dorsal Body Cavity

The dorsal body cavity can be subdivided into the **cranial cavity,** in which the brain is enclosed within the rigid skull, and the **spinal cavity,** within which the delicate spinal cord is protected by the bony vertebral column. Because the spinal cord is a continuation of the brain, these cavities are continuous with each other.

Ventral Body Cavity

Like the dorsal cavity, the ventral body cavity is subdivided. The superior **thoracic cavity** is separated from the rest of the

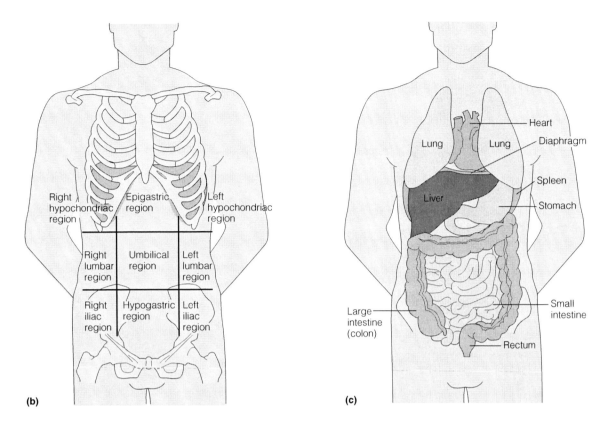

Figure 7 (continued) **(b)** Nine regions delineated by four planes. The superior horizontal plane is just inferior to the ribs; the inferior horizontal plane is at the superior aspect of the hip bones. The vertical planes are just medial to the nipples. **(c)** Anterior view of the abdominopelvic cavity showing superficial organs.

ventral cavity by the dome-shaped diaphragm. The heart and lungs, located in the thoracic cavity, are afforded some measure of protection by the bony rib cage. The cavity inferior to the diaphragm is often referred to as the **abdominopelvic cavity.** Although there is no further physical separation of the ventral cavity, some prefer to describe the abdominopelvic cavity in terms of a superior **abdominal cavity,** the area that houses the stomach, intestines, liver, and other organs, and an inferior **pelvic cavity,** the region that is partially enclosed by the bony pelvis and contains the reproductive organs, bladder, and rectum. Notice in Figure 6 that the abdominal and pelvic cavities are not continuous with each other in a straight plane but that the pelvic cavity is tipped away from the perpendicular.

Abdominopelvic Quadrants and Regions Because the abdominopelvic cavity is quite large and contains many organs, it is helpful to divide it up into smaller areas for discussion or study. The scheme used by most physicians and nurses divides the abdominal surface (and the abdominopelvic cavity deep to it) into four approximately equal regions called **quadrants.** These quadrants are named according to their relative position—that is, *right upper quadrant, right lower quadrant, left upper quadrant,* and *left lower quadrant* (see Figure 7a).

Another scheme, commonly used by anatomists, divides the abdominal surface and abdominopelvic cavity into nine separate regions by four planes, as shown in Figure 7b. Although the names of these nine regions are unfamiliar to you now, with a little patience and study they will become easier to remember. As you read through the descriptions of these nine regions below and locate them in the figure, notice the organs they contain by referring to Figure 7c.

Umbilical region: The centermost region, which includes the umbilicus

Epigastric region: Immediately superior to the umbilical region; overlies most of the stomach

Hypogastric (pubic) region: Immediately inferior to the umbilical region; encompasses the pubic area

Iliac regions: Lateral to the hypogastric region and overlying the superior parts of the hip bones

Lumbar regions: Between the ribs and the flaring portions of the hip bones; lateral to the umbilical region

Hypochondriac regions: Flanking the epigastric region laterally and overlying the lower ribs

A c t i v i t y :
Locating Abdominal Surface Regions

Locate the regions of the abdominal surface on a torso model and on yourself before continuing. ■

7

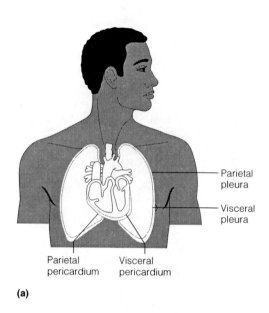

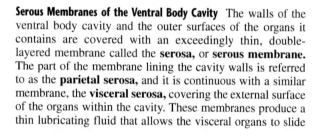

(a)

Figure 8 **Serous membranes.** **(a)** Serosae in the thoracic cavity are the pleurae surrounding the lungs and the pericardia surrounding the heart. **(b)** The peritoneums surround the digestive viscera in the abdominopelvic cavity.

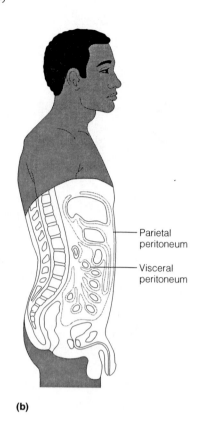

(b)

Serous Membranes of the Ventral Body Cavity The walls of the ventral body cavity and the outer surfaces of the organs it contains are covered with an exceedingly thin, double-layered membrane called the **serosa, or serous membrane.** The part of the membrane lining the cavity walls is referred to as the **parietal serosa,** and it is continuous with a similar membrane, the **visceral serosa,** covering the external surface of the organs within the cavity. These membranes produce a thin lubricating fluid that allows the visceral organs to slide over one another or to rub against the body wall without friction. Serous membranes also compartmentalize the various organs so that infection of one organ is prevented from spreading to others.

The specific names of the serous membranes depend on the structures they envelop. Thus the serosa lining the abdominal cavity and covering its organs is the **peritoneum,** that enclosing the lungs is the **pleura,** and that around the heart is the **pericardium** (Figure 8).

Illustrations: 2, 3, 5–8: Precision Graphics. **Photographs:** 1: © Benjamin/Cummings Publishing. Photo by BioMed Arts Associates, Inc. 4: © Jenny Thomas/Addison Wesley Longman.

The Language of Anatomy

Surface Anatomy

1. Match each of the following descriptions with a key equivalent, and record the key letter or term in front of the description.

   Key: a. buccal   c. deltoid   e. patellar
         b. calcaneal   d. digital   f. scapular

   a, buccal 1. cheek   _e, Patellar_ 4. anterior aspect of knee

   d. digital 2. pertaining to the fingers   _b. calcaneal_ 5. heel of foot

   f. scapular 3. shoulder blade region   _c. deltoid_ 6. curve of shoulder

2. Indicate the following body areas on the accompanying diagram by placing the correct key letter at the end of each line.

   Key:

   a. abdominal
   b. antecubital
   c. axillary
   d. brachial
   e. cervical
   f. femoral
   g. gluteal
   h. inguinal
   i. lumbar
   j. occipital
   k. oral
   l. popliteal
   m. pubic
   n. sural
   o. thoracic
   p. umbilical

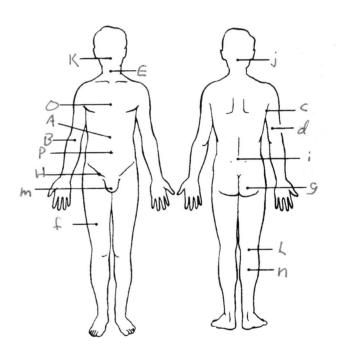

3. Classify each of the surface anatomy terms in the key of question 2 above, into one of the body regions indicated below. Insert the appropriate key letters on the answer blanks.

   _____ 1. Appendicular   _____ 2. Axial

Body Orientation, Direction, Planes, and Sections

1. Describe completely the standard human anatomical position. *body erect, arms at the side, palms facing foward*

2. Define *section*: *a certain region on the body*

3. Several incomplete statements are listed below. Correctly complete each statement by choosing the appropriate anatomical term from the key. Record the key letters and/or terms on the correspondingly numbered blanks below.

   Key: a. anterior   e. lateral   i. sagittal
         b. distal   f. medial   j. superior
         c. frontal   g. posterior   k. transverse
         d. inferior   h. proximal

   In the anatomical position, the face and palms are on the __1__ body surface; the buttocks and shoulder blades are on the __2__ body surface; and the top of the head is the most __3__ part of the body. The ears are __4__ and __4__ to the shoulders and __5__ to the nose. The heart is __6__ to the vertebral column (spine) and __7__ to the lungs. The elbow is __8__ to the fingers but __9__ to the shoulder. The abdominopelvic cavity is __10__ to the thoracic cavity and __11__ to the spinal cavity. In humans, the dorsal surface can also be called the __12__ surface; however, in quadruped animals, the dorsal surface is the __13__ surface.

   If an incision cuts the heart into right and left parts, the section is a __14__ section; but if the heart is cut so that superior and inferior portions result, the section is a __15__ section. You are told to cut a dissection animal along two planes so that the kidneys are observable in both sections. The two sections that meet this requirement are the __16__ and __17__ sections.

   1. *Anterior*
   2. *Posterior*
   3. *Superior*
   4. *Superior/medial*
   5. *lateral*
   6. *anterior*
   7. *medial*
   8. *Proximal*
   9. *distal*
   10. *inferior*
   11. *anterior*
   12. *Posterior*
   13. *5a Posterior*
   14. *Sagital*
   15. *transverse*
   16. *frontal*
   17. *transverse*

4. Correctly identify each of the body planes by inserting the appropriate term for each on the answer line below the drawing.

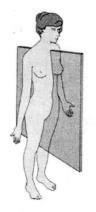

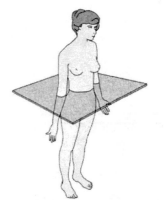

   1. *Sagital*
   2. *frontal*
   3. *transverse*

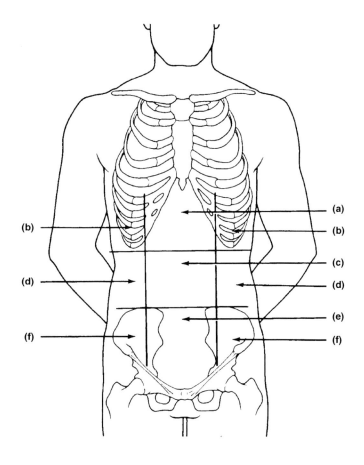

5. Correctly identify each of the nine areas of the abdominal surface by inserting the appropriate term for each of the letters indicated in the drawing just above.

a. _____   d. _____

b. _____   e. _____

c. _____   f. _____

Body Cavities

1. Which body cavity would have to be opened for the following types of surgery? (Insert letter of key choice in same-numbered blank. More than one choice may apply.)

Key: a. abdominopelvic   c. dorsal   e. thoracic
　　　 b. cranial　　　　　 d. spinal   f. ventral

1. surgery to remove a cancerous lung lobe
2. removal of the uterus or womb
3. removal of a brain tumor
4. appendectomy
5. stomach ulcer operation

　　The abdominopelvic and thoracic cavities are subdivisions of the ___6___ body cavity, while the cranial and spinal cavities are subdivisions of the ___7___ body cavity. The ___8___ body cavity is totally surrounded by bone, and thus affords its contained structures very good protection.

2. Name the serous membranes covering the lungs (#1), the heart (#2), and the organs of the abdominopelvic cavity (#3), and insert your responses in the blanks on the right.

1. _____

2. _____

3. _____

3. Name the muscle that subdivides the ventral body cavity. _____

4. Which of the following organ systems are represented in all three subdivisions of the ventral body cavity? (Circle all appropriate responses.)

respiratory	circulatory	reproductive	lymphatic
nervous	excretory (urinary)	muscular	integumentary

5. Which organ system would not be represented in any of the body cavities? _____

6. What are the bony landmarks of the abdominopelvic cavity? _____

_____

7. Which body cavity affords the least protection to its internal structures? _____

8. What is the function of the serous membranes of the body? _____

_____

_____

9. A nurse informs you that she is about to take blood from the antecubital region. What portion of your body should you present to her? _elbow_____

10. What do peritonitis, pleurisy, and pericarditis (pathologic conditions) have in common? _____

_____

11. Why are these conditions accompanied by a great deal of pain? _____

_____

12. The mouth, or buccal cavity, and its extension, which stretches through the body inside the digestive system, is not listed as an internal body cavity. Why is this so? _____

_____

_____

Anatomical Terminology

Let's play "Simon Says"
Your instructor is Simon. Follow the commands given in effort to identify body positions and directional terminology. Be sure to hear the phrase "Simon Says".

Who wants to be a Millionaire Doctor?

Take a piece of athletic tape and mark on your classmate where you (the surgeon) would make an incision using the following terminology (you need to show your instructor the patient when you think you have all the right incisions, if you have one wrong you are going to be slapped with a malpractice lawsuit!):

-A two inch incision starting on the right abdominal region, three inches superior, and two inches lateral to the umbilicus, extending superiorly.

-A two inch incision starting on the anterior part of the left shoulder, ½ inch medial to the AC joint, extending inferiorly.

-A two inch incision starting on the posterior right forearm, 1 inch proximal to the wrist, extending superiorly.

-A two inch incision starting on the midline of the left anterior knee at the inferior pole of the patella, extending distally.

Mark your incisions on the diagrams on page 9 as well.

Planes of sectioning
The three cardinal planes are shown in the diagrams on page10. Label the planes **and** the corresponding axis in each diagram about which motion occurs in that plane.

Which plane divides your body into right and left halves?

Which plane divides your body into superior and inferior parts?

Which plane divides your body into front (anterior) and back (posterior) sections?

Which plane is associated with medial and lateral?

What then is the "oblique plane"?

What plane are the 3 radiographs provided by your instructor?
1) transverse
2) saggital
3) frontal

Take your apple and draw a face on the surface. Using the plastic knife provided, make a sagittal plane cut, a coronal plane cut, and a transverse plane cut.

The Integumentary System

The **skin,** or **integument,** is often considered an organ system because of its extent and complexity. It is much more than an external body covering; architecturally the skin is a marvel. It is tough yet pliable, a characteristic that enables it to withstand constant insult from outside agents.

The skin has many functions, most (but not all) concerned with protection. It insulates and cushions the underlying body tissues and protects the entire body from mechanical damage (bumps and cuts), chemical damage (acids, alkalis, and the like), thermal damage (heat), and bacterial invasion (by virtue of its acid mantle and continuous surface). The hardened uppermost layer of the skin (the cornified layer) prevents water loss from the body surface. The skin's abundant capillary network (under the control of the nervous system) plays an important role in regulating heat loss from the body surface.

The skin has other functions as well. For example, it acts as a mini-excretory system; urea, salts, and water are lost through the skin pores in sweat. The skin also has important metabolic duties. For example, like liver cells, it carries out some chemical conversions that activate or inactivate certain drugs and hormones, and it is the site of vitamin D synthesis for the body. Finally, the cutaneous sense organs are located in the dermis.

Basic Structure of the Skin

The skin has two distinct regions—the superficial *epidermis* composed of epithelium and an underlying connective tissue *dermis.* These layers are firmly "cemented" together along an undulating border. But friction, such as the rubbing of a poorly fitting shoe, may cause them to separate, resulting in a blister. Immediately deep to the dermis is the **hypodermis** or **superficial fascia** (primarily adipose tissue), which is not considered part of the skin. The main skin areas and structures are described below.

Objectives

1. To recount several important functions of the skin, or integumentary system.

2. To recognize and name during observation of an appropriate model, diagram, projected slide, or microscopic specimen the following skin structures: epidermis (and indicate relative positioning of its strata), dermis (papillary and reticular layers), hair follicles and hair, sebaceous glands, and sweat glands.

3. To name the layers of the epidermis and describe the characteristics of each.

4. To compare the properties of the epidermis to those of the dermis.

5. To describe the distribution and function of the skin derivatives—sebaceous glands, sweat glands, and hairs.

6. To differentiate between eccrine and apocrine sweat glands.

7. To enumerate the factors determining skin color.

8. To describe the function of melanin.

9. To identify the major regions of nails.

Materials

- ❑ Skin model (three-dimensional, if available)
- ❑ Compound microscope
- ❑ Prepared slide of human skin with hair follicles
- ❑ Sheet of #20 bond paper ruled to mark off cm^2 areas
- ❑ Scissors
- ❑ Betadine swabs, or Lugol's iodine and cotton swabs
- ❑ Adhesive tape

From *Human Anatomy & Physiology Laboratory Manual,* Main Version, Fifth Edition, Elaine N. Marieb.
Copyright © 2000 by Addison Wesley Longman, Inc. This title published under the Benjamin/Cummings imprint. All rights reserved.

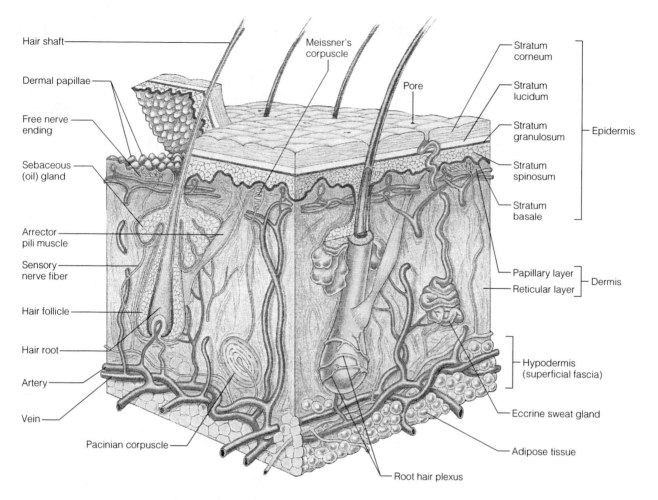

Hair shaft

Dermal papillae

Free nerve ending

Sebaceous (oil) gland

Arrector pili muscle

Sensory nerve fiber

Hair follicle

Hair root

Artery

Vein

Pacinian corpuscle

Meissner's corpuscle

Pore

Root hair plexus

Stratum corneum

Stratum lucidum

Stratum granulosum

Stratum spinosum

Stratum basale

Epidermis

Papillary layer

Reticular layer

Dermis

Hypodermis (superficial fascia)

Eccrine sweat gland

Adipose tissue

Figure 1 Skin structure. Three-dimensional view of the skin and the underlying hypodermis. The epidermis and dermis have been pulled apart at the left corner to reveal the dermal papillae.

Activity:
Locating Structures on a Skin Model

As you read, locate the following structures in Figure 1 and on a skin model. ■

Epidermis

Structurally, the avascular epidermis is a keratinized stratified squamous epithelium consisting of four distinct cell types and four or five distinct layers.

Cells of the Epidermis Most epidermal cells are **keratinocytes** (literally, keratin cells), epithelial cells that function mainly to produce keratin fibrils. **Keratin** is a fibrous protein that gives the epidermis its durability and protective capabilities.

Far less abundant are the following types of epidermal cells (Figure 2):

• **Melanocytes:** Spidery black cells that produce the brown-to-black pigment called **melanin.** The skin tans be-

cause melanin production increases when the skin is exposed to sunlight. The melanin provides a protective pigment umbrella over the nuclei of the cells in the deeper epidermal layers, thus shielding their genetic material (DNA) from the damaging effects of ultraviolet radiation. A concentration of melanin in one spot is called a *freckle*.

• **Langerhans' cells:** Also called *epidermal dendritic cells,* these phagocytic cells (macrophages) play a role in immunity.

• **Merkel cells:** In conjunction with sensory nerve endings, Merkel cells form sensitive touch receptors called *Merkel discs* located at the epidermal-dermal junction.

Layers of the Epidermis From deep to superficial, the layers of the epidermis are the stratum basale, stratum spinosum, stratum granulosum, stratum lucidum, and stratum corneum (Figure 1).

The **stratum basale** (basal layer) is a single row of cells immediately adjacent to the dermis. Its cells are constantly undergoing mitotic cell division to produce millions of new cells daily, hence its alternate name *stratum germinativum*.

About a quarter of the cells in this stratum are melanocytes, whose processes thread their way through this and the adjacent layers of keratinocytes (see Figure 2).

The **stratum spinosum** (spiny layer) is a stratum consisting of several cell layers immediately superficial to the basal layer. Its cells contain thick weblike bundles of intermediate filaments made of a prekeratin protein. The stratum spinosum cells appear spiky (hence their name) because, as the skin tissue is prepared for histological examination, they shrink but their desmosomes hold tight. Cells divide fairly rapidly in this stratum, but less so than in the stratum basale. Cells in the basal and spiny layers are the only ones to receive adequate nourishment (via diffusion of nutrients from the dermis). So as their daughter cells are pushed upward and away from the source of nutrition, they gradually die.

The **stratum granulosum** (granular layer) is a thin layer named for the abundant granules its cells contain. These granules are of two types: (1) *laminated granules,* which contain a waterproofing glycolipid that is secreted into the extracellular space; and (2) *keratohyalin granules,* which combine with the intermediate filaments in the more superficial layers to form the keratin fibrils. At the upper border of this layer, the cells are beginning to die.

The **stratum lucidum** (clear layer) is a very thin translucent band of flattened dead keratinocytes with indistinct boundaries. It is not present in regions of thin skin.

The outermost epidermal layer, the **stratum corneum** (horny layer), consists of some 20 to 30 cell layers, and accounts for the bulk of the epidermal thickness. Cells in this layer, like those in the stratum lucidum (where it exists), are dead and their flattened scalelike remnants are fully keratinized. They are constantly rubbing off and being replaced by division of the deeper cells.

Dermis

The dense irregular connective tissue making up the dermis consists of two principal regions—the papillary and reticular areas. Like the epidermis, the dermis varies in thickness. For example, the skin is particularly thick on the palms of the hands and soles of the feet and is quite thin on the eyelids.

The **papillary layer** is the more superficial dermal region. It is very uneven and has fingerlike projections from its superior surface, the **dermal papillae,** which attach it to the epidermis above. These projections lie on top of the larger dermal ridges. In the palms of the hands and soles of the feet, they produce the fingerprints, unique patterns of *epidermal ridges* that remain unchanged throughout life. Abundant capillary networks in the papillary layer furnish nutrients for the epidermal layers and allow heat to radiate to the skin surface. The pain and touch receptors (Meissner's corpuscles) are also found here.

The **reticular layer** is the deepest skin layer. It contains many arteries and veins, sweat and sebaceous glands, and pressure receptors.

Both the papillary and reticular layers are heavily invested with collagenic and elastic fibers. The elastic fibers give skin its exceptional elasticity in youth. In old age, the number of elastic fibers decreases and the subcutaneous layer loses fat, which leads to wrinkling and inelasticity of the skin. Fibroblasts, adipose cells, various types of macrophages (which are important in the body's defense), and other cell types are found throughout the dermis.

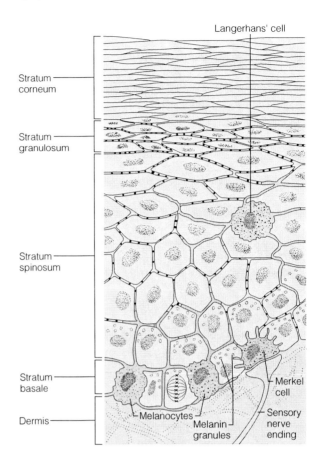

Figure 2 Diagram showing the main features—layers and relative numbers of the different cell types—in epidermis of thin skin. The keratinocytes form the bulk of the epidermis. Less numerous are the melanocytes, which produce the pigment melanin; Langerhans' cells, which function as macrophages; and Merkel cells. A sensory nerve ending, extending from the dermis, is depicted in association with the Merkel cell forming a Merkel disc (touch receptor). Notice that the keratinocytes, but not the other cell types, are joined by numerous desmosomes.

The abundant dermal blood supply allows the skin to play a role in the regulation of body temperature. When body temperature is high, the arterioles serving the skin dilate, and the capillary network of the dermis becomes engorged with the heated blood. Thus body heat is allowed to radiate from the skin surface. If the environment is cool and body heat must be conserved, the arterioles constrict so that blood bypasses the dermal capillary networks.

Any restriction of the normal blood supply to the skin results in cell death and, if severe enough, skin ulcers (Figure 3). **Bedsores (decubitus ulcers)** occur in bedridden patients who are not turned regularly enough. The weight of the body exerts pressure on the skin, especially over bony projections (hips, heels, etc.), which leads to restriction of the blood supply and death of tissue. ■

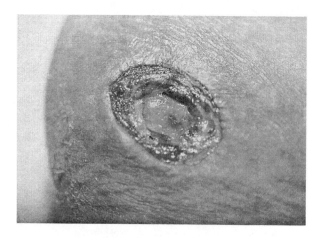

Figure 3   Photograph of a deep (stage III) decubitus ulcer.

The dermis is also richly provided with lymphatic vessels and a nerve supply. Many of the nerve endings bear highly specialized receptor organs that, when stimulated by environmental changes, transmit messages to the central nervous system for interpretation. Some of these receptors—bare nerve endings (pain receptors), a Meissner's corpuscle, a Pacinian corpuscle, and a root hair plexus—are shown in Figure 1.

Skin Color

Skin color is a result of three factors—the relative amount of two pigments (melanin and carotene) in skin and the degree of oxygenation of the blood. People who produce large amounts of melanin have brown-toned skin. In light-skinned people, who have less melanin, the dermal blood supply flushes through the rather transparent cell layers above, giving the skin a rosy glow. *Carotene* is a yellow-orange pigment present primarily in the stratum corneum and in the adipose tissue of the hypodermis. Its presence is most noticeable when large amounts of carotene-rich foods (carrots, for instance) are eaten.

Skin color may be an important diagnostic tool. For example, flushed skin may indicate hypertension, fever, or embarrassment, whereas pale skin is typically seen in anemic individuals. When the blood is inadequately oxygenated, as during asphyxiation and serious lung disease, both the blood and the skin take on a bluish or cyanotic cast. **Jaundice,** in which the tissues become yellowed, is almost always diagnostic for liver disease, whereas a bronzing of the skin hints that a person's adrenal cortex is hypoactive (**Addison's disease**). ■

Appendages of the Skin

The appendages of the skin—hair, nails, and cutaneous glands—are all derivatives of the epidermis, but they reside in the dermis. They originate from the stratum basale and grow downward into the deeper skin regions.

Cutaneous Glands

The cutaneous glands fall primarily into two categories: the sebaceous glands and the sweat glands (Figure 1). The **sebaceous glands** are found nearly all over the skin, except for the palms of the hands and the soles of the feet. Their ducts usually empty into a hair follicle, but some open directly onto the skin surface.

The product of the sebaceous glands, called **sebum,** is a mixture of oily substances and fragmented cells. The sebum is a lubricant that keeps the skin soft and moist (a natural skin cream) and keeps the hair from becoming brittle. The sebaceous glands become particularly active during puberty when more male hormones (androgens) begin to be produced; thus, the skin tends to become oilier during this period of life. *Blackheads* are accumulations of dried sebum and bacteria; *acne* is due to active infection of the sebaceous glands.

Epithelial openings, called *pores,* are the outlets for the **sweat (sudoriferous) glands.** These exocrine glands are widely distributed in the skin. Sweat glands are subcategorized by the composition of their secretions. The **eccrine glands,** which are distributed all over the body, produce clear perspiration, consisting primarily of water, salts (NaCl), and urea. The **apocrine glands,** found predominantly in the axillary and genital areas, secrete a milky protein- and fat-rich substance (also containing water, salts, and urea) that is an excellent nutrient medium for the microorganisms typically found on the skin.

The sweat glands, under the control of the nervous system, are an important part of the body's heat-regulating apparatus. They secrete perspiration when the external temperature or body temperature is high. When this water-based substance evaporates, it carries excess body heat with it. Thus evaporation of greater amounts of perspiration provides an efficient means of dissipating body heat when the capillary cooling system is not sufficient or is unable to maintain body temperature homeostasis.

Hair

Hairs are found over the entire body surface, except for thick-skinned areas (the palms of the hands, the soles of the feet), parts of the external genitalia, the nipples, and the lips. A hair, enclosed in a hair **follicle,** is also an epithelial structure (Figure 4). The portion of the hair enclosed within the follicle is called the **root;** the portion projecting from the scalp surface is called the **shaft.** The hair is formed by mitosis of the well-nourished germinal epithelial cells at the basal end of the follicle (the **hair bulb**). As the daughter cells are pushed farther away from the growing region, they die and become keratinized; thus the bulk of the hair shaft, like the bulk of the epidermis, is dead material.

A hair (Figure 4b) consists of a central region (medulla) surrounded first by the cortex and then by a protective cuticle. Abrasion of the cuticle results in "split ends." Hair color is a manifestation of the amount and kind of melanin pigment within the hair cortex.

The hair follicle is structured from both epidermal and dermal cells (Figure 4c). Its inner *epithelial root sheath,* with two parts (internal and external), is enclosed by the *connective tissue root sheath,* which is essentially dermal tissue. A small nipple of dermal tissue, the *connective tissue papilla,* protrudes into the hair bulb from the connective tissue sheath

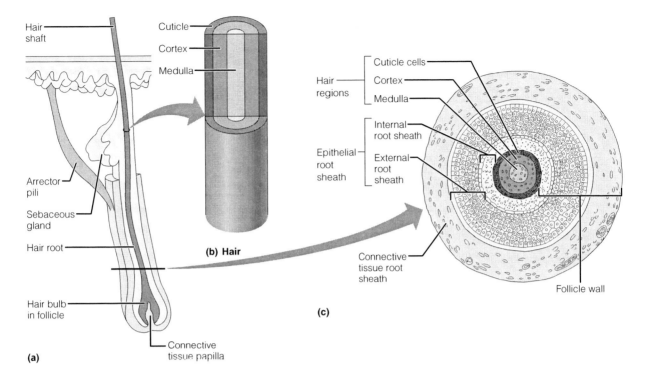

Figure 4 Structure of a hair and hair follicle. (a) Longitudinal section of a hair within its follicle. **(b)** Enlarged longitudinal section of a hair. **(c)** Cross section of a hair and hair follicle.

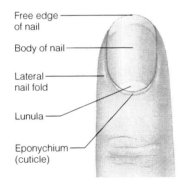

Figure 5 Structure of a nail. Surface view of the distal part of a finger showing nail parts. The nail matrix that forms the nail lies beneath the lunula; the epidermis of the nail bed underlies the nail.

Nails

Nails, the hornlike derivatives of the epidermis, consist of a *free edge,* a *body* (visible attached portion), and a *root* (embedded in the skin and adhering to an epithelial **nail bed**).The borders of the nail are overlapped by skin folds called **nail folds;** the thick proximal nail fold is the **eponychium,** commonly called the cuticle (Figure 5).

The germinal cells in the **nail matrix,** the thickened proximal part of the nail bed, are responsible for nail growth. As the nail cells are produced by the matrix, they become heavily keratinized and die. Thus, nails, like hairs, are mostly nonliving material.

Nails are transparent and nearly colorless, but they appear pink because of the blood supply in the underlying dermis. The exception to this is the proximal region of the thickened nail matrix which appears as a white crescent called the *lunula.* When someone is cyanotic due to a lack of oxygen in the blood, the nail beds take on a blue cast.

Activity:
Identifying Nail Structures

Identify the nail structures shown in Figure 5 on yourself or your lab partner. ■

and provides nutrition to the growing hair. If you look carefully at the structure of the hair follicle (see Figure 1), you will see that it generally is in a slanted position. Small bands of smooth muscle cells—**arrector pili**—connect each hair follicle to the papillary layer of the dermis. When these muscles contract (during cold or fright), the hair follicle is pulled upright, dimpling the skin surface with "goose bumps." This phenomenon is especially dramatic in a scared cat, whose fur actually stands on end to increase its apparent size. The activity of the arrector pili muscles also exerts pressure on the sebaceous glands surrounding the follicle, causing a small amount of sebum to be released.

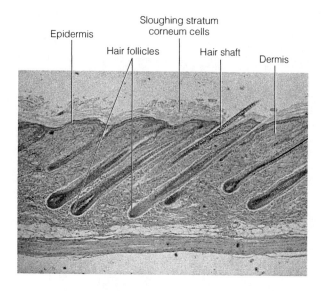

Epidermis | Sloughing stratum corneum cells | Hair follicles | Hair shaft | Dermis

Figure 6 Photomicrograph of skin (34×).

Microscopic Structure of the Skin

Activity:
Examining a Skin Slide

Obtain a prepared slide of human skin, and study it carefully under the microscope. Compare your tissue slide to the view shown in Figure 6, and identify as many of the structures diagrammed in Figure 1 as possible.

_____

_____

How do these differences relate to the functions of these two similar epithelia?

_____

_____

_____

_____ ■

Activity:
Plotting the Distribution of Sweat Glands

1.   For this simple experiment you will need two squares of bond paper (each 1 cm × 1 cm), adhesive tape, and a Beta-dine (iodine) swab *or* Lugol's iodine and a cotton-tipped swab. (The bond paper has been preruled in cm^2—just cut along the lines to obtain the required squares.)

2.   Paint an area of the medial aspect of your left palm (avoid the crease lines) and a region of your left forearm with the iodine solution, and allow it to dry thoroughly. The painted area in each case should be slightly larger than the paper squares to be used.

3.   Have your lab partner *securely* tape a square of bond paper over each iodine-painted area, and leave them in place for 20 minutes. (If it is very warm in the laboratory while this test is being conducted, good results may be obtained within 10 to 15 minutes.)

4.   After 20 minutes, remove the paper squares, and count the number of blue-black dots on each square. The presence of a blue-black dot on the paper indicates an active sweat gland. (The iodine in the pore is dissolved in the sweat and reacts chemically with the starch in the bond paper to produce the blue-black color.) Thus "sweat maps" have been produced for the two skin areas.

5.   Which skin area tested has the greater density of sweat glands?

_____

_____

_____ ■

Illustrations: 1: Elizabeth Morales-Denny. 2 and 4: Precision Graphics. 5: Barbara Cousins. **Photographs:** 3: © Addison Wesley Longman. 6: Courtesy of Marian Rice.

The Integumentary System

Basic Structure of the Skin

1. Complete the following statements by writing the appropriate word or phrase on the correspondingly numbered blank:

The two basic tissues of which the skin is composed are dense irregular connective tissue, which makes up the dermis, and __1__, which forms the epidermis. The tough water-repellent protein found in the epidermal cells is called __2__. The pigments, melanin and __3__, contribute to skin color. A localized concentration of melanin is referred to as a __4__.

1. _Stratified squamos_
2. _Keratin_
3. _Melanin cortih_
4. _freckle_

2. Four protective functions of the skin are _Protect against foreign bodies, water proof the body, Keep blood inside, warmth_.

3. Using the key choices, choose all responses that apply to the following descriptions.

Key: a. stratum basale
b. stratum corneum
c. stratum granulosum
d. stratum lucidum
e. stratum spinosum
f. papillary layer
g. reticular layer
h. epidermis as a whole
i. dermis as a whole

_D_ 1. translucent cells containing keratin fibrils

_H_ 2. dead cells

_F_ 3. dermis layer responsible for fingerprints

_C_ 4. vascular region

_G_ 5. major skin area where derivatives (nails and hair) arise

_I_ 6. epidermal region exhibiting rapid cell division
_B_

_A_ 7. scalelike dead cells, full of keratin, that constantly slough off

_E_ 8. also called the stratum germinativum

_B_ 9. has abundant elastic and collagenic fibers

_I_ 10. site of melanin formation

11. area where weblike prekeratin filaments first appear

4. Label the skin structures and areas indicated in the accompanying diagram of skin. Then, complete the statements that follow.

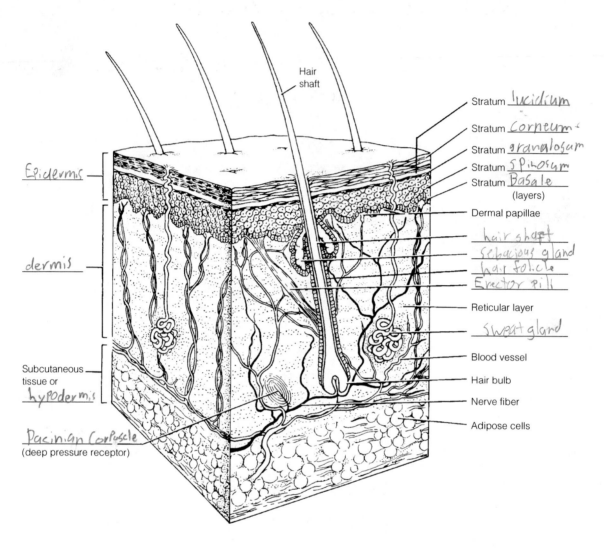

Hair shaft

Stratum _lucidium_

Stratum _corneum_

Stratum _granalogum_

Stratum _Spinosum_

Stratum _Basale_
(layers)

Dermal papillae

hair shaft

sebacious gland

hair folicle

Erector pili

Reticular layer

Sweat gland

Blood vessel

Hair bulb

Nerve fiber

Adipose cells

Epidermis

dermis

Subcutaneous tissue or
hypodermis

Pacinian Corpuscle
(deep pressure receptor)

1. _____ granules extruded from the keratinocytes prevent water loss by diffusion through the epidermis.

2. The origin of the fibers in the dermis is _____.

3. Glands that respond to rising androgen levels are the _____ glands.

4. Phagocytic cells that occupy the epidermis are called _____.

5. A unique touch receptor formed from a stratum basale cell and a nerve fiber is a _____.

5. What substance is manufactured in the skin (but is not a secretion) to play a role elsewhere in the body?

_____

Review Sheet

6. What sensory receptors are found in the skin? _Pacinian corPuscle (deeP Pressure)_ _Meissners CorPuscle, Cutaneous RecePtors_

7. A nurse tells a doctor that a patient is cyanotic. What is cyanosis? _The skin turns blue b/c lack of O₂_ What does its presence imply? _lack of oxygen to the skin_

8. What is the mechanism of a suntan? _Melanin Synthesis_

9. What is a decubitus ulcer? _An ulcer forms becaus blood is traPPed_ Why does it occur? _A Patient that is in a bed for a long time, blood gets traPPed and skin decays_

10. Some injections hurt more than others. On the basis of what you have learned about skin structure, can you determine why this is so? _Some shots go into the blood stream and it may Take them longer to get in causing irritation_

Appendages of the Skin

1. Using key choices, respond to the following descriptions.

   Key: a. arrector pili   d. hair follicle   g. sweat gland—apocrine
          b. cutaneous receptors   e. nail   h. sweat gland—eccrine
          c. hair   f. sebaceous glands

   _H_   1. A blackhead is an accumulation of oily material that is produced by _____.

   _A_   2. Tiny muscles, attached to hair follicles, that pull the hair upright during fright or cold.

   _F_   3. More numerous variety of perspiration gland.

   _D_   4. Sheath formed of both epithelial and connective tissues.

   _G_   5. Less numerous type of perspiration-producing gland; found mainly in the pubic and axillary regions.

   _C_   6. Found everywhere on body except palms of hands and soles of feet.

   _E_   7. Primarily dead/keratinized cells.

   _B_   8. Specialized nerve endings that respond to temperature, touch, etc.

   _F_   9. Its secretion contains cell fragments.

   _C_   10. "Sports" a lunula and a cuticle.

2. How does the skin help in regulating body temperature? (Describe two different mechanisms.) _____

Sweat - As the body heats up the skin releases sweat to cool the internal temp.

hair sticks up - when a person is cold the erector Pili is activated and the hair stands up making the body warmer

3. Several structures or skin regions are lettered in the photomicrograph below. Identify each by matching its letter with the appropriate description that follows.

_____ Adipose cells	_____ Hair follicle
_____ Dermis	_____ Sebaceous gland
_____ Epidermis	_____ Sloughing stratum corneum cells

Plotting the Distribution of Sweat Glands

1. With what substance in the bond paper does the iodine painted on the skin react? _____

2. Which skin area—the forearm or palm of hand—has more sweat glands? _palm of hand_

Which other body areas would, if tested, prove to have a high density of sweat glands? _Armpits and Pubic region_

3. What organ system controls the activity of the eccrine sweat glands? _____

Integumentary System

Find and label these structures on the skin model provided.

Epidermis	**Dermis**	**Sweat pores**
Sebaceous gland **Apocrine sweat gland**		**Hypodermis**
Piloerector muscle	**Blood capillaries**	**Hair**

Look at the skin model; explain in your own words the differences between a 1st, 2nd, and 3rd degree burn to your skin.

1. epidermis   2. dermis   3. hypodermis

Based upon what you know about the structure and function of skin cells, what is the real danger of tanning or deep sunburn?

Cancer

What does SPF stand for on your sunscreen? What minimal SPF should you use?

Sun Protection factor   15

Fingerprints

Finger prints are specific to each individual. Not even identical twins have the same fingerprints. Fingerprints can be broadly classified into ridge flow patterns: loop, arch, and whorl. Your instructor will provide you with an example of each.

Take your right index finger-apply ink as directed. Put your fingerprint on the sheet of paper.

What basic pattern is this fingerprint?   Do all of your fingers have the same print?

Whorl   Similar

How do we get fingerprints?

From moving around in the womb

Why do we have them on your fingers, toes, palms, and soles-what function do they serve?

Provides a grip so our skin is not as smooth

Why do you leave behind fingerprints when you touch certain surfaces?

Oil of your finger

Touch receptor distribution.

You have seen that we have fine-touch receptors in the dermis; however, we have higher numbers of these receptors on different parts of our bodies. Using the instrument provided, perform the two-point discrimination test on the following different body areas (arm, hand, and lower back) and record your results in the following table. Have the subjects eyes closed during the experiment. Put the points together and touch the skin with both points at the same time. Increase the distance between caliper points. Increase the distance about 1 mm, continue until the subject feels two points.

Area of Body	Touch Receptor Distance (mm)
Lower Back	3 cm
Palm of the hand	1 cm
Posterior side of the arm	5 cm

What is one reason we have so many receptors in this area of the body?

We use the Palm to feel

Skin samples

Put on a pair of latex gloves and feel the sample of human skin. See if you can identify the epidermis, dermis, and hypodermis.

Can you identify where on the person's body these samples are from?

A heel

B Arm

C

What do you notice about human skin-how does it feel?

feels tough and flexible

Why is the ability to be flexible so important in these tissues?

To be able to move with the persons movement

What is the function of hair?

warmth/Protection

Why doesn't it hurt to cut hair (or fingernails)?

dead tissue

Tattoos consist of ink being injected into the skin. In which layer do you think the ink is injected? Why?

dermis   it would flake off if not

Explain why a superficial skin scrape such as a paper cut or rug burn doesn't bleed.

Look at your own skin.

Do you have any "moles" or "freckles"?

Yes

Are your moles round?

yes

Are they all one color?

yes

Do you have any that are larger than a pencil eraser?

no

Response to cold

Apply a small bag of ice to your forearm for 5 minutes.

What color does your skin turn?

Red

Why?

blood capilaries

Did you get "goose bumps"? What causes them?

being cold and shivering

Open Lab:

Instructions: See your Open Lab Proctor for the set-up. They will give you 6 structures to identify on the Skin Model (you can use your notes). In addition, they will ask you to identify the 5 layers of epidermis. When finished, go over the list with your proctor and thank them for helping you.

***(Proctors-please sign this list when the student has <u>satisfactorily</u> finished this exercise-<u>Thank You!</u>)

Identify 6 structures on the Skin Model:

1 sebaceous gland
2 sweat gland
3 Pacinian corPuscle
4 errector Pili
5 dermis
6 hyPo dermis

What are the 5 layers of epidermis?

1 B - Basale
2 S - spinosum
3 G - Granulosum
4 L - Lucidium
5 C - corneum

Signature _____

Overview of the Skeleton: Classification and Structure of Bones and Cartilages

Objectives

1. To list three functions of the skeletal system.
2. To identify the four main kinds of bones.
3. To identify surface bone markings and functions.
4. To identify the major anatomical areas on a longitudinally cut long bone (or diagram of one).
5. To identify the major regions and structures of an osteon in a histologic specimen of compact bone (or diagram of one).
6. To explain the role of the inorganic salts and organic matrix in providing flexibility and hardness to bone.
7. To locate and identify the three major types of skeletal cartilages.

Materials

- ❑ Disarticulated bones (identified by name or number) that demonstrate classic examples of the four bone classifications (long, short, flat, and irregular)
- ❑ Long bone sawed longitudinally (beef bone from a slaughterhouse, if possible, or prepared laboratory specimen)
- ❑ Disposable plastic gloves
- ❑ Long bone soaked in 10% nitric acid (or vinegar) until flexible
- ❑ Long bone baked at 250°F for more than 2 hours
- ❑ Compound microscope
- ❑ Prepared slides of ground bone (cross section), hyaline cartilage, elastic cartilage, and fibrocartilage
- ❑ 3-D model of microscopic structure of compact bone
- ❑ Articulated skeleton

 See Appendix C, Exercise 9 for links to A.D.A.M. Interactive Anatomy.

The **skeleton** is constructed of two of the most supportive tissues found in the human body—cartilage and bone. In embryos, the skeleton is predominantly composed of hyaline cartilage, but in the adult, most of the cartilage is replaced by more rigid bone. Cartilage persists only in such isolated areas as the bridge of the nose, the larynx, the trachea, joints, and parts of the rib cage.

Besides supporting and protecting the body as an internal framework, the skeleton provides a system of levers with which the skeletal muscles work to move the body. In addition, the bones store lipids and many minerals (most importantly calcium). Finally, the red marrow cavities of bones provide a site for hematopoiesis (blood cell formation).

The skeleton is made up of bones that are connected at joints, or articulations. The skeleton is subdivided into two divisions: the **axial skeleton** (those bones that lie around the body's center of gravity) and the **appendicular skeleton** (bones of the limbs, or appendages) (Figure 1).

Before beginning your study of the skeleton, imagine for a moment that your bones have turned to putty. What if you were running when this metamorphosis took place? Now imagine your bones forming a continuous metal framework within your body, somewhat like a network of plumbing pipes. What problems could you envision with this arrangement? These images should help you understand how well the skeletal system provides support and protection, as well as facilitating movement.

Bone Markings

Even a casual observation of the bones will reveal that bone surfaces are not featureless smooth areas but are scarred with an array of bumps, holes, and ridges. These **bone markings** reveal where bones form joints with other bones, where muscles, tendons, and ligaments were attached, and where blood vessels and nerves passed. Bone markings fall into two categories: projections, or processes that grow out from the bone and serve as sites of muscle attachment or help form joints; and depressions or cavities, indentations or openings in the bone that often serve as conduits for nerves and blood vessels. The bone markings are summarized in Table 1.

Classification of Bones

The 206 bones of the adult skeleton are composed of two basic kinds of osseous tissue that differ in their texture. **Compact** bone looks smooth and homogeneous; **spongy** (or *cancellous*) bone is composed of small trabeculae (bars) of bone and lots of open space.

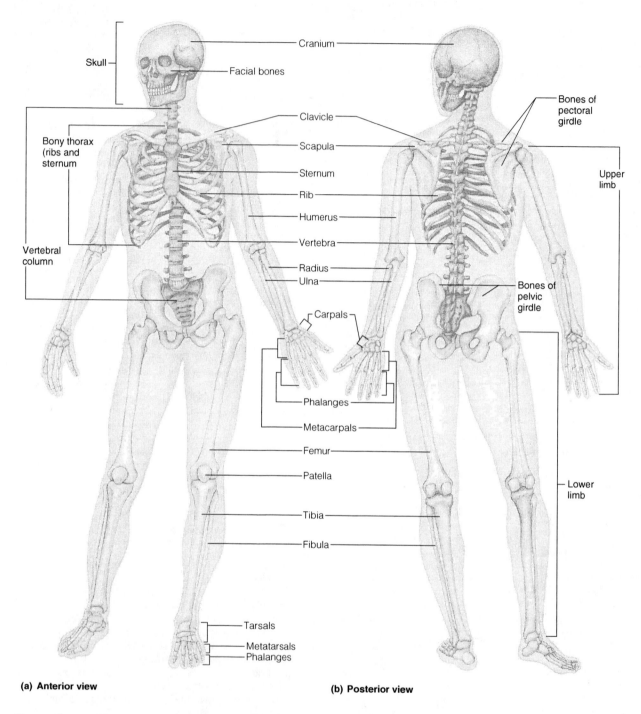

(a) **Anterior view**   (b) **Posterior view**

Figure 1   The human skeleton. The bones of the axial skeleton are colored green to distinguish them from the bones of the appendicular skeleton.

Bones may be classified further on the basis of their relative gross anatomy into four groups: long, short, flat, and irregular bones.

Long bones, such as the femur (Figure 1), are much longer than they are wide, generally consisting of a shaft with heads at either end. Long bones are composed predominantly of compact bone. **Short bones** are typically cube-shaped, and they contain more spongy bone than compact bone. See the tarsals and carpals in Figure 1.

Flat bones are generally thin, with two waferlike layers of compact bone sandwiching a layer of spongy bone between them. Although the name "flat bone" implies a structure that is level or horizontal, many flat bones are curved (for example, the bones of the skull). Bones that do not fall

30

Table 1	Bone Markings

Name of bone marking	Description	Illustration
Projections that are sites of muscle and ligament attachment		
Tuberosity (too"bĕ-ros'ĭ-te)	Large rounded projection; may be roughened	
Crest	Narrow ridge of bone; usually prominent	
Trochanter (tro-kan'ter)	Very large, blunt, irregularly shaped process. (The only examples are on the femur.)	
Line	Narrow ridge of bone; less prominent than a crest	
Tubercle (too'ber-kl)	Small rounded projection or process	
Epicondyle (ep"ĭ-kon'dīl)	Raised area on or above a condyle	
Spine	Sharp, slender, often pointed projection	
Projections that help to form joints		
Head	Bony expansion carried on a narrow neck	
Facet	Smooth, nearly flat articular surface	
Condyle (kon'dīl)	Rounded articular projection	
Ramus (ra'mus)	Armlike bar of bone	
Depressions and openings allowing blood vessels and nerves to pass		
Meatus (me-a'tus)	Canal-like passageway	
Sinus	Cavity within a bone, filled with air and lined with mucous membrane	
Fossa (fos'ah)	Shallow, basinlike depression in a bone, often serving as an articular surface	
Groove	Furrow	
Fissure	Narrow, slitlike opening	
Foramen (fo-ra'men)	Round or oval opening through a bone	

into one of the preceding categories are classified as **irregular bones.** The vertebrae are irregular bones (see Figure 1).

Some anatomists also recognize two other subcategories of bones. **Sesamoid bones** are small bones formed in tendons. The patellas (kneecaps) are sesamoid bones. **Wormian bones** are tiny bones between cranial bones. Except for the patellas, the sesamoid and Wormian bones are not included in the bone count of 206 because they vary in number and location in different individuals.

Activity:
Examining and Classifying Bones

Examine the isolated (disarticulated) bones on display. See if you can find specific examples of the bone markings described in Table 1. Then classify each of the bones into one of the four anatomical groups by recording its name or number in the chart at right. Verify your identifications with your instructor before leaving the laboratory. ■

Long	Short	Flat	Irregular

31

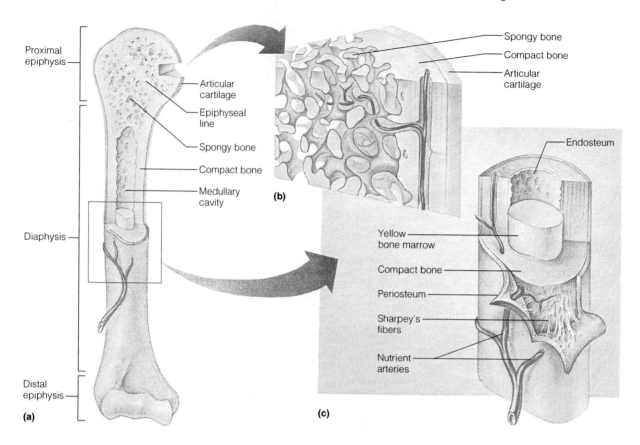

Figure 2 The structure of a long bone (humerus of the arm). (a) Anterior view with longitudinal section cut away at the proximal end. **(b)** Pie-shaped, three-dimensional view of spongy bone and compact bone of the epiphysis. **(c)** Cross section of shaft (diaphysis). Note that the external surface of the diaphysis is covered by a periosteum, but the articular surface of the epiphysis is covered with hyaline cartilage.

Gross Anatomy of the Typical Long Bone

Activity:
Examining a Long Bone

1.   Obtain a long bone that has been sawed along its longitudinal axis. If a cleaned dry bone is provided, no special preparations need be made.

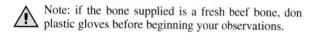 Note: if the bone supplied is a fresh beef bone, don plastic gloves before beginning your observations.

With the help of Figure 2, identify the shaft, or **diaphysis.** Observe its smooth surface, which is composed of compact bone. If you are using a fresh specimen, carefully pull away the **periosteum,** or fibrous membrane covering, to view the bone surface. Notice that many fibers of the periosteum penetrate into the bone. These fibers are called **Sharpey's fibers.** The periosteum is the source of the blood vessels and nerves that invade the bone. **Osteoblasts** (bone-forming cells) on its inner face secrete the bony matrix that increases the girth of the long bone.

2.   Now inspect the **epiphysis,** the end of the long bone. Notice that it is composed of a thin layer of compact bone that encloses spongy bone.

3.   Identify the **articular cartilage,** which covers the epiphyseal surface in place of the periosteum. Because it is composed of glassy hyaline cartilage, it provides a smooth surface to prevent friction at joint surfaces.

4.   If the animal was still young and growing, you will be able to see the **epiphyseal plate,** a thin area of hyaline cartilage that provides for longitudinal growth of the bone during youth. Once the long bone has stopped growing, these areas are replaced with bone and appear as thin, barely discernible remnants—the **epiphyseal lines.**

5.   In an adult animal, the central cavity of the shaft (*medullary cavity*) is essentially a storage region for adipose tissue, or **yellow marrow.** In the infant, this area is involved in forming blood cells, and so **red marrow** is found in the

marrow cavities. In adult bones, the red marrow is confined to the interior of the epiphyses, where it occupies the spaces between the trabeculae of spongy bone.

6.   If you are examining a fresh bone, look carefully to see if you can distinguish the delicate **endosteum** lining the shaft. In a living bone, **osteoclasts** (bone-destroying cells) are found on the inner surface of the endosteum, against the compact bone of the diaphysis. As the bone grows in diameter on its external surface, it is constantly being broken down on its inner surface. Thus the thickness of the compact bone layer composing the shaft remains relatively constant.

⚠ 7.   If you have been working with a fresh bone specimen, return it to the appropriate area and properly dispose of your gloves, as designated by your instructor. Wash your hands before continuing on to the microscope study. ■

▧ Longitudinal bone growth at epiphyseal discs follows a predictable sequence and provides a reliable indicator of the age of children exhibiting normal growth. In cases in which problems of long-bone growth are suspected (for example, pituitary dwarfism), X rays are taken to view the width of the growth plates. An abnormally thin epiphyseal plate indicates growth retardation. ■

Chemical Composition of Bone

Bone is one of the hardest materials in the body. Although relatively light, bone has a remarkable ability to resist tension and shear forces that continually act on it. An engineer would tell you that a cylinder (like a long bone) is one of the strongest structures for its mass. Thus nature has given us an extremely strong, exceptionally simple (almost crude), and flexible supporting system without sacrificing mobility.

The hardness of bone is due to the inorganic calcium salts deposited in its ground substance. Its flexibility comes from the organic elements of the matrix, particularly the collagenic fibers.

Activity:
Examining the Effects of Heat and Nitric Acid on Bones

Obtain a bone sample that has been soaked in nitric acid (or vinegar) and one that has been baked. Heating removes the organic part of bone, while acid dissolves out the minerals. Do the treated bones retain the structure of untreated specimens?

retain the structure

Gently apply pressure to each bone sample. What happens to the heated bone?

bone breaks

The bone treated with acid?

bend and very flexible

What does the acid appear to remove from the bone?

Calcium

What does baking appear to do to the bone?

remove the collagen fibers

In rickets, the bones are not properly calcified. Which of the demonstration specimens would more closely resemble the bones of a child with rickets?

Acid ■

Microscopic Structure of Compact Bone

As you have seen, spongy bone has a spiky, open-work appearance, resulting from the arrangement of the **trabeculae** that compose it, while compact bone appears to be dense and homogeneous. However, microscopic examination of compact bone reveals that it is riddled with passageways carrying blood vessels, nerves, and lymphatic vessels that provide the living bone cells with needed substances and a way to eliminate wastes. Indeed, bone histology is much easier to understand when you recognize that bone tissue is organized around its blood supply.

Activity:
Examining the Microscopic Structure of Compact Bone

1.   Obtain a prepared slide of ground bone and examine it under low power. Using Figure 3 as a guide, focus on a **central (Haversian) canal.** The central canal runs parallel to the long axis of the bone and carries blood vessels, nerves, and lymph vessels through the bony matrix. Identify the **osteocytes** (mature bone cells) in **lacunae** (chambers), which are arranged in concentric circles (concentric **lamellae**) around the central canal. A central canal and all the concentric lamellae surrounding it are referred to as an **osteon** or **Haversian system.** Also identify **canaliculi**, tiny canals radiating outward from a central canal to the lacunae of the first lamella and then from lamella to lamella. The canaliculi form a dense transportation network through the hard bone matrix, con-

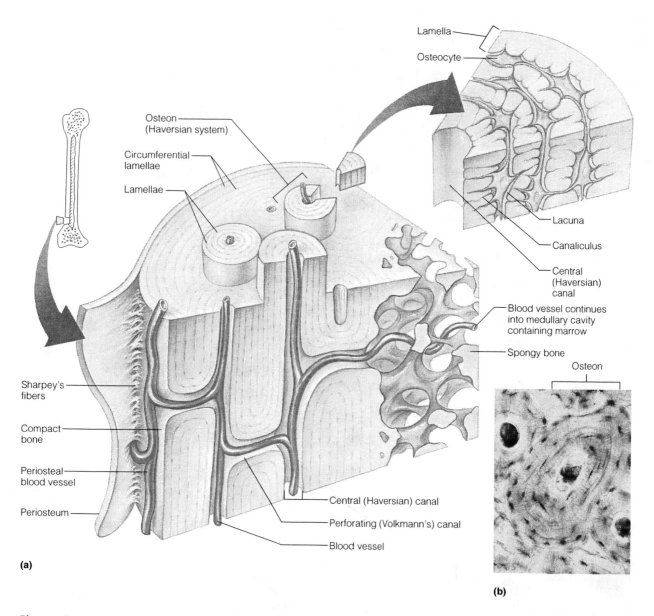

Figure 3 Microscopic structure of compact bone. (a) Diagrammatic view of a pie-shaped segment of compact bone, illustrating its structural units (osteons). The inset shows a more highly magnified view of a portion of one osteon. Notice the position of osteocytes in lacunae (cavities of the matrix). **(b)** Photomicrograph of a cross-sectional view of one osteon (90×).

necting all the living cells of the osteon to the nutrient supply. The canaliculi allow each cell to take what it needs for nourishment and to pass along the excess to the next osteocyte. You may need a higher-power magnification to see the fine canaliculi.

2. Also note the **perforating (Volkmann's) canals** in Figure 3. These canals run into the compact bone and marrow cavity from the periosteum, at right angles to the shaft. With the central canals, the perforating canals complete the communication pathway between the bone interior and its external surface.

3. If a model of bone histology is available, identify the same structures on the model. ■

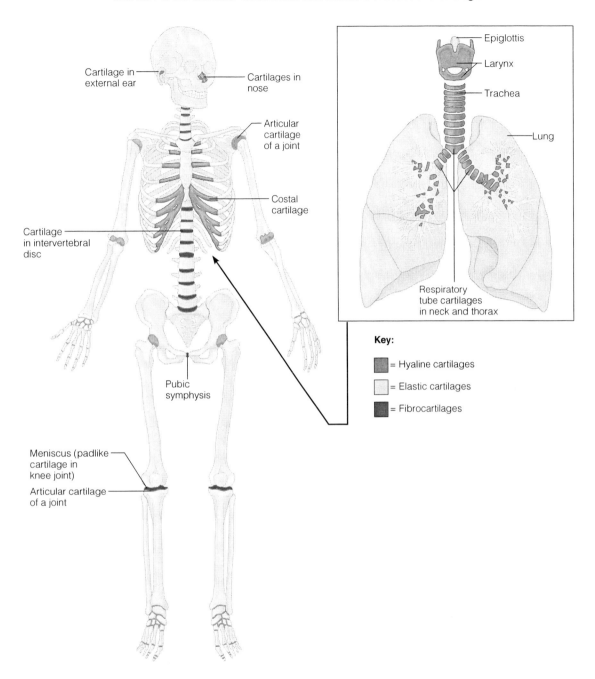

Figure 4 **Cartilages in the adult skeleton and body.** The cartilages that support the respiratory tubes and larynx are shown separately above.

Cartilages of the Skeleton

Location and Basic Structure

As mentioned earlier, cartilaginous regions of the skeleton have a fairly limited distribution in adults (Figure 4). The most important of these skeletal cartilages are (1) **articular cartilages,** which cover the bone ends at movable joints; (2) **costal cartilages,** found connecting the ribs to the sternum (breastbone); (3) **laryngeal cartilages,** which largely construct the larynx (voice box); (4) **tracheal** and **bronchial cartilages,** which reinforce other passageways of the respiratory system; (5) **nasal cartilages,** which support the external nose; (6) **intervertebral discs,** which separate and cushion bones of the spine (vertebrae); and (7) the cartilage supporting the external ear.

The skeletal cartilages consist of some variety of *cartilage tissue,* which typically consists primarily of water and is fairly resilient. Additionally, cartilage tissues are distinguished by the fact that they contain no nerves or blood vessels. Like bones, each cartilage is surrounded by a covering of dense connective tissue, called a *perichondrium* (rather than a periosteum). The perichondrium acts like a girdle to resist distortion of the cartilage when the cartilage is subjected to pressure. It also plays a role in cartilage growth and repair.

Classification of Cartilage

The skeletal cartilages have representatives from each of the three cartilage tissue types—hyaline, elastic, and fibrocartilage. Although you have already studied cartilage tissues (Exercise 6), some of that information will be recapped briefly here and you will have a chance to review the microscope structure unique to each cartilage type.

Activity:
Observing the Microscopic Structure of Different Types of Cartilage

Obtain prepared slides of hyaline cartilage, elastic cartilage, and fibrocartilage and bring them to your laboratory bench for viewing.

As you read through the descriptions of these cartilage types, keep in mind that the bulk of cartilage tissue consists of a nonliving *matrix* (containing a jellylike ground substance and fibers) secreted by chondrocytes.

Hyaline Cartilage **Hyaline cartilage** looks like frosted glass when viewed by the unaided eye. As easily seen in Figure 4, most skeletal cartilages are composed of hyaline cartilage. Its chondrocytes, snugly housed in lacunae, appear spherical and collagen fibers are the only fiber type in its matrix. Hyaline cartilage provides sturdy support with some resilience or "give." Draw a small section of hyaline cartilage in the circle below. Label the chrondrocytes, lacunae, and the cartilage matrix.

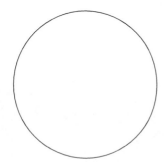

Elastic Cartilage **Elastic cartilage** can be envisioned as "hyaline cartilage with more elastic fibers." Consequently, it is much more flexible than hyaline cartilage and it tolerates repeated bending better. Essentially, only the cartilages of the external ear and the epiglottis (which flops over and covers the larynx when we swallow) are made of elastic cartilage. Focus on how this cartilage differs from hyaline cartilage as you diagram it in the circle below.

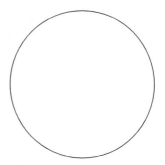

Fibrocartilage **Fibrocartilage** consists of rows of chondrocytes alternating with rows of thick collagen fibers. This tissue looks like a cartilage-dense regular connective tissue hybrid, and it is always found where hyaline cartilage joins a tendon or ligament. Fibrocartilage has great tensile strength and can withstand heavy compression. Hence, its use to construct the intervertebral discs and the cartilages within the knee joint makes a lot of sense (see Figure 4). Sketch a section of this tissue in the circle provided. ■

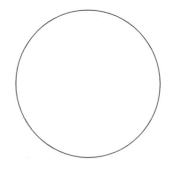

Illustrations: Table 1: Kristin Mount. 1: Laurie O'Keefe. 2 and 3: Barbara Cousins. 4: Precision Graphics.
Photographs: 3b: © Benjamin/Cummings Publishing Company. Photo by Allen Bell, University of New England.

NAME ______________________ LAB TIME/DATE ______________________

REVIEW SHEET

Overview of the Skeleton

Bone Markings

Match the terms in column B with the appropriate description in column A:

	Column A	Column B
K	1. sharp, slender process*	a. condyle
m	2. small rounded projection*	b. crest
B	3. narrow ridge of bone*	c. epicondyle
n	4. large rounded projection*	d. fissure
G	5. structure supported on neck†	e. foramen
I	6. armlike projection†	f. fossa
A	7. rounded, convex projection†	g. head
D	8. narrow depression or opening‡	h. meatus
H	9. canal-like structure‡	i. ramus
E	10. opening through a bone‡	j. sinus
F	11. shallow depression†	k. spine
J	12. air-filled cavity	l. trochanter
L	13. large, irregularly shaped projection*	m. tubercle
C	14. raised area of a condyle*	n. tuberosity

* A site of muscle attachment.
† Takes part in joint formation.
‡ A passageway for nerves or blood vessels.

Classification of Bones

1. The four major anatomical classifications of bones are long, short, flat, and irregular. Which category has the least amount of spongy bone relative to its total volume? long bones

2. Classify each of the bones in the next chart into one of the four major categories by checking the appropriate column. Use appropriate references as necessary.

	Long	Short	Flat	Irregular
humerus	X			
phalanx		X		
parietal			X	
calcaneus		X		
rib			X	
vertebra				X
ulna	X			

Gross Anatomy of the Typical Long Bone

1. Use the terms below to identify the structures marked by leader lines and braces in the diagrams (some terms are used more than once). After labeling the diagrams, use the listed terms to characterize the statements following the diagrams.

Key: a. articular cartilage f. epiphysis i. red marrow cavity
 b. compact bone g. medullary cavity j. trabeculae of spongy bone
 c. diaphysis h. periosteum k. yellow marrow
 d. endosteum
 e. epiphyseal line

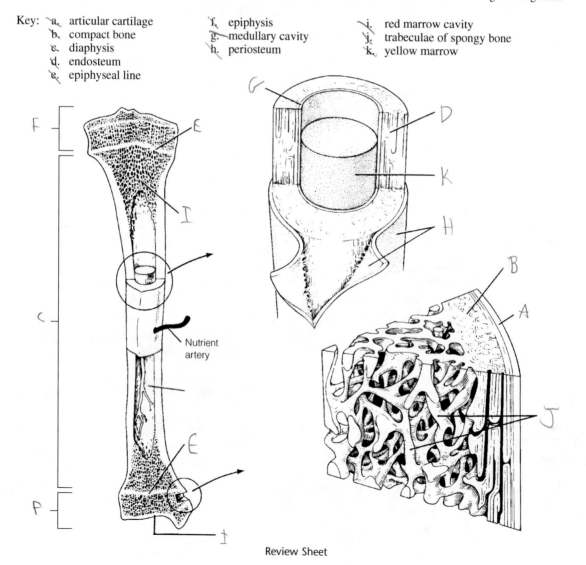

Nutrient artery

Review Sheet

38

_____ 1. contains spongy bone in adults

_____ 2. made of compact bone

_____ 3. site of blood cell formation

_____ 4. major submembranous site of osteoclasts

_____ 5. scientific term for bone shaft

_____ 6. contains fat in adult bones

_____ 7. growth plate remnant

_____ 8. major submembranous site of osteoblasts

2. What differences between compact and spongy bone can be seen with the naked eye? _____

_____

3. What is the function of the periosteum? _an attachment point for muscles and_
Bone

Microscopic Structure of Compact Bone

1. Trace the route taken by nutrients through a bone, starting with the periosteum and ending with an osteocyte in a lacuna.

Periosteum ___→_____ → _____

_____ → _____ → osteocyte

2. Several descriptions of bone structure are given in column B. Identify the structure involved by choosing the appropriate term from column A and placing its letter in the blank.

Column A

a. canaliculi

b. central canal

c. concentric lamellae

d. lacunae

Column B

__C__ 1. layers of bony matrix around a central canal

__D__ 2. site of osteocytes

__B__ 3. longitudinal canal carrying blood vessels, lymphatics, and nerves

__A__ 4. minute canals connecting osteocytes of an osteon

3. On the photomicrograph of bone below (208×), identify all structures named in column A in question 2 above.

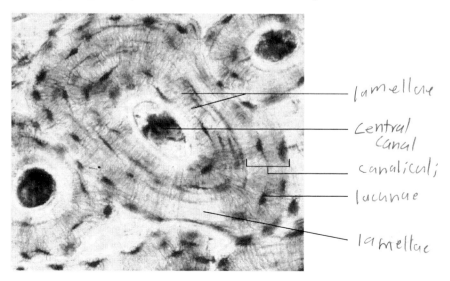

lamellae

central canal

canaliculi

lacunae

lamellae

Review Sheet

Chemical Composition of Bone

1. What is the function of the organic matrix in bone? *Gives bone its toughness and strength*

2. Name the important organic bone components. *collagen fibers, calcium*

3. Calcium salts form the bulk of the inorganic material in bone. What is the function of the calcium salts?

   Provide hardness + strength

4. Which is responsible for bone structure? (circle the appropriate response)

   inorganic portion   organic portion   both contribute

Cartilages of the Skeleton

1. Using key choices, identify each type of cartilage described (in terms of its body location or function) below.

   Key: a. elastic   b. fibrocartilage   c. hyaline

   _____ 1. supports the external ear   _____ 6. meniscus in a knee joint

   _____ 2. between the vertebrae   _____ 7. connects the ribs to the sternum

   _____ 3. forms the walls of the   _____ 8. most effective at resisting
                         voice box (larynx)   compression

   _____ 4. the epiglottis   _____ 9. most springy and flexible

   _____ 5. articular cartilages   _____ 10. most abundant

2. Identify the two types of cartilage diagrammed below. On each, label the *chondrocytes in lacunae* and the *matrix*.

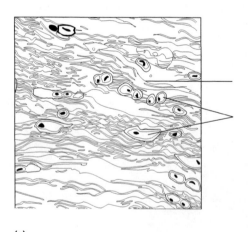

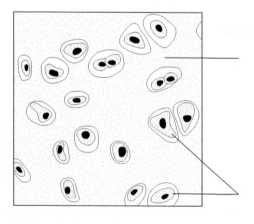

(a) _____   (b) _____

The Axial Skeleton

Objectives

1. To identify the three bone groups composing the axial skeleton.
2. To identify the bones composing the axial skeleton, either by examining isolated bones or by pointing them out on an articulated skeleton or a skull, and to name the important bone markings on each.
3. To distinguish the different types of vertebrae.
4. To discuss the importance of intervertebral discs and spinal curvatures.
5. To distinguish three abnormal spinal curvatures.

Materials

- ❑ Intact skull and Beauchene skull
- ❑ X rays of individuals with scoliosis, lordosis, and kyphosis (if available)
- ❑ Articulated skeleton, articulated vertebral column
- ❑ Isolated cervical, thoracic, and lumbar vertebrae, sacrum, and coccyx

 See Appendix C, Exercise 10 for links to A.D.A.M. Interactive Anatomy.

The **axial skeleton** can be divided into three parts: the skull, the vertebral column, and the bony thorax.

The Skull

The **skull** is composed of two sets of bones. Those of the **cranium** enclose and protect the fragile brain tissue. The **facial bones** present the eyes in an anterior position and form the base for the facial muscles, which make it possible for us to present our feelings to the world. All but one of the bones of the skull are joined by interlocking joints called *sutures*. The mandible, or lower jawbone, is attached to the rest of the skull by a freely movable joint.

Activity:
Identifying the Bones of the Skull

The bones of the skull, shown in Figures 1 through 7, are described below. As you read through this material, identify each bone on an intact (and/or Beauchene*) skull. Note that important bone markings are listed beneath the bones on which they appear and that a color-coded dot before each bone name indicates its color in the figures. ■

The Cranium

The cranium may be divided into two major areas for study—the **cranial vault** or **calvaria,** forming the superior, lateral, and posterior walls of the skull, and the **cranial floor** or **base,** forming the skull bottom. Internally, the cranial floor has three distinct concavities, the **anterior, middle,** and **posterior cranial fossae** (see Figure 3). The brain sits in these fossae, completely enclosed by the cranial vault.

Eight large flat bones construct the cranium. *With the exception of two paired bones (the parietals and the temporals), all are single bones.* Sometimes the six ossicles of the middle ear are also considered part of the cranium. Because the ossicles are functionally part of the hearing apparatus, their consideration is deferred to later, Special Senses: Hearing and Equilibrium.

○ **Frontal** See Figures 1, 3, and 6. Anterior portion of cranium; forms the forehead, superior part of the orbit, and floor of anterior cranial fossa.

Supraorbital foramen (notch): Opening above each orbit allowing blood vessels and nerves to pass.

Glabella: Smooth area between the eyes.

○ **Parietal** See Figures 1 and 6. Posterolateral to the frontal bone, forming sides of cranium.

Sagittal suture: Midline articulation point of the two parietal bones.

Coronal suture: Point of articulation of parietals with frontal bone.

○ **Temporal** See Figures 1 through 3 and 6. Inferior to parietal bone on lateral skull. The temporals can be divided into four major parts: the **squamous region** abuts the parietals; the **tympanic region** surrounds the external ear opening; the **mastoid region** is the area posterior to the ear; and the **petrous region** forms the lateral region of the skull base.

Important markings associated with the flaring squamous region (Figures 1 and 2) include:

Squamous suture: Point of articulation of the temporal bone with the parietal bone.

Zygomatic process: A bridgelike projection joining the zy-

*Two views (Plates A and B) of a Beauchene skull are provided in the Human Anatomy Atlas.

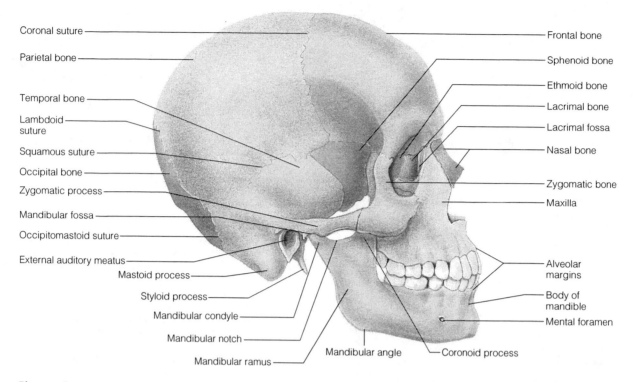

Coronal suture — Parietal bone — Temporal bone — Lambdoid suture — Squamous suture — Occipital bone — Zygomatic process — Mandibular fossa — Occipitomastoid suture — External auditory meatus — Mastoid process — Styloid process — Mandibular condyle — Mandibular notch — Mandibular ramus — Mandibular angle — Coronoid process

Frontal bone — Sphenoid bone — Ethmoid bone — Lacrimal bone — Lacrimal fossa — Nasal bone — Zygomatic bone — Maxilla — Alveolar margins — Body of mandible — Mental foramen

Figure 1   External anatomy of the right lateral aspect of the skull.

gomatic bone (cheekbone) anteriorly. Together these two bones form the *zygomatic arch.*

Mandibular fossa: Rounded depression on the inferior surface of the zygomatic process (anterior to the ear); forms the socket for the mandibular condyle, the point where the mandible (lower jaw) joins the cranium.

Tympanic region markings (Figures 1 and 2) include:

External auditory meatus: Canal leading to eardrum and middle ear.

Styloid (*stylo*=stake, pointed object) **process:** Needlelike projection inferior to external auditory meatus; attachment point for muscles and ligaments of the neck. This process is often broken off demonstration skulls.

Prominent structures in the mastoid region (Figures 1 and 2) are:

Mastoid process: Rough projection inferior and posterior to external auditory meatus; attachment site for muscles.

The mastoid process, full of air cavities and so close to the middle ear—a trouble spot for infections—often becomes infected too, a condition referred to as **mastoiditis.** Because the mastoid area is separated from the brain by only a thin layer of bone, an ear infection that has spread to the mastoid process can inflame the brain coverings or the meninges. The latter condition is known as **meningitis.** ■

Stylomastoid foramen: Tiny opening between the mastoid and styloid processes through which cranial nerve VII leaves the cranium.

The petrous region (Figures 2 and 3), which helps form the middle and posterior cranial fossae, exhibits several obvious

foramina with important functions:

Jugular foramen: Opening medial to styloid process through which the internal jugular vein and cranial nerves IX, X, and XI pass.

Carotid canal: Opening medial to the styloid process through which the internal carotid artery passes into the cranial cavity.

Internal acoustic meatus: Opening on posterior aspect (petrous portion) of temporal bone allowing passage of cranial nerves VII and VIII (Figure 3).

Foramen lacerum: A jagged opening between the petrous temporal bone and the sphenoid providing passage for a number of small nerves, and for the internal carotid artery to enter the middle cranial fossa (after it passes through part of the temporal bone).

○ **Occipital**   See Figures 1, 2, 3, and 6. Most posterior bone of cranium—forms floor and back wall. Joins sphenoid bone anteriorly via its narrow basioccipital region.

Lambdoid suture: Site of articulation of occipital bone and parietal bones.

Foramen magnum: Large opening in base of occipital, which allows the spinal cord to join with the brain.

Occipital condyles: Rounded projections lateral to the foramen magnum that articulate with the first cervical vertebra (atlas).

Hypoglossal canal: Opening medial and superior to the occipital condyle through which the hypoglossal nerve (cranial nerve XII) passes.

External occipital crest and protuberance: Midline prominences posterior to the foramen magnum.

42

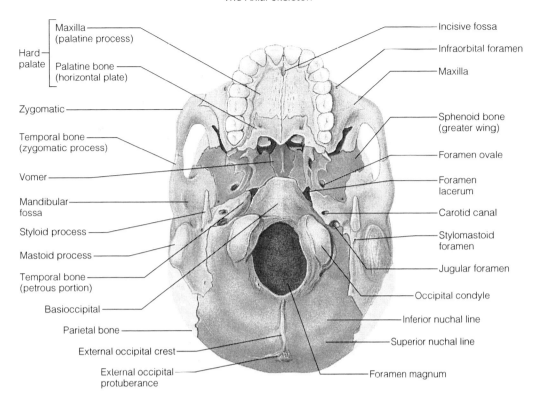

Figure 2   Inferior superficial view of the skull, mandible removed.

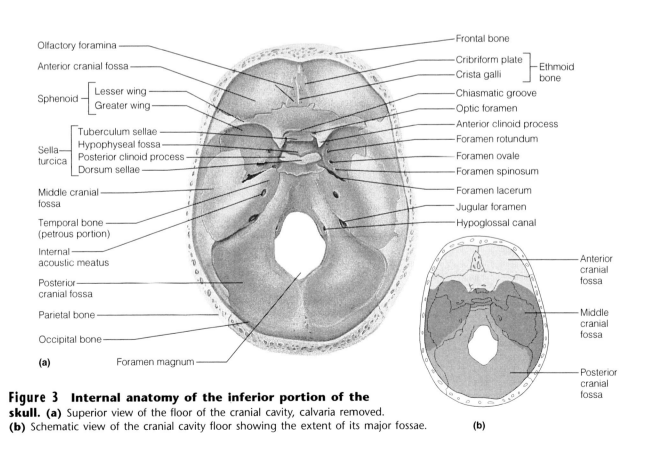

Figure 3   Internal anatomy of the inferior portion of the skull. (a) Superior view of the floor of the cranial cavity, calvaria removed. **(b)** Schematic view of the cranial cavity floor showing the extent of its major fossae.

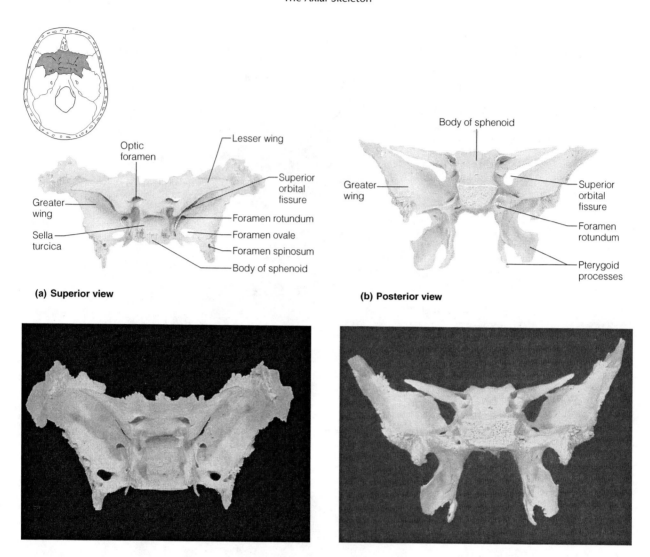

Figure 4 The sphenoid bone. (a) Superior view. **(b)** Posterior view.

○ **Sphenoid** See Figures 1 through 4 and 6. Bat-shaped bone forming the anterior plateau of the middle cranial fossa across the width of the skull.

Greater wings: Portions of the sphenoid seen exteriorly anterior to the temporal and forming a portion of the orbits of the eyes.

Superior orbital fissures: Jagged openings in orbits providing passage for cranial nerves III, IV, V, and VI to enter the orbit where they serve the eye.

The sphenoid bone can be seen in its entire width if the top of the cranium (calvaria) is removed (Figure 3).

Sella turcica (Turk's saddle): A saddle-shaped region in the sphenoid midline which nearly encloses the pituitary gland in a living person. The pituitary gland sits in the **hypophyseal fossa** portion of the sella turcica. This fossa is abutted before

and aft respectively by the **tuberculum sellae** and the **dorsum sellae.** The dorsum sellae terminates laterally in the **posterior clinoid processes.**

Lesser wings: Bat-shaped portions of the sphenoid anterior to the sella turcica. Posteromedially these terminate in the pointed **anterior clinoid processes,** which provide an anchoring site for securing the brain within the skull.

Optic foramina: Openings in the bases of the lesser wings through which the optic nerves enter the orbits to serve the eyes; these foramina are connected by the *chiasmatic groove.*

Foramen rotundum: Opening lateral to the sella turcica providing passage for a branch of the fifth cranial nerve. (This foramen is not visible on an inferior view of the skull.)

Foramen ovale: Opening posterior to the sella turcica that allows passage of a branch of the fifth cranial nerve.

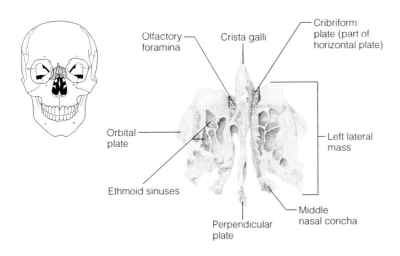

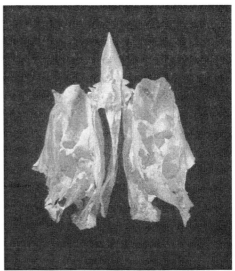

Figure 5 The ethmoid bone. Anterior view.

○ **Ethmoid** See Figures 1, 3, 5, and 6. Irregularly shaped bone anterior to the sphenoid. Forms the roof of the nasal cavity, upper nasal septum, and part of the medial orbit walls.

Crista galli (cock's comb): Vertical projection providing a point of attachment for the dura mater (outermost membrane covering of the brain).

Cribriform plates: Bony plates lateral to the crista galli through which olfactory fibers pass to the brain from the nasal mucosa. Together the cribriform plates and the midline crista galli form the *horizontal plate* of the ethmoid bone.

Perpendicular plate: Inferior projection of the ethmoid that forms the superior part of the nasal septum.

Lateral masses: Irregularly shaped thin-walled bony regions flanking the perpendicular plate laterally. Their lateral surfaces (*orbital plates*) shape part of the medial orbit wall.

Superior and middle nasal conchae (turbinates): Thin, delicately coiled plates of bone extending medially from the lateral masses of the ethmoid into the nasal cavity. The conchae make air flow through the nasal cavity more efficient and greatly increase the surface area of the mucosa that covers them, thus increasing the mucosa's ability to warm and humidify incoming air.

Facial Bones

Of the 14 bones composing the face, 12 are paired. *Only the mandible and vomer are single bones.* An additional bone, the hyoid bone, although not a facial bone, is considered here because of its location.

○ **Mandible** See Figures 1, 6, and 7. The lower jawbone, which articulates with the temporal bones in the only freely movable joints of the skull.

Body: Horizontal portion; forms the chin.

Ramus: Vertical extension of the body on either side.

Mandibular condyle: Articulation point of the mandible with the mandibular fossa of the temporal bone.

Coronoid process: Jutting anterior portion of the ramus; site of muscle attachment.

Angle: Posterior point at which ramus meets the body.

Mental foramen: Prominent opening on the body (lateral to the midline) that transmits the mental blood vessels and nerve to the lower jaw.

Mandibular foramen: Open the lower jaw of the skull to identify this prominent foramen on the medial aspect of the mandibular ramus. This foramen permits passage of the nerve involved with tooth sensation (mandibular branch of cranial nerve V) and is the site where the dentist injects Novocain to prevent pain while working on the lower teeth.

Alveolar margin: Superior margin of mandible, contains sockets in which the teeth lie.

Mandibular symphysis: Anterior median depression indicating point of mandibular fusion.

○ **Maxillae** See Figures 1, 2, 6, and 7. Two bones fused in a median suture; form the upper jawbone and part of the orbits. All facial bones, except the mandible, join the maxillae. Thus they are the main, or keystone, bones of the face.

Alveolar margin: Inferior margin containing sockets (alveoli) in which teeth lie.

Palatine processes: Form the anterior hard palate.

Infraorbital foramen: Opening under the orbit carrying the infraorbital nerves and blood vessels to the nasal region.

Incisive fossa: Large bilateral opening located posterior to the central incisor tooth of the maxilla and piercing the hard palate; transmits the nasopalatine arteries and blood vessels.

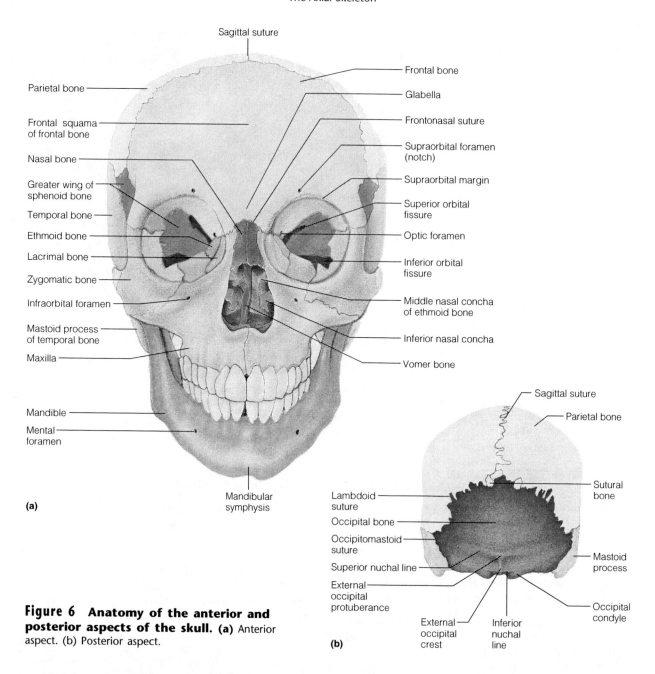

Figure 6 Anatomy of the anterior and posterior aspects of the skull. (a) Anterior aspect. (b) Posterior aspect.

○ **Palatine** See Figures 2 and 7. Paired bones posterior to the palatine processes; form posterior hard palate and part of the orbit.

○ **Zygomatic** See Figures 1, 2, and 6. Lateral to the maxilla; forms the portion of the face commonly called the cheekbone, and forms part of the lateral orbit. Its three processes are named for the bones with which they articulate.

○ **Lacrimal** See Figures 1 and 6. Fingernail-sized bones forming a part of the medial orbit walls between the maxilla and the ethmoid. Each lacrimal bone is pierced by an

opening, the **lacrimal fossa,** which serves as a passageway for tears (*lacrima* means "tear").

○ **Nasal** See Figures 1 and 6. Small rectangular bones forming the bridge of the nose.

○ **Vomer** (*vomer* = **plow**) See Figures 2 and 6. Blade-shaped bone in median plane of nasal cavity that forms the posterior and inferior nasal septum.

○ **Inferior Nasal Conchae (turbinates)** See Figure 6. Thin curved bones protruding medially from the lateral walls of the nasal cavity; serve the same purpose as the turbinate portions of the ethmoid bone (described earlier).

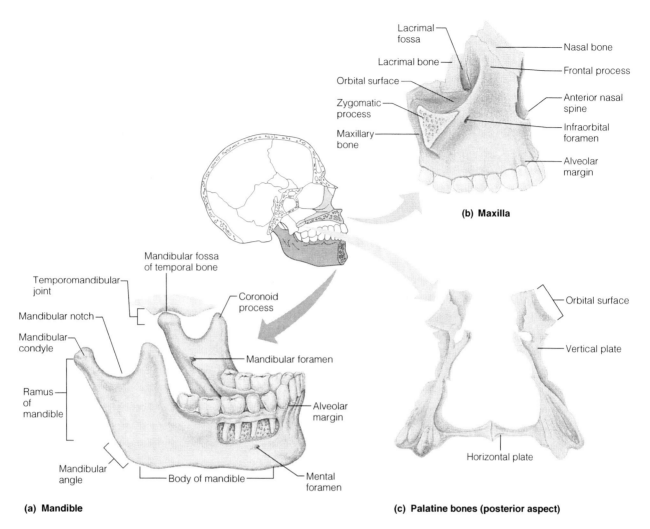

(b) Maxilla

(a) Mandible

(c) Palatine bones (posterior aspect)

Figure 7 Detailed anatomy of some isolated facial bones. (Note that the mandible, maxilla, and palatine bones are not drawn in proportion to each other.)

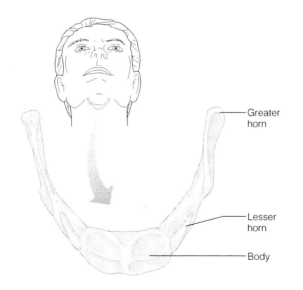

Figure 8 Hyoid bone.

Hyoid Bone

Not really considered or counted as a skull bone. Located in the throat above the larynx (Figure 8); serves as a point of attachment for many tongue and neck muscles. Does not articulate with any other bone, and is thus unique. Horseshoe-shaped with a body and two pairs of **horns,** or **cornua.**

Paranasal Sinuses

Four skull bones—maxillary, sphenoid, ethmoid, and frontal—contain sinuses (mucosa-lined air cavities), which lead into the nasal passages (see Figure 9). These paranasal sinuses lighten the facial bones and may act as resonance chambers for speech. The maxillary sinus is the largest of the sinuses found in the skull.

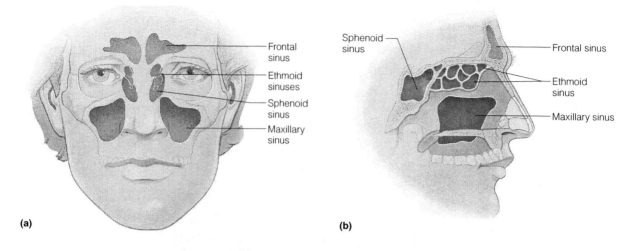

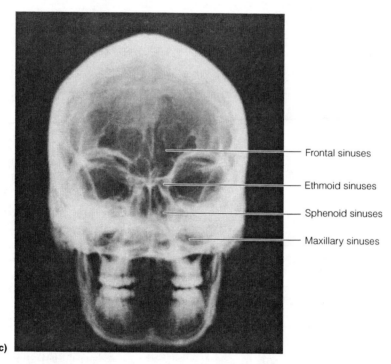

Figure 9 Paranasal sinuses. (a) Anterior "see-through" view.
(b) As seen in a sagittal section of the head. **(c)** Skull X ray showing three of
the paranasal sinuses, anterior view.

Sinusitis, or inflammation of the sinuses, sometimes occurs as a result of an allergy or bacterial invasion of the sinus cavities. In such cases, some of the connecting passageways between the sinuses and nasal passages may become blocked with thick mucus or infectious material. Then, as the air in the sinus cavities is absorbed, a partial vacuum forms. The result is a sinus headache localized over the inflamed sinus area. Severe sinus infections may require surgical drainage to relieve this painful condition. ■

Activity:
Palpating Skull Markings

Palpate the following areas on yourself:

• Zygomatic bone and arch. (The most prominent part of your cheek is your zygomatic bone. Follow the posterior course of the zygomatic arch to its junction with your temporal bone.)

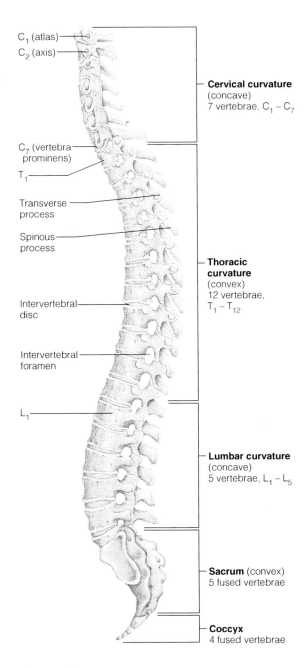

C₁ (atlas)
C₂ (axis)

Cervical curvature
(concave)
7 vertebrae, C₁ – C₇

C₇ (vertebra prominens)
T₁

Transverse process

Spinous process

Thoracic curvature
(convex)
12 vertebrae, T₁ – T₁₂

Intervertebral disc

Intervertebral foramen

L₁

Lumbar curvature
(concave)
5 vertebrae, L₁ – L₅

Sacrum (convex)
5 fused vertebrae

Coccyx
4 fused vertebrae

Figure 10   The vertebral column. Notice the curvatures in the lateral view. (The terms *convex* and *concave* refer to the curvature of the posterior aspect of the vertebral column.)

- Mastoid process (the rough area behind your ear).

- Temporomandibular joints. (Open and close your jaws to locate these.)

- Greater wing of sphenoid. (Find the indentation posterior to the orbit and superior to the zygomatic arch on your lateral skull.)

- Superior orbital foramen. (Apply firm pressure along the superior orbital margin to find the indentation resulting from this foramen.)

- Inferior orbital foramen. (Apply firm pressure along the inferomedial border of the orbit to locate this large foramen.)

- Mandibular angle (most inferior and posterior aspect of the mandible).

- Mandibular symphysis (midline of chin).

- Nasal bones. (Run your index finger and thumb along opposite sides of the bridge of your nose until they "slip" medially at the inferior end of the nasal bones.)

- External occipital protuberance. (This midline projection is easily felt by running your fingers up the furrow at the back of your neck to the skull.)

- Hyoid bone. (Place a thumb high behind the lateral edge of the mandible and squeeze medially.) ■

The Vertebral Column

The **vertebral column,** extending from the skull to the pelvis, forms the body's major axial support. Additionally, it surrounds and protects the delicate spinal cord while allowing the spinal nerves to issue from the cord via openings between adjacent vertebrae. The term *vertebral column* might suggest a rather rigid supporting rod, but this is far from the truth. The vertebral column consists of 24 single bones called **vertebrae** and two composite, or fused, bones (the sacrum and coccyx) that are connected in such a way as to provide a flexible curved structure (Figure 10). Of the 24 single vertebrae, the seven bones of the neck are called *cervical vertebrae;* the next 12 are *thoracic vertebrae;* and the 5 supporting the lower back are *lumbar vertebrae.* Remembering common mealtimes for breakfast, lunch, and dinner (7 A.M., 12 noon, and 5 P.M.) may help you to remember the number of bones in each region.

The vertebrae are separated by pads of fibrocartilage, **intervertebral discs,** that cushion the vertebrae and absorb shocks. Each disc is composed of two major regions, a central gelatinous *nucleus pulposus* that behaves like a fluid, and an outer ring of encircling collagen fibers called the *annulus fibrosus* that stabilizes the disc and contains the pulposus.

As a person ages, the water content of the discs decreases (as it does in other tissues throughout the body), and the discs become thinner and less compressible. This situation, along with other degenerative changes such as weakening of the ligaments and tendons of the vertebral column, predisposes older people to **ruptured discs.** In a ruptured disc, the nucleus pulposus herniates through the annulus portion and typically compresses adjacent nerves. ■

The presence of the discs and the S-shaped or springlike construction of the vertebral column prevent shock to the head in walking and running and provide flexibility to the body trunk. The thoracic and sacral curvatures of the spine are referred to as *primary curvatures* because they are present and well developed at birth. Later the *secondary curvatures* are formed. The cervical curvature becomes prominent when the baby begins to hold its head up independently, and the lumbar curvature develops when the baby begins to walk.

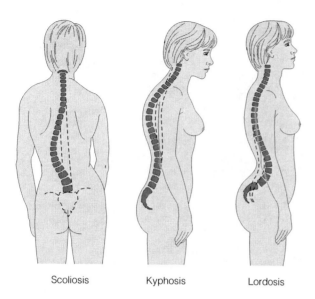

Scoliosis   Kyphosis   Lordosis

Figure 11   Abnormal spinal curvatures.

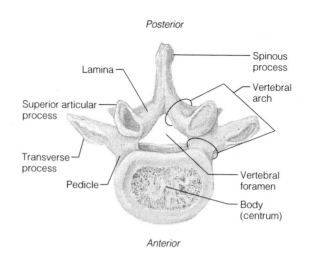

Figure 12   A typical vertebra, superior view. Inferior articulating surfaces not shown.

Activity:
Examining Spinal Curvatures

1.   Observe the normal curvature of the vertebral column in your laboratory specimen, and compare it to Figure 10. Then examine Figure 11, which depicts three abnormal spinal curvatures—*scoliosis, kyphosis,* and *lordosis.* These abnormalities may result from disease or poor posture. Also examine X rays, if they are available, showing these same conditions in a living patient.

2.   Then using an articulated vertebral column (or an articulated skeleton), examine the freedom of movement between two lumbar vertebrae separated by an intervertebral disc.

When the fibrous disc is properly positioned, are the spinal cord or peripheral nerves impaired in any way?

_____

Remove the disc and put the two vertebrae back together. What happens to the nerve?

_____

_____

What would happen to the spinal nerves in areas of malpositioned or "slipped" discs?

_____

_____

_____ ∎

Structure of a Typical Vertebra

Although they differ in size and specific features, all vertebrae have some features in common (Figure 12).

Body (or centrum): Rounded central portion of the vertebra, which faces anteriorly in the human vertebral column.

Vertebral arch: composed of pedicles, laminae, and a spinous process, it represents the junction of all posterior extensions from the vertebral body.

Vertebral foramen: Opening enclosed by the body and vertebral arch; a conduit for the spinal cord.

Transverse processes: Two lateral projections from the vertebral arch.

Spinous process: Single medial and posterior projection from the vertebral arch.

Superior and inferior articular processes: Paired projections lateral to the vertebral foramen that enable articulation with adjacent vertebrae. The superior articular processes typically face toward the spinous process, whereas the inferior articular processes face away from the spinous process.

Intervertebral foramina: The right and left pedicles have notches on their inferior and superior surfaces that create openings, the intervertebral foramina, for spinal nerves to leave the spinal cord between adjacent vertebrae.

Figures 13 and 14 and Table 1 show how specific vertebrae differ; refer to them as you read the following sections.

Cervical Vertebrae

The seven cervical vertebrae (referred to as C_1 through C_7) form the neck portion of the vertebral column. The first two cervical vertebrae (atlas and axis) are highly modified to perform special functions (see Figure 13). The **atlas** (C_1) lacks a body, and its lateral processes contain large concave

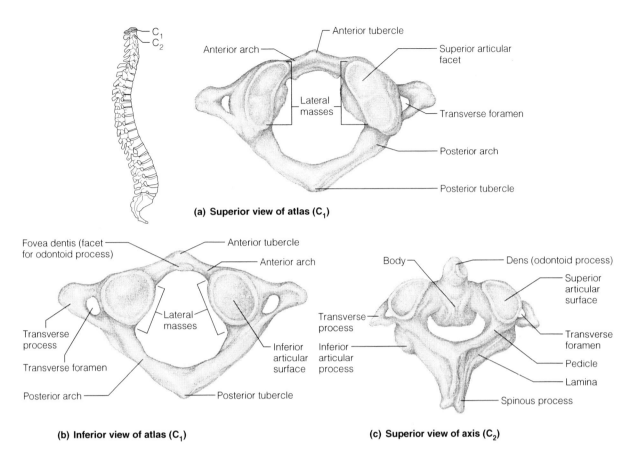

(a) Superior view of atlas (C₁)

(b) Inferior view of atlas (C₁)

(c) Superior view of axis (C₂)

Figure 13 Cervical vertebrae C₁ and C₂. (a) Superior view of the atlas (C₁). **(b)** Inferior view of the atlas (C₁). **(c)** Superior view of the axis (C₂).

depressions on their superior surfaces that receive the occipital condyles of the skull. This joint enables you to nod "yes." The **axis** (C₂) acts as a pivot for the rotation of the atlas (and skull) above. It bears a large vertical process, the **odontoid process,** or **dens,** that serves as the pivot point. The articulation between C₁ and C₂ allows you to rotate your head from side to side to indicate "no."

The more typical cervical vertebrae (C₃ through C₇) are distinguished from the thoracic and lumbar vertebrae by several features (see Table 1). They are the smallest, lightest vertebrae and the vertebral foramen is triangular. The spinous process is short and often bifurcated, or divided into two branches. The spinous process of C₇ is not branched, however, and is substantially longer than that of the other cervical vertebrae. Because the spinous process of C₇ is visible through the skin, it is called the *vertebra prominens* and is used as a landmark for counting the vertebrae. Transverse processes of the cervical vertebrae are wide, and they contain foramina through which the vertebral arteries pass superiorly on their way to the brain. Any time you see these foramina in a vertebra, you can be sure that it is a cervical vertebra.

- Palpate your vertebra prominens.

Thoracic Vertebrae

The 12 thoracic vertebrae (referred to as T₁ through T₁₂) may be recognized by the following structural characteristics. As shown in Table 1, they have a larger body than the cervical vertebrae. The body is somewhat heart shaped, with two small articulating surfaces, or *costal demifacets,* on each side (one superior, the other inferior) close to the origin of the vertebral arch. These demifacets articulate with the heads of the corresponding ribs. The vertebral foramen is oval or round, and the spinous process is long, with a sharp downward hook. The closer the thoracic vertebra is to the lumbar region, the less sharp and shorter the spinous process. Articular facets on the transverse processes articulate with the tubercles of the ribs. Besides forming the thoracic part of the spine, these vertebrae form the posterior aspect of the bony thoracic cage (rib cage). Indeed, they are the only vertebrae that articulate with the ribs.

Lumbar Vertebrae

The five lumbar vertebrae (L₁ through L₅) have massive blocklike bodies and short, thick, hatchet-shaped spinous processes extending directly backward (see Table 1). The superior articular facets face posteromedially; the inferior ones

Table 1	Regional Characteristics of Cervical, Thoracic, and Lumbar Vertebrae		
Characteristic	**(a) Cervical (3–7)**	**(b) Thoracic**	**(c) Lumbar**
Body	Small, wide side to side	Larger than cervical; heart shaped; bears two costal demifacets	Massive; kidney shaped
Spinous process	Short; bifid; projects directly posteriorly	Long; sharp; projects inferiorly	Short; blunt; projects directly posteriorly
Vertebral foramen	Triangular	Circular	Triangular
Transverse processes	Contain foramina	Bear facets for ribs (except T_{11} and T_{12})	No special features
Superior and inferior articulating processes	Superior facets directed superoposteriorly	Superior facets directed posteriorly	Superior facets directed posteromedially (or medially)
	Inferior facets directed inferoanteriorly	Inferior facets directed anteriorly	Inferior facets directed anterolaterally (or laterally)
Movements allowed	Flexion and extension; lateral flexion; rotation; the spine region with the greatest range of movement	Rotation; lateral flexion possible but limited by ribs; flexion and extension prevented	Flexion and extension; some lateral flexion; rotation prevented

Superior view

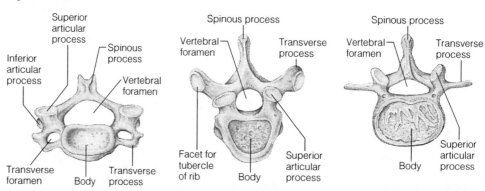

Right lateral view

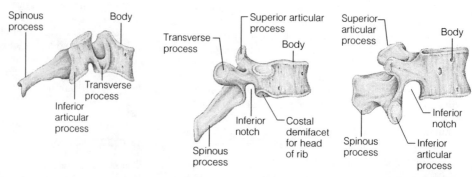

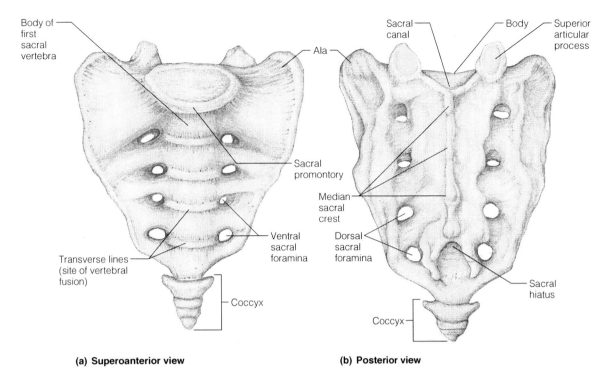

Body of first sacral vertebra

Ala

Sacral promontory

Transverse lines (site of vertebral fusion)

Ventral sacral foramina

Coccyx

Sacral canal

Body

Superior articular process

Median sacral crest

Dorsal sacral foramina

Sacral hiatus

Coccyx

(a) Superoanterior view

(b) Posterior view

Figure 14   Sacrum and coccyx. (a) Superoanterior view. **(b)** Posterior view.

are directed anterolaterally. These structural features reduce the mobility of the lumbar region of the spine. Since most stress on the vertebral column occurs in the lumbar region, these are also the sturdiest of the vertebrae.

The spinal cord ends at the superior edge of L_2, but the outer covering of the cord, filled with cerebrospinal fluid, extends an appreciable distance beyond. Thus a *lumbar puncture* (for examination of the cerebrospinal fluid) or the administration of "saddle block" anesthesia for childbirth is normally done between L_3 and L_4 or L_4 and L_5, where there is little or no chance of injuring the delicate spinal cord.

The Sacrum

The **sacrum** (Figure 14) is a composite bone formed from the fusion of five vertebrae. Superiorly it articulates with L_5, and inferiorly it connects with the coccyx. The **median sacral crest** is a remnant of the spinous processes of the fused vertebrae. The winglike **alae,** formed by fusion of the transverse processes, articulate laterally with the hip bones. The sacrum is slightly concave anteriorly and forms the posterior border of the pelvis. Four ridges (lines of fusion) cross the anterior part of the sacrum, and **sacral foramina** are located at either end of these ridges. These foramina allow blood vessels and nerves to pass. The vertebral canal continues inside the sacrum as the **sacral canal** and terminates near the coccyx via an enlarged opening called the **sacral hiatus.** The **sacral promontory** (anterior border of the body of S_1) is an important anatomical landmark for obstetricians.

• Attempt to palpate the median sacral crest of your sacrum. (This is more easily done by thin people and [obviously] in privacy.)

The Coccyx

The **coccyx** (see Figure 14) is formed from the fusion of three to five small irregularly shaped vertebrae. It is literally the human tailbone, a vestige of the tail that other vertebrates have. The coccyx is attached to the sacrum by ligaments.

A c t i v i t y :
Examining Vertebral Structure

Obtain examples of each type of vertebra and examine them carefully, comparing them to Figures 13, 14, and Table 1, and to each other. ■

The Bony Thorax

The **bony thorax** is composed of the sternum, ribs, and thoracic vertebrae (Figure 15). It is also referred to as the **thoracic cage** because of its appearance and because it forms a protective cone-shaped enclosure around the organs of the thoracic cavity (heart and lungs, for example).

The Sternum

The **sternum** (breastbone), a typical flat bone, is a result of the fusion of three bones—the manubrium, body, and xiphoid process. It is attached to the first seven pairs of ribs. The superiormost **manubrium** looks like the knot of a tie; it articulates with the clavicle (collarbone) laterally. The **body (gladiolus)** forms the bulk of the sternum. The **xiphoid**

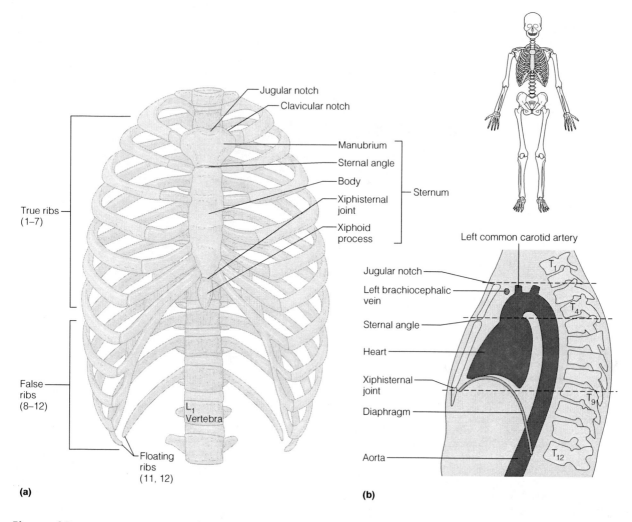

Figure 15 The bony thorax. (a) Skeleton of the bony thorax, anterior view (costal cartilages are shown in blue). **(b)** Left lateral view of the thorax, illustrating the relationship of the surface anatomical landmarks of the thorax to the vertebral column (thoracic portion).

process constructs the inferior end of the sternum and lies at the level of the fifth intercostal space. Although it is made of hyaline cartilage in children, it is usually ossified in adults.

In some people, the xiphoid process projects dorsally. This may present a problem because physical trauma to the chest can push such a xiphoid into the heart or liver (both immediately deep to the process), causing massive hemorrhage. ■

The sternum has three important bony landmarks—the jugular notch, the sternal angle, and the xiphisternal joint. The **jugular notch** (concave upper border of the manubrium) can be palpated easily; generally it is at the level of the third thoracic vertebra. The **sternal angle** is a result of the manubrium and body meeting at a slight angle to each other, so that a transverse ridge is formed at the level of the second ribs. It provides a handy reference point for counting ribs to locate the second intercostal space for listening to certain

heart valves, and is an important anatomical landmark for thoracic surgery. The **xiphisternal joint,** the point where the sternal body and xiphoid process fuse, lies at the level of the ninth thoracic vertebra.

• Palpate your sternal angle and jugular notch.

Because of its accessibility, the sternum is a favored site for obtaining samples of blood-forming (hematopoietic) tissue for the diagnosis of suspected blood diseases. A needle is inserted into the marrow of the sternum and the sample withdrawn (sternal puncture).

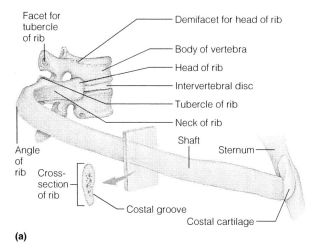

(a)

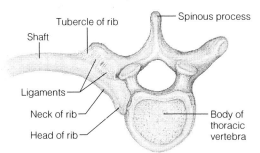

(b)

Figure 16 Structure of a "typical" true rib and its articulations. (a) Vertebral and sternal articulations of a typical true rib. **(b)** Superior view of the articulation between a rib and a thoracic vertebra, with costovertebral ligaments shown on left side only.

The Ribs

The 12 pairs of **ribs** form the walls of the thoracic cage (see Figures 15 and 16). All of the ribs articulate posteriorly with the vertebral column via their heads and tubercles and then curve downward and toward the anterior body surface. The first seven pairs, called the *true,* or *vertebrosternal, ribs,* attach directly to the sternum by their "own" costal cartilages. The next five pairs are called *false ribs;* they attach indirectly to the sternum or entirely lack a sternal attachment. Of these, rib pairs 8–10, which are also called *vertebrochondral ribs,* have indirect cartilage attachments to the sternum. The last two pairs, called *floating,* or *vertebral, ribs,* have no sternal attachment.

A c t i v i t y :
Examining the Relationship Between Ribs and Vertebrae

First take a deep breath to expand your chest. Notice how your ribs seem to move outward and how your sternum rises. Then examine an articulated skeleton to observe the relationship between the ribs and the vertebrae. ■

Illustrations: Table 1: Kristin Otwell. 1, 2, 3a, 6, and 12: Nadine Sokol. 3b, 8, and 15: Precision Graphics. 4 and 5: Wendy Hiller-Gee and Precision Graphics. 7, 13, 14, and 16: Laurie O'Keefe. 9: Vincent Perez. 10: Kristin Otwell. 11: Kristin Mount. **Photographs:** 4 and 5 From *A Stereoscopic Atlas of Human Anatomy,* by David L. Bassett. 9c: © Dr. Robert A. Chase.

The Axial Skeleton

The Skull

1. The skull is one of the major components of the axial skeleton. Name the other two:

   _____Spine cord_____ and _____Ribs_____

   What structures do each of these areas protect? _Skull protects brain_
   Spine Protects spinal cord
   Ribs protect heart, lungs, + liver

2. Define *suture*: _____

3. With one exception, the skull bones are joined by sutures. Name the exception. _____
   Parital to temporal bones

4. What are the four major sutures of the skull, and what bones do they connect? _____
   Coronal: frontal - Parietal
   Lamboidal: Parietal - occipital
   Squamos: Parietal - temporal
   Sagital: Parietal - Parietal

5. Name the eight bones composing the cranium.

   frontal   _temporal_   _sphenoid_   _____
   Parietal   _occipital_   _ethmoid_   _____

6. Give two possible functions of the sinuses. _lighten the bones,_
   act as resonance chambers for speech

7. What is the orbit? _eye socket_

   What bones contribute to the formation of the orbit? _frontal, sphenoid, maxilla, Ethmoid,_
   Zygomatic

8. Why can the sphenoid bone be called the keystone of the cranial floor? _It is located_
   in the center of the cranium and everything expands
   from that point

9. What is a cleft palate? _____

_____

10. Match the bone names in column B with the descriptions in column A.

	Column A		Column B
b	1. forehead bone		a. ethmoid
n	2. cheekbone		b. frontal
e	3. lower jaw		c. hyoid
c	4. bridge of nose		d. lacrimal
i	5. posterior bones of the hard palate		e. mandible
j	6. much of the lateral and superior cranium		f. maxilla
h	7. most posterior part of cranium		g. nasal
k	8. single, irregular, bat-shaped bone forming part of the cranial floor		h. occipital
d	9. tiny bones bearing tear ducts		i. palatine
~~f~~ i	10. anterior part of hard palate		j. parietal
a	11. superior and medial nasal conchae formed from its projections		k. sphenoid
l	12. site of mastoid process		l. temporal
k	13. site of sella turcica		m. vomer
a	14. site of cribriform plate		n. zygomatic
e	15. site of mental foramen		
l	16. site of styloid processes		
a , b , f , and			
k	17. four bones containing paranasal sinuses		
h	18. condyles here articulate with the atlas		
h	19. foramen magnum contained here		
c	20. small U-shaped bone in neck, where many tongue muscles attach		
l	21. middle ear found here		
c	22. nasal septum		
a	23. bears an upward protrusion, the "cock's comb," or crista galli		
e , f	24. contain alveoli bearing teeth		

Review Sheet

11. Using choices from column B in question 10 and from the numbered key to the right, identify all bones and bone markings provided with leader lines in the two diagrams below.

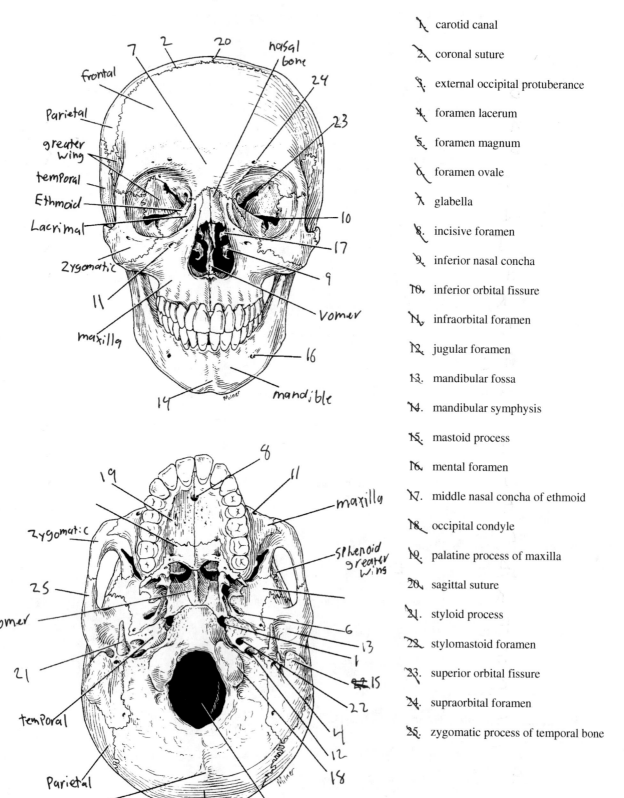

1. carotid canal
2. coronal suture
3. external occipital protuberance
4. foramen lacerum
5. foramen magnum
6. foramen ovale
7. glabella
8. incisive foramen
9. inferior nasal concha
10. inferior orbital fissure
11. infraorbital foramen
12. jugular foramen
13. mandibular fossa
14. mandibular symphysis
15. mastoid process
16. mental foramen
17. middle nasal concha of ethmoid
18. occipital condyle
19. palatine process of maxilla
20. sagittal suture
21. styloid process
22. stylomastoid foramen
23. superior orbital fissure
24. supraorbital foramen
25. zygomatic process of temporal bone

Review Sheet

The Vertebral Column

1. Using the key, correctly identify the vertebral parts/areas described below. (More than one choice may apply in some cases.) Also use the key letters to correctly identify the vertebral areas in the diagram.

Key: a. body   d. pedicle   g. transverse process
         b. intervertebral foramina   e. spinous process   h. vertebral arch
         c. lamina   f. superior articular process   i. vertebral foramen

_____I_____ 1. cavity enclosing the nerve cord

_____A_____ 2. weight-bearing portion of the vertebra

_____D_____ 3. provide levers against which muscles pull

_____g_____ 4. provide an articulation point for the ribs

_____B_____ 5. openings providing for exit of spinal nerves

_____I_____ 6. structures that form an enclosure for the spinal cord

2. The distinguishing characteristics of the vertebrae composing the vertebral column are noted below. Correctly identify each described structure/region by choosing a response from the key.

Key: a. atlas   d. coccyx   f. sacrum
         b. axis   e. lumbar vertebra   g. thoracic vertebra
         c. cervical vertebra—typical

___cervical___ 1. vertebral type containing foramina in the transverse processes, through which the vertebral arteries ascend to reach the brain

___axis___ 2. dens here provides a pivot for rotation of the first cervical vertebra (C_1)

___thoracic___ 3. transverse processes faceted for articulation with ribs; spinous process pointing sharply downward

___sacrum___ 4. composite bone; articulates with the hip bone laterally

___lumbar___ 5. massive vertebrae; weight-sustaining

___coccyx___ 6. "tail bone"; vestigial fused vertebrae

___atlas___ 7. supports the head; allows a rocking motion in conjunction with the occipital condyles

___cervical___ 8. seven components; unfused

___thoracic___ 9. twelve components; unfused

3. Identify specifically each of the vertebra types shown in the diagrams below. Also identify and label the following markings on each: transverse processes, spinous process, body, superior articular processes.

transverse
process

superior
articular
process

spinous
process

body

___transverse___

body

transverse
process

superior
articular
surface

spinous
process

___cervicle___

4. Describe how a spinal nerve exits from the vertebral column. _they leave through the intervertebral foraman_

5. Name two factors/structures that allow for flexibility of the vertebral column.

_____ and _____

6. What kind of tissue comprises the intervertebral discs? _____

7. What is a herniated disc? _____

What problems might it cause? _____

_____

8. Which two spinal curvatures are obvious at birth? ___Lordosis___ and

___scoliosis___

Under what conditions do the secondary curvatures develop? _____

_____

_____

9. On this illustration of an articulated vertebral column, identify each curvature indicated as a primary or a secondary curvature. Also identify by letter the terms in the column below and to the left.

a. atlas
b. axis
c. a disc
d. two thoracic vertebrae
e. two lumbar vertebrae
f. sacrum
g. vertebra prominens

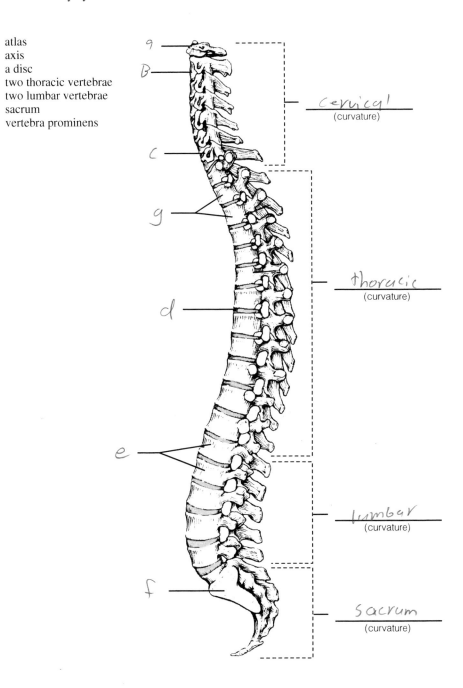

cervical
(curvature)

thoracic
(curvature)

lumbar
(curvature)

sacrum
(curvature)

10. Diagram the abnormal spinal curvatures named below. (Use posterior or lateral views as necessary.)

Lordosis   Scoliosis   Kyphosis

The Bony Thorax

1. The major components of the thorax (excluding the vertebral column) are the _ribs_
and the _Sternum_.

2. Differentiate between a true rib and a false rib. _True ribs attach to the sternum_
false ribs are ~~not~~ attached through cartilage

Is a floating rib a true or a false rib? _False_

3. What is the general shape of the thoracic cage? _____

4. Provide the more scientific name for the following rib types.

a. True ribs _____

b. False ribs (not including c) _____

c. Floating ribs _____

5. Using the terms at the right, identify the regions and landmarks of the bony thorax.

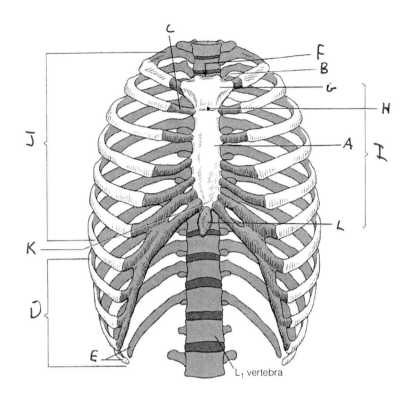

L₁ vertebra

a. body
b. clavicular notch
c. costal cartilage
d. false ribs
e. floating ribs
f. jugular notch
g. manubrium
h. sternal angle
i. sternum
j. true ribs
k. xiphisternal joint
l. xiphoid process

Axial Skeleton

Activity: Vertebra classification

The cervical, thoracic, and lumbar vertebra all have very distinct characteristics which enable you to tell them apart from each other. Inspect the three vertebra that are provided in the box of bones. Describe the differences that you see between them. How many vertebrae make up each section of the spine?

The Appendicular Skeleton

The **appendicular skeleton** is composed of the 126 bones of the appendages and the pectoral and pelvic girdles, which attach the limbs to the axial skeleton. Although the upper and lower limbs differ in their functions and mobility, they have the same fundamental plan, with each limb composed of three major segments connected together by freely movable joints.

Activity:
Examining and Identifying Bones of the Appendicular Skeleton

Carefully examine each of the bones described throughout this exercise and identify the characteristic bone markings of each. The markings aid in determining whether a bone is the right or left member of its pair. *This is a very important instruction because, before completing this laboratory exercise, you will be constructing your own skeleton.* Additionally, when corresponding X rays are available, compare the actual bone specimen to its X-ray image. ■

Bones of the Pectoral Girdle and Upper Extremity
The Pectoral (Shoulder) Girdle

The paired **pectoral,** or **shoulder, girdles** (Figure 1) each consist of two bones—the anterior clavicle and the posterior scapula. The shoulder girdles function to attach the upper

Objectives

1. To identify on an articulated skeleton the bones of the pectoral and pelvic girdles and their attached limbs.
2. To arrange unmarked, disarticulated bones in proper relative position to form the entire skeleton.
3. To differentiate between a male and a female pelvis.
4. To discuss the common features of the human appendicular girdles (pectoral and pelvic), and to note how their structure relates to their specialized functions.
5. To identify specific bone markings in the appendicular skeleton.

Materials

- ❑ Articulated skeletons
- ❑ Disarticulated skeletons (complete)
- ❑ Articulated pelves (male and female for comparative study)
- ❑ X rays of bones of the appendicular skeleton

See Appendix C, Exercise 11 for links to A.D.A.M. Interactive Anatomy.

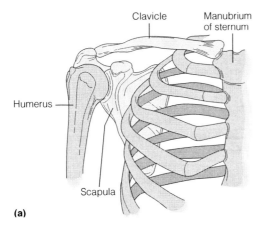

(a)

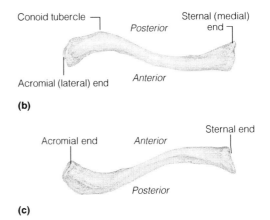

(b)

(c)

Figure 1 Bones of the pectoral (shoulder) girdle. (a) Right pectoral girdle articulated to show the relationship of the girdle to the bones of the thorax and arm. **(b)** Right clavicle, superior view. **(c)** Right clavicle, inferior view.

From *Human Anatomy & Physiology Laboratory Manual,* Main Version, Fifth Edition, Elaine N. Marieb.

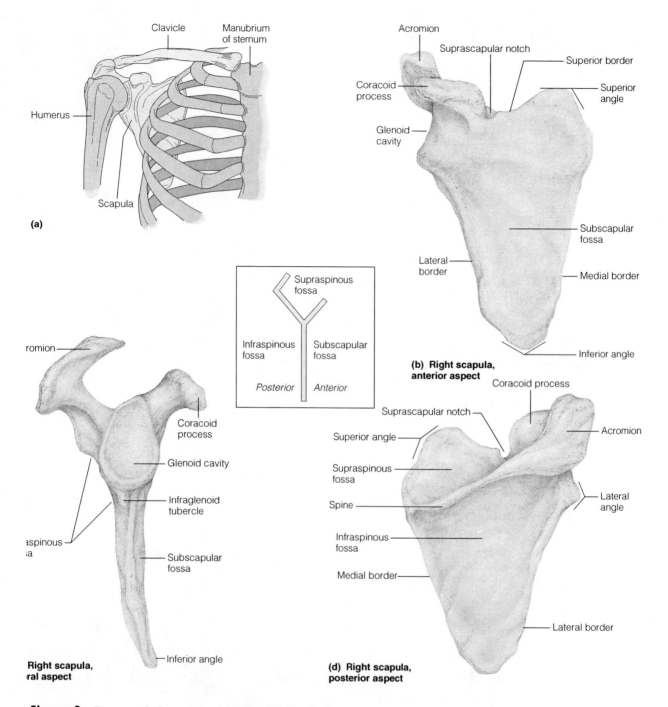

Figure 2 Bones of the pectoral (shoulder) girdle. (a) Right pectoral girdle articulated to show the relationship of the girdle to the bones of the thorax and arm. **(b–d)** Right scapula, anterior, lateral, and posterior views. View **(c)** is accompanied by a schematic representation of its orientation.

limbs to the axial skeleton. In addition, the bones of the shoulder girdles serve as attachment points for many trunk and neck muscles.

The **clavicle,** or collarbone, is a slender doubly curved bone—convex forward on its medial two-thirds and concave laterally. Its *sternal* (medial) *end,* which attaches to the sternal manubrium, is rounded or triangular in cross section. The

sternal end projects above the manubrium and can be felt and (usually) seen forming the lateral walls of the *jugular notch.* The *acromial* (lateral) *end* of the clavicle is flattened where it articulates with the scapula to form part of the shoulder joint. On its posteroinferior surface is the prominent **conoid tubercle.** This projection anchors a ligament and provides a handy landmark for determining whether a given clavicle is from

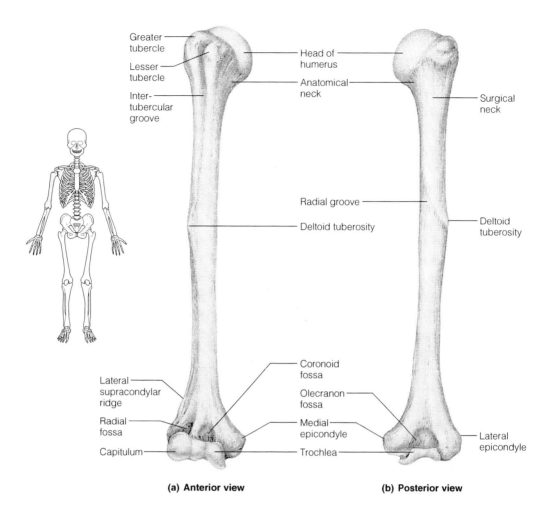

Greater tubercle

Lesser tubercle

Inter-tubercular groove

Head of humerus

Anatomical neck

Surgical neck

Radial groove

Deltoid tuberosity

Deltoid tuberosity

Lateral supracondylar ridge

Radial fossa

Capitulum

Coronoid fossa

Olecranon fossa

Medial epicondyle

Trochlea

Lateral epicondyle

(a) Anterior view

(b) Posterior view

Figure 3 Bone of the right arm. (a) Humerus, anterior view. **(b)** Humerus, posterior view.

the right or left side of the body. The clavicle serves as an anterior brace, or strut, to hold the arm away from the top of the thorax.

The **scapulae** (Figure 2), or shoulder blades, are generally triangular and are commonly called the "wings" of humans. Each scapula has a flattened body and two important processes—the **acromion** (the enlarged end of the spine of the scapula) and the beaklike **coracoid process** (*corac* = crow, raven). The acromion connects with the clavicle; the coracoid process points anteriorly over the tip of the shoulder joint and serves as an attachment point for some of the upper limb muscles. The **suprascapular notch** at the base of the coracoid process allows nerves to pass. The scapula has no direct attachment to the axial skeleton but is loosely held in place by trunk muscles.

The scapula has three angles: superior, inferior, and lateral. The inferior angle provides a landmark for auscultating (listening to) lung sounds. The scapula also has three named borders: superior, medial (vertebral), and lateral (axillary). Several shallow depressions (fossae) appear on both sides of the scapula and are named according to location; i.e., there are the *anterior subscapular fossa* and the *posterior infraspinous* and *supraspinous fossae*. The **glenoid cavity,** a shal-

low socket that receives the head of the arm bone (humerus), is located in the lateral angle.

The shoulder girdle is exceptionally light and allows the upper limb a degree of mobility not seen anywhere else in the body. This is due to the following factors:

• The sternoclavicular joints are the *only* site of attachment of the shoulder girdles to the axial skeleton.

• The relative looseness of the scapular attachment allows it to slide back and forth against the thorax with muscular activity.

• The glenoid cavity is shallow, and does little to stabilize the shoulder joint.

However, this exceptional flexibility exacts a price: the arm bone (humerus) is very susceptible to dislocation, and fracture of the clavicle disables the entire upper limb.

The Arm

The arm (Figure 3) consists of a single bone—the **humerus,** a typical long bone. Proximally its rounded *head* fits into the shallow glenoid cavity of the scapula. The head is

69

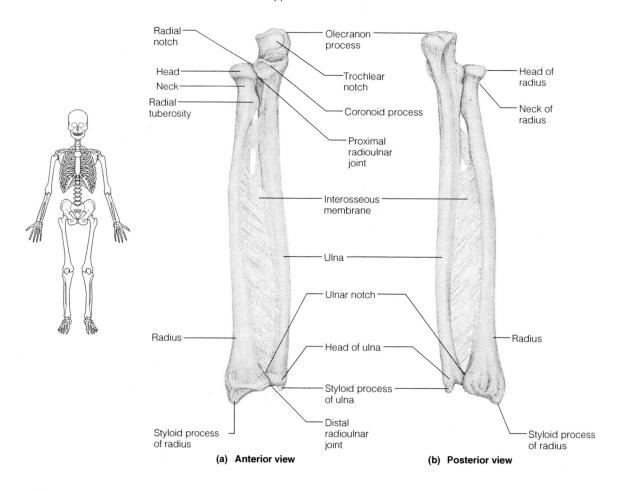

Radial notch

Head
Neck
Radial tuberosity

Olecranon process

Trochlear notch

Coronoid process

Proximal radioulnar joint

Interosseous membrane

Ulna

Ulnar notch

Head of ulna

Styloid process of ulna

Distal radioulnar joint

Radius

Styloid process of radius

Head of radius

Neck of radius

Radius

Styloid process of radius

(a) Anterior view

(b) Posterior view

Figure 4   Bones of the right forearm. (a) Radius and ulna, anterior view. **(b)** Posterior view.

separated from the shaft by the *anatomical neck* and the more constricted *surgical neck,* which is a common site of fracture. Opposite the head are two prominences, the **greater** and **lesser tubercles** (from lateral to medial aspect), separated by a groove (the **intertubercular** or **bicipital groove**) that guides the tendon of the biceps muscle to its point of attachment (the superior rim of the glenoid cavity). In the midpoint of the shaft is a roughened area, the **deltoid tuberosity,** where the large fleshy shoulder muscle, the deltoid, attaches. Just inferior to the deltoid tuberosity is the **radial groove,** which indicates the pathway of the radial nerve.

At the distal end of the humerus are two condyles—the medial **trochlea** (looking rather like a spool), which articulates with the ulna, and the lateral **capitulum,** which articulates with the radius of the forearm. This condyle pair is flanked medially by the **medial epicondyle** and laterally by the **lateral epicondyle.**

The medial epicondyle is commonly called the "funny bone." The large ulnar nerve runs in a groove beneath the medial epicondyle, and when this region is sharply bumped, we are likely to experience a temporary, but excruciatingly painful, tingling sensation. This event is called "hitting the funny bone," a strange expression, because it is certainly *not* funny!

Above the trochlea on the anterior surface is a depression, the **coronoid fossa;** on the posterior surface is the **olecranon fossa.** These two depressions allow the corresponding processes of the ulna to move freely when the elbow is flexed and extended. The small **radial fossa,** lateral to the coronoid fossa, receives the head of the radius when the elbow is flexed.

The Forearm

Two bones, the radius and the ulna, compose the skeleton of the forearm, or antebrachium (see Figure 4). When the body is in the anatomical position, the **radius** is in the lateral position in the forearm and the radius and ulna are parallel. Proximally, the disc-shaped head of the radius articulates with the capitulum of the humerus. Just below the head, on

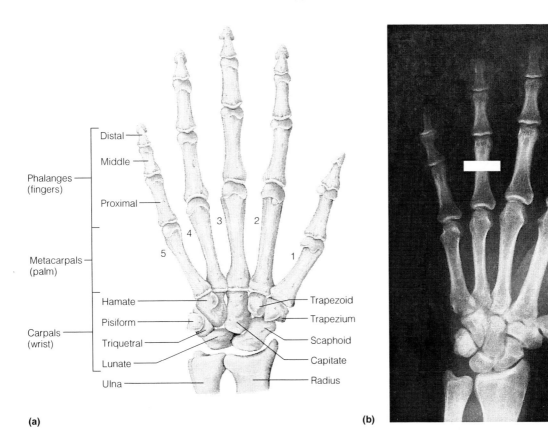

Figure 5 Bones of the right hand. (a) Anterior view showing the relationships of the carpals, metacarpals, and phalanges. **(b)** X ray. White bar on the proximal phalanx of the ring finger shows the position at which a ring would be worn.

the medial aspect of the shaft, is a prominence called the **radial tuberosity,** the point of attachment for the tendon of the biceps muscle of the arm. Distally, the small **ulnar notch** reveals where it articulates with the end of the ulna.

The **ulna** is the medial bone of the forearm. Its proximal end bears the anterior **coronoid process** and the posterior **olecranon process,** which are separated by the **trochlear notch.** Together these processes grip the trochlea of the humerus in a plierslike joint. The small **radial notch** on the lateral side of the coronoid process articulates with the head of the radius. The slimmer distal end, the ulnar head, bears a small medial **styloid process,** which serves as a point of attachment for the ligaments of the wrist.

The Hand

The skeleton of the hand, or manus (Figure 5), includes three groups of bones, those of the carpus (wrist), the metacarpals (bones of the palm), and the phalanges (bones of the fingers).

The wrist is the proximal portion of the hand. It is referred to anatomically as the **carpus;** the eight bones composing it are the **carpals.** (So you actually wear your wristwatch over the distal part of your forearm.) The carpals are arranged in two irregular rows of four bones each, which are illustrated in Figure 5. In the proximal row (lateral to medial)

are the scaphoid, lunate, triangular, and pisiform bones; the scaphoid and lunate articulate with the distal end of the radius. In the distal row are the trapezium, trapezoid, capitate, and hamate. The carpals are bound closely together by ligaments, which restrict movements between them.

The **metacarpals,** numbered 1 to 5 from the thumb side of the hand toward the little finger, radiate out from the wrist like spokes to form the palm of the hand. The *bases* of the metacarpals articulate with the carpals of the wrist; their more bulbous *heads* articulate with the phalanges of the fingers distally. When the fist is clenched, the heads of the metacarpals become prominent as the knuckles.

Like the bones of the palm, the fingers are numbered from 1 to 5, beginning from the thumb (*pollex*) side of the hand. The 14 bones of the fingers, or digits, are miniature long bones, called **phalanges** as noted above. Each finger contains three phalanges (proximal, middle, and distal) except the thumb which has only two (proximal and distal).

A c t i v i t y :
Palpating the Surface Anatomy of the Pectoral Girdle and the Upper Limb

Before continuing on to study the bones of the pelvic girdle, take the time to identify the following bone markings on the skin surface of the upper limb. It is usually preferable to observe and palpate the bone markings on your lab partner, particularly since many of these markings can only be seen from the dorsal aspect.

- Clavicle: Palpate the clavicle along its entire length from sternum to shoulder.

- Acromioclavicular joint: The high point of the shoulder, which represents the junction point between the clavicle and the acromion of the scapular spine.

- Spine of the scapula: Extend your arm at the shoulder so that your scapula moves posteriorly. As you do this, your scapular spine will be seen as a winglike protrusion on your dorsal thorax and can be easily palpated by your lab partner.

- Lateral epicondyle of the humerus: The inferiormost projection at the lateral aspect of the distal humerus. After you have located the epicondyle, run your finger posteriorly into the hollow immediately dorsal to the epicondyle. This is the site where the extensor muscles of the hand are attached and is a common site of the excruciating pain of tennis elbow, a condition in which those muscles and their tendons are abused physically.

- Medial epicondyle of the humerus: Feel this medial projection at the distal end of the humerus.

- Olecranon process of the ulna: Work your elbow—flexing and extending—as you palpate its dorsal aspect to feel the olecranon process of the ulna moving into and out of the olecranon fossa on the dorsal aspect of the humerus.

- Styloid process of the ulna: With the hand in the anatomical position, feel out this small inferior projection on the medial aspect of the distal end of the ulna.

- Styloid process of the radius: Find this projection at the distal end of the radius (lateral aspect). It is most easily located by moving the hand medially at the wrist. Once you have palpated the styloid process, move your fingers just medially onto the anterior wrist. Press firmly and then let up slightly on the pressure. You should be able to feel your pulse at this pressure point, which lies over the radial artery (radial pulse).

- Metacarpophalangeal joints (knuckles): Clench your fist and find the first set of flexed-joint protrusions beyond the wrist—these are your metacarpophalangeal joints. ■

Bones of the Pelvic Girdle and Lower Limb

The Pelvic (Hip) Girdle

As with the bones of the pectoral girdle and upper limb, pay particular attention to bone markings needed to identify right and left bones.

The **pelvic girdle,** or **hip girdle** (Figure 6), is formed by the two **coxal** (*coxa* = hip) **bones** (also called the **ossa coxae** or hip bones). The two coxal bones together with the sacrum and coccyx form the **bony pelvis.** In contrast to the bones of the shoulder girdle, those of the pelvic girdle are heavy and massive, and they attach securely to the axial skeleton. The sockets for the heads of the femurs (thigh bones) are deep and heavily reinforced by ligaments to ensure a stable, strong limb attachment. The ability to bear

weight is more important here than mobility and flexibility. The combined weight of the upper body rests on the pelvis (specifically, where the hip bones meet the sacrum).

Each coxal bone is a result of the fusion of three bones—the ilium, ischium, and pubis—which are distinguishable in the young child. The **ilium,** a large flaring bone, forms the major portion of the coxal bone. It connects posteriorly, via its **auricular surface,** with the sacrum at the **sacroiliac joint.** The superior margin of the iliac bone, the **iliac crest,** is rough; when you rest your hands on your hips, you are palpating your iliac crests. The iliac crest terminates anteriorly in the **anterior superior spine** and posteriorly in the **posterior superior spine.** Two inferior spines are located below these. The shallow **iliac fossa** marks its internal surface, and a prominent ridge, the **arcuate line,** outlines the pelvic inlet, or pelvic brim.

The **ischium** is the "sit-down" bone, forming the most inferior and posterior portion of the coxal bone. The most outstanding marking on the ischium is the rough **ischial tuberosity,** which receives the weight of the body when sitting. The **ischial spine,** superior to the ischial tuberosity, is an important anatomical landmark of the pelvic cavity. (See Comparison of the Male and Female Pelves, below.) The obvious **lesser** and **greater sciatic notches** allow nerves and blood vessels to pass to and from the thigh. The sciatic nerve passes through the latter.

The **pubis** is the most anterior portion of the coxal bone. Fusion of the **rami** of the pubic bone anteriorly and the ischium posteriorly forms a bar of bone enclosing the **obturator foramen,** through which blood vessels and nerves run from the pelvic cavity into the thigh. The pubic bones of each hip bone meet anteriorly at the **pubic crest** to form a cartilaginous joint called the **pubic symphysis.** At the lateral end of the pubic crest is the *pubic tubercle* (see Figure 6c) to which the important *inguinal ligament* attaches.

The ilium, ischium, and pubis fuse at the deep hemispherical socket called the **acetabulum** (literally, "vinegar cup"), which receives the head of the thigh bone.

Activity:
Observing Pelvic Articulations

Before continuing with the bones of the lower limbs, take the time to examine an articulated pelvis. Notice how each coxal bone articulates with the sacrum posteriorly and how the two coxal bones join at the pubic symphysis. The sacroiliac joint is a common site of lower back problems because of the pressure it must bear. ■

Comparison of the Male and Female Pelves Although bones of males are usually larger, heavier, and have more prominent bone markings, the male and female skeletons are very similar. The outstanding exception to this generalization is pelvic structure.

The female pelvis reflects modifications for childbearing. Generally speaking, the female pelvis is wider, shallower, lighter, and rounder than that of the male. Not only must her pelvis support the increasing size of a fetus, but it must also be large enough to allow the infant's head (its largest dimension) to descend through the birth canal at birth.

To describe pelvic sex differences, we need to introduce a few more terms. Anatomically, the pelvis is described in

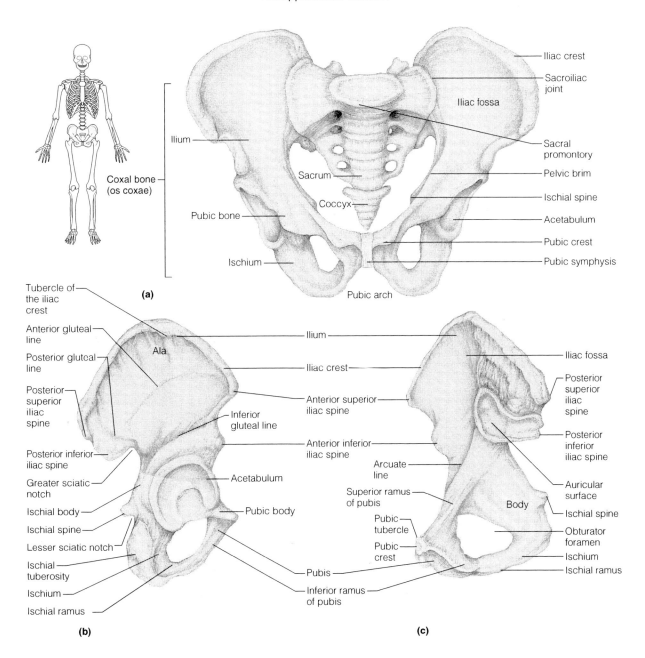

Figure 6 **Bones of the pelvic girdle.** **(a)** Articulated bony pelvis, showing the two coxal bones, which together comprise the pelvic girdle, and the sacrum. **(b)** Right coxal bone, lateral view, showing the point of fusion of the ilium, ischium, and pubic bones. **(c)** Right coxal bone, medial view.

terms of a false pelvis and a true pelvis. The **false pelvis** is that portion superior to the arcuate line; it is bounded by the alae of the ilia laterally and the sacral promontory and lumbar vertebrae posteriorly. Although the false pelvis supports the abdominal viscera, it does not restrict childbirth in any way. The **true pelvis** is the region inferior to the arcuate line that is almost entirely surrounded by bone. Its posterior boundary is formed by the sacrum. The ilia, ischia, and pubic bones define its limits laterally and anteriorly.

The dimensions of the true pelvis, particularly its inlet and outlet, are critical if delivery of a baby is to be uncomplicated; and they are carefully measured by the obstetrician. The **pelvic inlet,** or **pelvic brim,** is the opening delineated by the sacral promontory posteriorly and the arcuate lines of the ilia anterolaterally. It is the superiormost margin of the true pelvis. Its widest dimension is from left to right, that is, along the frontal plane. The **pelvic outlet** is the inferior margin of the true pelvis. It is bounded anteriorly by the pelvic arch, laterally by the ischia, and posteriorly by the sacrum and coccyx.

Table 1	Comparison of the Male and Female Pelves	
Characteristic	**Female**	**Male**
General structure and functional modifications	Tilted forward; adapted for childbearing; true pelvis defines the birth canal; cavity of the true pelvis is broad, shallow, and has a greater capacity	Tilted less far forward; adapted for support of a male's heavier build and stronger muscles; cavity of the true pelvis is narrow and deep
Bone thickness	Less; bones lighter, thinner, and smoother	Greater; bones heavier and thicker, and markings are more prominent
Acetabula	Smaller; farther apart	Larger; closer
Pubic angle/arch	Broader (80° to 90°); more rounded	Angle is more acute (50° to 60°)
Anterior view	Pelvic brim	
Sacrum	Wider; shorter; sacral curvature is accentuated	Narrow; longer; sacral promontory more ventral
Coccyx	More movable; straighter	Less movable; curves ventrally
Left lateral view		
Pelvic inlet (brim)	Wider; oval from side to side	Narrow; basically heart shaped
Pelvic outlet	Wider; ischial tuberosities shorter, farther apart and everted	Narrower; ischial tuberosities longer, sharper, and point more medially
Posteroinferior view		

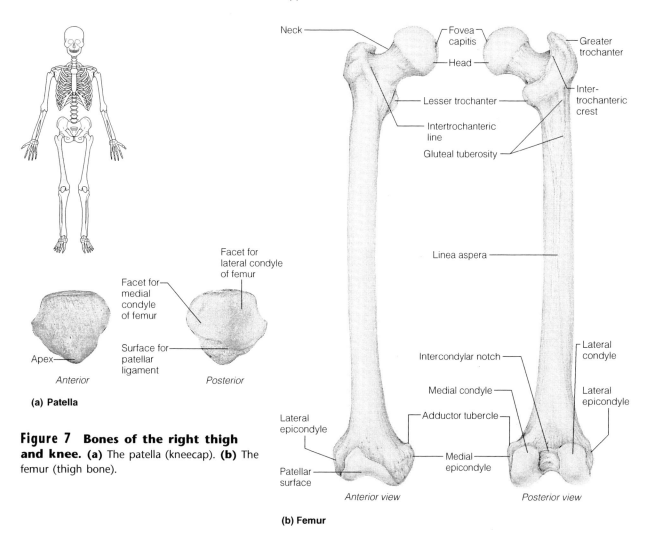

Figure 7 **Bones of the right thigh and knee. (a)** The patella (kneecap). **(b)** The femur (thigh bone).

(a) Patella

Facet for lateral condyle of femur

Facet for medial condyle of femur

Surface for patellar ligament

Apex

Anterior

Posterior

Neck

Fovea capitis

Head

Greater trochanter

Lesser trochanter

Inter-trochanteric crest

Intertrochanteric line

Gluteal tuberosity

Linea aspera

Intercondylar notch

Medial condyle

Lateral epicondyle

Lateral condyle

Lateral epicondyle

Adductor tubercle

Patellar surface

Medial epicondyle

Anterior view

Posterior view

(b) Femur

Since both the coccyx and the ischial spines protrude into the outlet opening, a sharply angled coccyx or large, sharp ischial spines can dramatically narrow the outlet. The largest dimension of the outlet is the anterior-posterior diameter.

The major differences between the male and female pelves are summarized in Table 1.

Activity:
Comparing Male and Female Pelves

Examine male and female pelves for the following differences:

• The female inlet is larger and more circular.

• The female pelvis as a whole is shallower, and the bones are lighter and thinner.

• The female sacrum is broader and less curved, and the pubic arch is more rounded.

• The female acetabula are smaller and farther apart, and the ilia flare more laterally.

• The female ischial spines are shorter, farther apart, and everted, thus enlarging the pelvic outlet. ■

The Thigh

The **femur,** or thigh bone (Figure 7b), is the sole bone of the thigh. It is the heaviest, strongest bone in the body. The ball-like head of the femur articulates with the hip bone via the deep, secure socket of the acetabulum. Obvious in the femur's head is a small central pit called the **fovea capitis** ("pit of the head") from which a small ligament runs to the acetabulum. The head of the femur is carried on a short, constricted *neck,* which angles laterally to join the shaft. The neck is the weakest part of the femur and is a common fracture site (an injury called a broken hip), particularly in the elderly. At the junction of the shaft and neck are the **greater** and **lesser trochanters** (separated posteriorly by the **intertrochanteric crest** and anteriorly by the **intertrochanteric line**). The trochanters and trochanteric crest, as well as the **gluteal tuberosity** and the **linea aspera** located on the shaft, are sites of muscle attachment.

The femur inclines medially as it runs downward to the leg bones; this brings the knees in line with the body's center

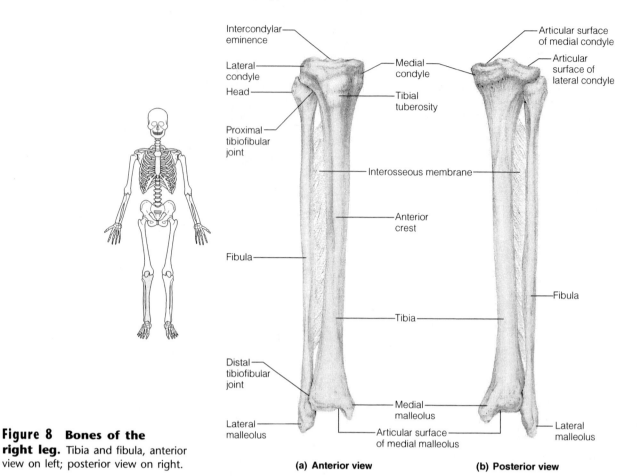

Figure 8 Bones of the right leg. Tibia and fibula, anterior view on left; posterior view on right.

(a) Anterior view

(b) Posterior view

of gravity, or maximum weight. The medial course of the femur is more noticeable in females because of the wider female pelvis.

Distally, the femur terminates in the **lateral** and **medial condyles,** which articulate with the tibia below, and the **patellar surface,** which forms a joint with the patella (kneecap) anteriorly. The **lateral** and **medial epicondyles,** just superior to the condyles, are separated by the **intercondylar notch.** On the superior part of the medial epicondyle is a bump, the **adductor tubercle,** to which the large adductor magnus muscle attaches.

The **patella** (Figure 7a) is a triangular sesamoid bone enclosed in the (quadriceps) tendon that secures the anterior thigh muscles to the tibia. It guards the knee joint anteriorly and improves the leverage of the thigh muscles acting across the knee joint.

The Leg

Two bones, the tibia and the fibula, form the skeleton of the leg (see Figure 8). The **tibia,** or *shinbone,* is the larger and more medial of the two leg bones. At the proximal end, the **medial** and **lateral condyles** (separated by the **intercondylar eminence**) receive the distal end of the femur to form the knee joint. The **tibial tuberosity,** a roughened protrusion on the anterior tibial surface (just below the condyles), is the site of attachment of the patellar (kneecap) ligament. Small facets on its superior and inferior lateral surface articulate with the

fibula. Distally, a process called the **medial malleolus** forms the inner (medial) bulge of the ankle, and the smaller distal end articulates with the talus bone of the foot. The anterior surface of the tibia bears a sharpened ridge that is relatively unprotected by muscles. This so-called **anterior crest** is easily felt beneath the skin.

The **fibula,** which lies parallel to the tibia, takes no part in forming the knee joint. Its proximal head articulates with the lateral condyle of the tibia. The fibula is thin and sticklike with a sharp anterior crest. It terminates distally in the **lateral malleolus,** which forms the outer part, or lateral bulge, of the ankle.

The Foot

The bones of the foot include the 7 **tarsal** bones, 5 **metatarsals,** which form the instep, and 14 **phalanges,** which form the toes (see Figure 9). Body weight is concentrated on the two largest tarsals which form the posterior aspect of the foot, the *calcaneus* (heel bone) and the *talus,* which lies between the tibia and the calcaneus. The other tarsals are named and identified in Figure 9. Like the fingers of the hand, each toe has 3 phalanges except the great toe, which has 2.

The bones in the foot are arranged to produce three strong arches—two longitudinal arches (medial and lateral) and one transverse arch (Figure 9b). Ligaments, binding the foot bones together, and tendons of the foot muscles hold the

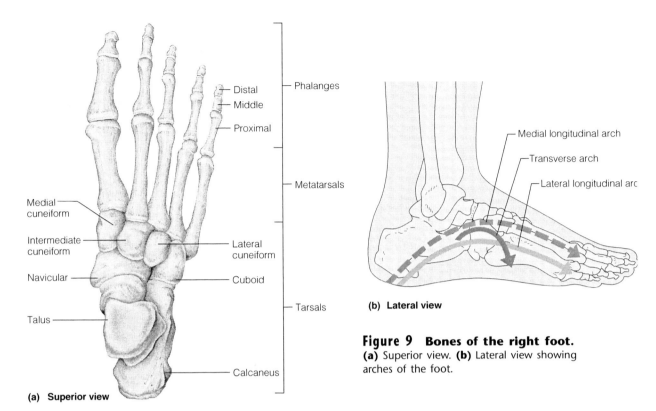

(a) **Superior view**

Figure 9   Bones of the right foot.
(a) Superior view. (b) Lateral view showing arches of the foot.

bones firmly in the arched position but still allow a certain degree of give. Weakened arches are referred to as fallen arches or flat feet.

Activity:
Palpating the Surface Anatomy of the Pelvic Girdle and Lower Limb

Locate and palpate the following bone markings on yourself and/or your lab partner.

•   Iliac crest and anterior superior iliac spine: Rest your hands on your hips—they will be overlying the iliac crests. Trace the crest as far posteriorly as you can and then follow it anteriorly to the anterior superior iliac spine. This latter bone marking is easily felt in almost everyone, and is clearly visible through the skin (and perhaps the clothing) of very slim people. (The posterior superior iliac spine is much less obvious and is usually indicated only by a dimple in the overlying skin. Check it out in the mirror tonight.)

•   Greater trochanter of the femur: This is easier to locate in females than in males because of the wider female pelvis; also it is more likely to be clothed by bulky muscles in males. Try to locate it on yourself as the most lateral point of the proximal femur. It typically lies about 6–8 inches below the iliac crest.

•   Patella and tibial tuberosity: Feel your kneecap and palpate the ligaments attached to its borders. Follow the inferior patellar ligament to the tibial tuberosity.

•   Medial and lateral condyles of the femur and tibia: As you move from the patella inferiorly on the medial (and then the lateral) knee surface, you will feel first the femoral and then the tibial condyle.

•   Medial malleolus: Feel the medial protrusion of your ankle, the medial malleolus of the distal tibia.

•   Lateral malleolus: Feel the bulge of the lateral aspect of your ankle, the lateral malleolus of the fibula.

•   Calcaneus: Attempt to follow the extent of your calcaneus or heel bone. ■

Activity:
Constructing a Skeleton

1.   When you finish examining the disarticulated bones of the appendicular skeleton and yourself, work with your lab partner to arrange the disarticulated bones on the laboratory bench in their proper relative positions to form an entire skeleton. Careful observations of the bone markings should help you distinguish between right and left members of bone pairs.

2.   When you believe that you have accomplished this task correctly, ask the instructor to check your arrangement to ensure that it is correct. If it is not, go to the articulated skeleton and check your bone arrangements. Also review the descriptions of the bone markings as necessary to correct your bone arrangement. ■

Illustrations: Table 1: Kristin Otwell. 1a, 2a, and 9b: Precision Graphics. 1b and c, 2b–d, and 3–8: Laurie O'Keefe. 9a: Kristin Otwell.
Photographs: Table 1: From *A Stereoscopic Atlas of Human Anatomy,* by David L. Bassett. 5b: Department of Anatomy and Histology, University of California, San Francisco. 7a: © Benjamin/Cummings Publishing. Photo by BioMed Arts Associates, Inc.

The Appendicular Skeleton

Bones of the Pectoral Girdle and Upper Extremity

1. Match the bone names or markings in column B with the descriptions in column A.

Column A

_____G_____ 1. raised area on lateral surface of humerus to which deltoid muscle attaches

_____I_____ 2. arm bone

_____P_____ , _____D_____ 3. bones of the shoulder girdle

_____O_____ , _____T_____ 4. forearm bones

_____q_____ 5. scapular region to which the clavicle connects

_____P_____ 6. shoulder girdle bone that is unattached to the axial skeleton

_____D_____ 7. shoulder girdle bone that transmits forces from the upper limb to the bony thorax

_____H_____ 8. depression in the scapula that articulates with the humerus

_____E_____ 9. process above the glenoid cavity that permits muscle attachment

_____d_____ 10. the "collarbone"

_____S_____ 11. distal condyle of the humerus that articulates with the ulna

_____t_____ 12. medial bone of forearm in anatomical position

_____b_____ 13. rounded knob on the humerus; adjoins the radius

_____K_____ 14. anterior depression, superior to the trochlea, which receives part of the ulna when the forearm is flexed

_____t_____ 15. forearm bone involved in formation of the elbow joint

_____C_____ 16. wrist bones

_____m_____ 17. finger bones

_____m_____ 18. heads of these bones form the knuckles

_____Q_____ , _____P_____ 19. bones that articulate with the clavicle

Column B

a. acromion

b. capitulum

c. carpals

d. clavicle

e. coracoid process

f. coronoid fossa

g. deltoid tuberosity

h. glenoid cavity

i. humerus

j. metacarpals

k. olecranon fossa

l. olecranon process

m. phalanges

n. radial tuberosity

o. radius

p. scapula

q. sternum

r. styloid process

s. trochlea

t. ulna

2. Why is the clavicle at risk to fracture when a person falls on his or her shoulder? _____

_____

3. Why is there generally no problem in the arm clearing the widest dimension of the thoracic cage?

_____

_____

4. What is the total number of phalanges in the hand? _____14_____

5. What is the total number of carpals in the wrist? _____8_____

In the proximal row, the carpals are (medial to lateral) _triquetral, Lunate, scaphoid_____

In the distal row, they are (medial to lateral) _Pisiform, hamate, capitate, trapezoid, trapezium_

6. Using items from the list at the right, identify the anatomical landmarks and regions of the scapula.

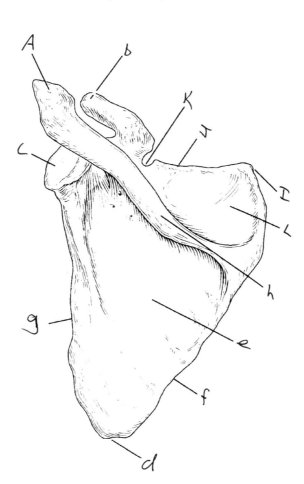

a. acromion

b. coracoid process

c. glenoid cavity

d. inferior angle

e. infraspinous fossa

f. lateral border

g. medial border

h. spine

i. superior angle

j. superior border

k. suprascapular notch

l. supraspinous fossa

7. Match the terms in the key with the appropriate leader lines on the photos of the humerus and the radius and ulna. Also decide whether these bones are right or left bones.

Key:

Key:

a. anatomical neck

b. coronoid process

c. distal radioulnar joint

d. greater tubercle

e. head of humerus

f. head of radius

g. head of ulna

h. lateral epicondyle

i. medial epicondyle

j. olecranon fossa

k. olecranon process

l. proximal radioulnar joint

m. radial groove

n. radial notch

o. radial tuberosity

p. styloid process of radius

q. styloid process of ulna

r. surgical neck

s. trochlea

t. trochlear notch

The humerus is a ___Left___ bone; the radius and ulna are ___Right___ bones.

Bones of the Pelvic Girdle and Lower Limb

1. Compare the pectoral and pelvic girdles by choosing appropriate descriptive terms from the key.

Key: a. flexibility most important d. insecure axial and limb attachments
     b. massive e. secure axial and limb attachments
     c. lightweight f. weight-bearing most important

Pectoral: _____, _____, _____   Pelvic: _____, _____, _____

2. What organs are protected, at least in part, by the pelvic girdle? _____

_____

3. Distinguish between the true pelvis and the false pelvis. _____

_____

_____

4. Use letters from the key to identify the bone markings on this illustration of an articulated pelvis. Make an educated guess as to whether the illustration shows a male or female pelvis and provide two reasons for your decision.

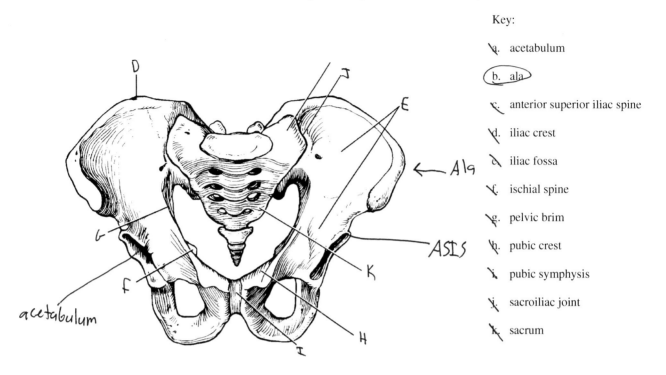

Key:

a. acetabulum

b. ala

c. anterior superior iliac spine

d. iliac crest

e. iliac fossa

f. ischial spine

g. pelvic brim

h. pubic crest

i. pubic symphysis

j. sacroiliac joint

k. sacrum

This is a __male__ (female/male) pelvis because:

a female pelvis has more of a U shape

5. Deduce why the pelvic bones of a four-legged animal such as the cat or pig are much less massive than those of the human.

6. A person instinctively curls over his abdominal area in times of danger. Why? _____

7. For what anatomical reason do many women appear to be slightly knock-kneed? _____

8. What does *fallen arches* mean? _____

9. Match the bone names and markings in column B with the descriptions in column A.

Column A

_____I_____, _____K_____, and

_____T_____ 1. fuse to form the coxal bone

_____K_____ 2. inferoposterior "bone" of the coxal bone

_____S_____ 3. point where the coxal bones join anteriorly

_____H_____ 4. superiormost margin of the coxal bone

_____A_____ 5. deep socket in the coxal bone that receives the head of the thigh bone

_____U_____ 6. joint between axial skeleton and pelvic girdle

_____C_____ 7. longest, strongest bone in body

_____D_____ 8. thin lateral leg bone

_____X_____ 9. heavy medial leg bone

_____C_____, _____X_____ 10. bones forming knee joint

_____Y_____ 11. point where the patellar ligament attaches

_____R_____ 12. kneecap

_____X_____ 13. shin bone

_____O_____ 14. medial ankle projection

_____L_____ 15. lateral ankle projection

_____B_____ 16. largest tarsal bone

_____W_____ 17. ankle bones

_____Q_____ 18. bones forming the instep of the foot

_____P_____ 19. opening in hip bone formed by the pubic and ischial rami

_____E_____ and _____G_____ 20. sites of muscle attachment on the proximal femur

_____V_____ 21. tarsal bone that "sits" on the calcaneus

Column B

a. acetabulum

b. calcaneus

c. femur

d. fibula

e. gluteal tuberosity

f. greater sciatic notch

g. greater and lesser trochanters

h. iliac crest

i. ilium

j. ischial tuberosity

k. ischium

l. lateral malleolus

m. lesser sciatic notch

n. linea aspera

o. medial malleolus

p. obturator foramen

q. metatarsals

r. patella

s. pubic symphysis

t. pubis

u. sacroiliac joint

v. talus

w. tarsals

x. tibia

y. tibial tuberosity

10. Match the terms in the key with the appropriate leader lines on the photos of the femur and the tibia and fibula. Also decide if these bones are right or left bones.

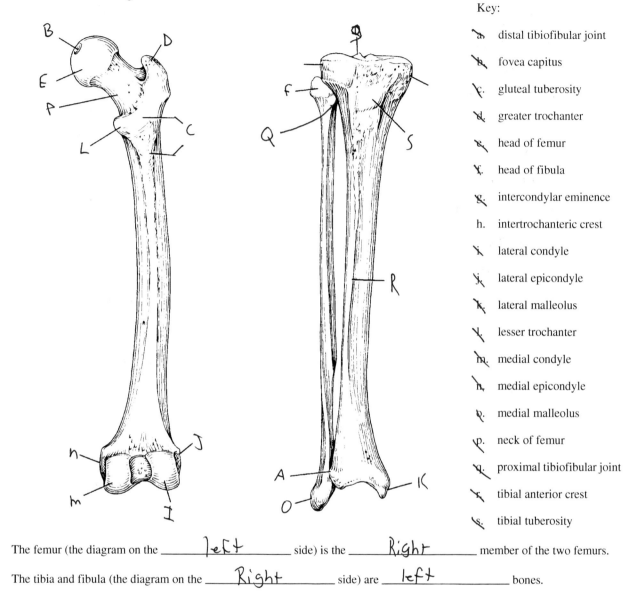

Key:

a. distal tibiofibular joint

b. fovea capitus

c. gluteal tuberosity

d. greater trochanter

e. head of femur

f. head of fibula

g. intercondylar eminence

h. intertrochanteric crest

i. lateral condyle

j. lateral epicondyle

k. lateral malleolus

l. lesser trochanter

m. medial condyle

n. medial epicondyle

o. medial malleolus

p. neck of femur

q. proximal tibiofibular joint

r. tibial anterior crest

s. tibial tuberosity

The femur (the diagram on the _____left_____ side) is the _____Right_____ member of the two femurs.

The tibia and fibula (the diagram on the _____Right_____ side) are _____left_____ bones.

Summary of Skeleton

1. Identify all indicated bones (or groups of bones) in the diagram of the articulated skeleton on the next page.

@ do this

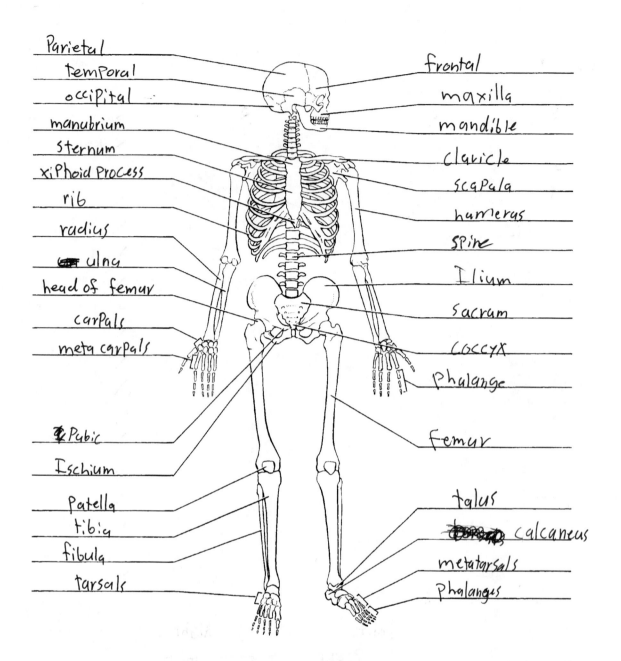

Parietal

temporal

occipital

manubrium

sternum

xiPhoid Process

rib

radius

ulna

head of femur

carpals

meta carpals

Pubic

Ischium

Patella

tibia

fibula

tarsals

frontal

maxilla

mandible

clavicle

scapula

humerus

spine

Ilium

sacrum

coccyx

Phalange

femur

talus

calcaneus

metatarsals

phalanges

Review Sheet

84

Appendicular Skeleton

Activity: Long bone identification

Identify the following structures on the x-rays provided by your lab instructor.
1. epiphysis
2. diaphysis
3. spongy bone
4. compact bone
5. epiphyseal line
6. medullary canal

Articulations and Body Movements

Objectives

1. To name the three structural categories of joints, and to compare their structure and mobility.
2. To identify the types of synovial joints.
3. To define *origin* and *insertion* of muscles.
4. To demonstrate or identify the various body movements.

Materials

❑ Articulated skeleton
❑ Skull
❑ Diarthrotic beef joint (fresh or preserved), preferably a knee joint
❑ Disposable gloves
❑ Anatomical chart of joint types (if available)
❑ X rays of normal and arthritic joints (if available)

 See Appendix C, Exercise 13 for links to A.D.A.M. Interactive Anatomy.

With rare exceptions, every bone in the body is connected to, or forms a joint with, at least one other bone. **Articulations,** or joints, perform two functions for the body. They (1) hold the bones together and (2) allow the rigid skeletal system some flexibility so that gross body movements can occur.

Joints may be classified structurally or functionally. The *structural classification* is based on whether there is connective tissue fiber, cartilage, or a joint cavity between the articulating bones. Structurally, there are *fibrous, cartilaginous,* and *synovial joints.*

The functional classification focuses on the amount of movement allowed at the joint. On this basis, there are **synarthroses,** or immovable joints; **amphiarthroses,** or slightly movable joints; and **diarthroses,** or freely movable joints. Freely movable joints predominate in the limbs, whereas immovable and slightly movable joints are largely restricted to the axial skeleton, where firm bony attachments and protection of enclosed organs are a priority.

As a general rule, fibrous joints are immovable, and synovial joints are freely movable. Cartilaginous joints offer both rigid and slightly movable examples. Since the structural categories are more clear-cut, we will use the structural classification here and indicate functional properties as appropriate.

Fibrous Joints

In **fibrous joints,** the bones are joined by fibrous tissue. No joint cavity is present. The amount of movement allowed depends on the length of the fibers uniting the bones. Although some fibrous joints are slightly movable, most are synarthrotic and permit virtually no movement.

The two major types of fibrous joints are sutures and syndesmoses. In **sutures** (Figure 1d) the irregular edges of the bones interlock and are united by very short connective tissue fibers, as in most joints of the skull. In **syndesmoses** the articulating bones are connected by short ligaments of dense fibrous tissue; the bones do not interlock. The joint at the distal end of the tibia and fibula is an example of a syndesmosis (Figure 1e). Although this syndesmosis allows some give, it is classed functionally as a synarthrosis.

Activity:
Identifying Fibrous Joints

Examine a human skull again. Notice that adjacent bone surfaces do not actually touch but are separated by fibrous connective tissue. Also examine a skeleton and anatomical chart of joint types for examples of fibrous joints. ∎

Cartilaginous Joints

In **cartilaginous joints,** the articulating bone ends are connected by a plate or pad of cartilage. No joint cavity is present. The two major types of cartilaginous joints are synchondroses and symphyses. Although there is variation, most cartilaginous joints are *slightly movable* (amphiarthroses)

From *Human Anatomy & Physiology Laboratory Manual,* Main Version, Fifth Edition, Elaine N. Marieb.

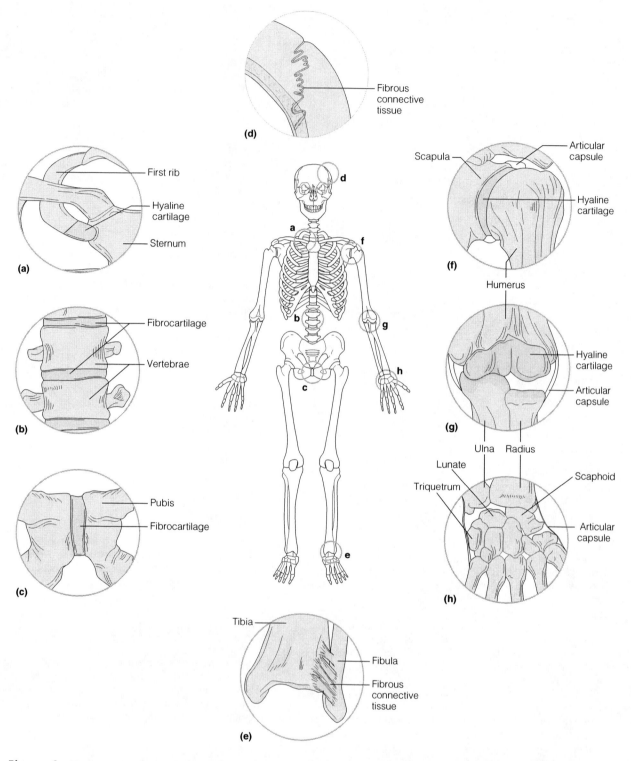

Figure 1 Types of joints. Joints to the left of the skeleton are cartilaginous joints; joints above and below the skeleton are fibrous joints; joints to the right of the skeleton are synovial joints. **(a)** Synchondrosis (joint between costal cartilage of rib 1 and the sternum). **(b)** Symphyses (intervertebral discs of fibrocartilage connecting adjacent vertebrae). **(c)** Symphysis (fibrocartilaginous pubic symphysis connecting the pubic bones anteriorly). **(d)** Suture (fibrous connective tissue connecting interlocking skull bones). **(e)** Syndesmosis (fibrous connective tissue connecting the distal ends of the tibia and fibula). **(f)** Synovial joint (multiaxial shoulder joint). **(g)** Synovial joint (uniaxial elbow joint). **(h)** Synovial joints (biaxial intercarpal joints of the hand).

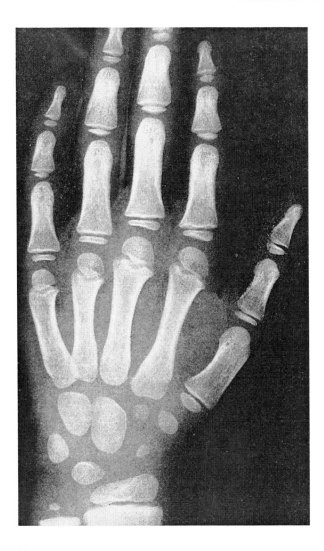

Figure 2 X ray of the hand of a child.
Notice the cartilaginous epiphyseal plates, examples of temporary synchondroses.

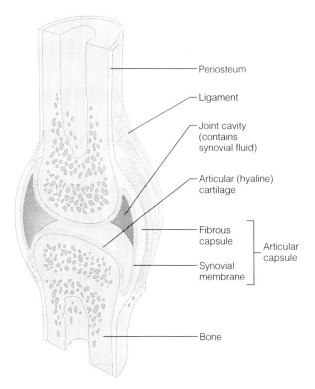

Figure 3 Major structural features of a synovial joint.

functionally. In **symphyses** (*symphysis* means "a growth to-gether") the bones are connected by a broad, flat disc of **fibrocartilage.** The intervertebral joints and the pubic symphysis of the pelvis are symphyses (see Figure 1b and c). In **synchondroses** the bony portions are united by hyaline cartilage. The articulation of the costal cartilage of the first rib with the sternum (Figure 1a) is a synchondrosis, but perhaps the best examples of synchondroses are the epiphyseal plates seen in the long bones of growing children (Figure 2). The epiphyseal plates are flexible during childhood but eventually they are totally ossified.

Activity:
Identifying Cartilaginous Joints

Identify the cartilaginous joints on a human skeleton and on an anatomical chart of joint types. ■

Synovial Joints

Synovial joints are those in which the articulating bone ends are separated by a joint cavity containing synovial fluid (see Figure 1f–h). All synovial joints are diarthroses, or freely movable joints. Their mobility varies, however; some synovial joints can move in only one plane, and others can move in several directions (multiaxial movement). Most joints in the body are synovial joints.

All synovial joints have the following structural characteristics (Figure 3):

• The joint surfaces are enclosed by an *articular capsule* (a sleeve of fibrous connective tissue), creating a joint cavity.

• The interior of this capsule is lined with a smooth connective tissue membrane, called *synovial membrane,* which produces a lubricating fluid (synovial fluid) that reduces friction.

• Articulating surfaces of the bones forming the joint are covered with hyaline (*articular*) cartilage.

• The articular capsule is typically reinforced with ligaments and may contain bursae (fluid-filled sacs that reduce friction where tendons cross bone).

• Fibrocartilage pads (articular discs) may be present within the capsule.

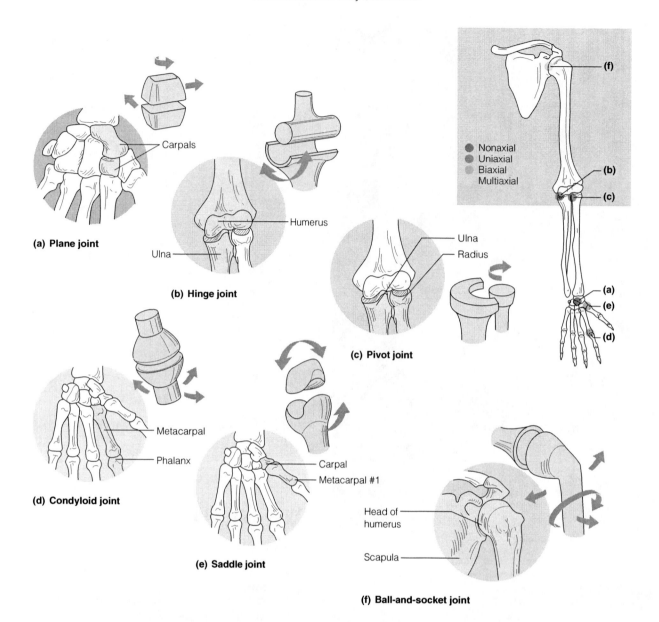

Figure 4 Types of synovial joints. Articulating bones being referenced are shown in gold; noninvolved bones are left white. **(a)** Plane joint (e.g., intercarpal and intertarsal joints). **(b)** Hinge joint (e.g., elbow joints and interphalangeal joints). **(c)** Pivot joint (e.g., proximal radioulnar joint). **(d)** Condyloid joint (e.g., metacarpophalangeal joints). **(e)** Saddle joint (e.g., carpometacarpal joint of the thumb). **(f)** Ball-and-socket joint (e.g., shoulder joint).

Activity:
Examining Synovial Joint Structure

Examine a beef joint to identify the general structural features of diarthrotic joints.

⚠ If the joint is freshly obtained from the slaughterhouse and you will be handling it, don plastic gloves before beginning your observations. ∎

Types of Synovial Joints

Because there are so many types of synovial joints, they have been divided into the following subcategories on the basis of movements allowed (Figure 4):

● Plane: Articulating surfaces are flat or slightly curved, allowing sliding movements in one or two planes. Examples are the intercarpal and intertarsal joints and the vertebrocostal joints.

● Hinge: The rounded process of one bone fits into the concave surface of another to allow movement in one plane (uniaxial), usually flexion and extension. Examples are the elbow and interphalangeal joints.

● Pivot: The rounded or conical surface of one bone articulates with a shallow depression or foramen in another bone. Pivot joints allow uniaxial rotation, as in the joint between the atlas and axis (C_1 and C_2).

● Condyloid: The oval condyle of one bone fits into an ellipsoidal depression in another bone, allowing biaxial (two-way) movement. The wrist joint and the metacarpalphalangeal joints (knuckles) are examples.

● Saddle: Articulating surfaces are saddle shaped; the articulating surface of one bone is convex, and the reciprocal surface is concave. Saddle joints, which are biaxial, include the joint between the thumb metacarpal and the trapezium of the wrist.

● Ball and socket: The ball-shaped head of one bone fits into a cuplike depression of another. These are multiaxial joints, allowing movement in all directions and pivotal rotation. Examples are the shoulder and hip joints.

Activity:
Identifying Types of Synovial Joints

Examine the articulated skeleton, anatomical charts, and yourself to identify the subcategories of synovial joints. Make sure you understand the terms *uniaxial, biaxial,* and *multiaxial.* ∎

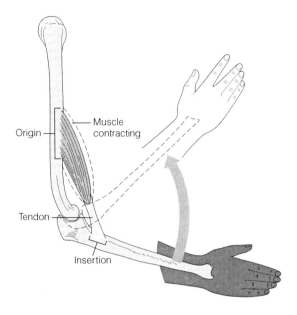

Figure 5 Muscle attachments (origin and insertion). When a skeletal muscle contracts, its insertion moves toward its origin.

Movements Allowed by Synovial Joints

Every muscle of the body is attached to bone (or other connective tissue structures) at two points–the **origin** (the stationary, immovable, or less movable attachment) and the **insertion** (the movable attachment). Body movement occurs when muscles contract across diarthrotic synovial joints (Figure 5). When the muscle contracts and its fibers shorten, the insertion moves toward the origin. The type of movement depends on the construction of the joint (uniaxial, biaxial, or multiaxial) and on the placement of the muscle relative to the joint. The most common types of body movements are described below and illustrated in Figure 6.

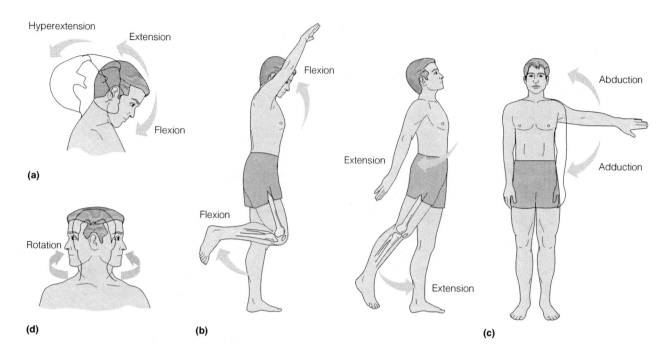

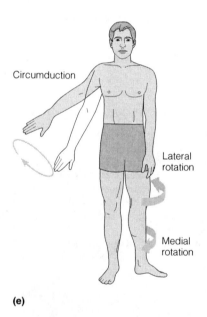

Figure 6 Movements occurring at synovial joints of the body. (a) Flexion and extension of the head. **(b)** Flexion and extension of the knee and shoulder. **(c)** Abduction and adduction of the arm. **(d)** Rotation of the head. **(e)** Circumduction of the arm and lateral and medial rotation of the lower limb around its long axis.

Activity:

Demonstrating Movements of Synovial Joints

Attempt to demonstrate each movement as you read through the following material:

Flexion (Figure 6a and b): A movement, generally in the sagittal plane, that decreases the angle of the joint and reduces the distance between the two bones. Flexion is typical of hinge joints (bending the knee or elbow), but is also common at ball-and-socket joints (bending forward at the hip).

Extension (Figure 6a and b): A movement that increases the angle of a joint and the distance between two bones or parts of the body (straightening the knee or elbow). Extension is the opposite of flexion. If extension is greater than 180 degrees (bending the trunk backward), it is termed *hyperextension*.

Abduction (Figure 6c): Movement of a limb away from the midline or median plane of the body, generally on the frontal plane, or the fanning movement of fingers or toes when they are spread apart.

Adduction (Figure 6c): Movement of a limb toward the midline of the body. Adduction is the opposite of abduction.

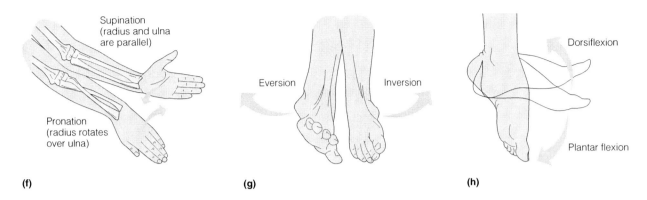

(f)   (g)   (h)

Figure 6 (continued) **(f)** Supination and pronation of the forearm. **(g)** Eversion and inversion of the foot. **(h)** Dorsiflexion and plantar flexion of the foot.

Rotation (Figure 6d and e): Movement of a bone around its longitudinal axis without lateral or medial displacement. Rotation, a common movement of ball-and-socket joints, also describes the movement of the atlas around the odontoid process of the axis.

Circumduction (Figure 6e): A combination of flexion, extension, abduction, and adduction commonly observed in ball-and-socket joints like the shoulder. The proximal end of the limb remains stationary, and the distal end moves in a circle. The limb as a whole outlines a cone.

Pronation (Figure 6f): Movement of the palm of the hand from an anterior or upward-facing position to a posterior or downward-facing position. This action moves the distal end of the radius across the ulna.

Supination (Figure 6f): Movement of the palm from a posterior position to an anterior position (the anatomical position). Supination is the opposite of pronation. During supination, the radius and ulna are parallel.

The last four terms refer to movements of the foot:

Inversion (Figure 6g): A movement that results in the medial turning of the sole of the foot.

Eversion (Figure 6g): A movement that results in the lateral turning of the sole of the foot; the opposite of inversion.

Dorsiflexion (Figure 6h): A movement of the ankle joint in a dorsal direction (standing on one's heels).

Plantar flexion (Figure 6h): A movement of the ankle joint in which the foot is flexed downward (standing on one's toes or pointing the toes). ■

Activity:

Examining Selected Synovial Joints

Now you will have the opportunity to compare and contrast the structure of the hip and knee joints using Figures 7 and 8 as your guides. Both of these joints are large weight-bearing joints of the lower limb, but they differ substantially in their security. Read through the brief descriptive material below, and look at the questions in the review section that pertain to this exercise before beginning your comparison.

The Knee Joint The knee is the largest and most complex joint in the body. Three joints in one (Figure 7), it allows extension, flexion, and a little rotation. The tibiofemoral joint, actually a duplex joint between the femoral condyles above and the menisci (semilunar cartilages) of the tibia below, is functionally a hinge joint, a very unstable one made slightly more secure by the menisci. Some rotation occurs when the knee is partly flexed, but during extension, rotation and side-to-side movements are counteracted by the menisci and ligaments. The other joint is the femoropatellar joint, the intermediate joint anteriorly. The knee is unique in that it is only partly enclosed by an articular capsule. The capsule is reinforced by three broad ligaments, the *patellar ligament* and the *medial* and *lateral patellar retinacula,* which merge with the capsule. Extracapsular ligaments including the *fibular* and *tibial collateral ligaments* (which prevent rotation during extension) and the *oblique popliteal* and *arcuate popliteal ligaments* are crucial in reinforcing the knee. The *cruciate ligaments,* which are intracapsular ligaments, prevent anterior-posterior displacement of the joint and overflexion and hyperextension of the joint.

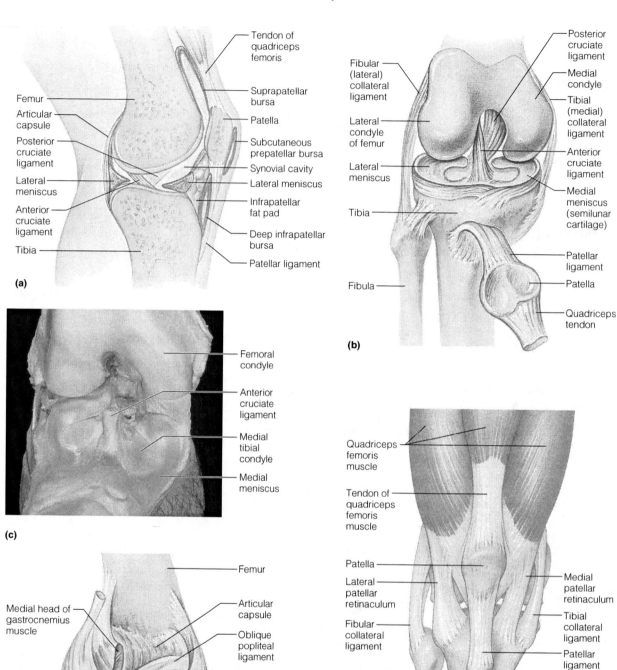

(a)

(b)

(c)

(d)

(e)

Figure 7 Knee joint relationships. (a) Mid-sagittal section of right knee joint. **(b)** Anterior view of slightly flexed right knee joint showing the cruciate ligaments. Articular capsule has been removed; the quadriceps tendon has been cut and reflected distally. **(c)** Photograph of an opened knee joint corresponds to view in (b). **(d)** Anterior superficial view of the right knee. **(e)** Posterior superficial view of the ligaments clothing the knee joint.

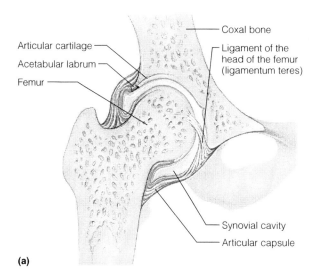

(a)

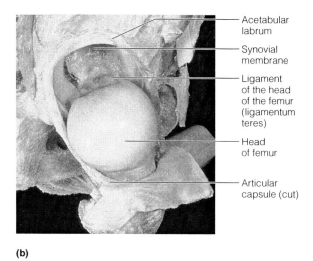

(b)

Figure 8 Hip joint relationships. (a) Frontal section through the right hip joint. **(b)** Photograph of the interior of the hip joint, lateral view. **(c)** Anterior superficial view of the right hip joint.

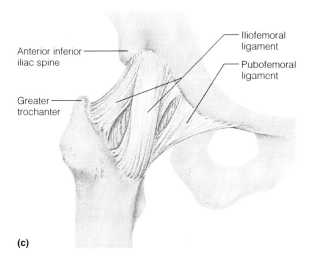

(c)

The Hip Joint The hip joint is a ball-and-socket joint, so movements can occur in all possible planes. However, its movements are definitely limited by its deep socket and strong reinforcing ligaments, the two factors that account for its exceptional stability (Figure 8).

The deeply cupped acetabulum that receives the head of the femur is enhanced by a circular rim of fibrocartilage called the *acetabular labrum.* Because the diameter of the labrum is smaller than that of the femur's head, dislocations of the hip are rare. A short ligament, *the ligament of the head of the femur* or *ligamentum teres* runs from the pitlike *fovea capitus* on the femur head to the acetabulum where it helps to secure the femur. Several strong ligaments, including the *iliofemoral* and *pubofemoral* anteriorly and the *ischiofemoral* that spirals posteriorly (not shown), are arranged so that they "screw" the femur head into the socket when a person stands upright. ∎

Joint Disorders

Most of us don't think about our joints until something goes wrong with them. Joint pains and malfunctions are caused by a variety of things. For example, a hard blow to the knee can cause a painful bursitis, known as "water on the knee," due to damage to, or inflammation of, the patellar bursa. Slippage of a fibrocartilage pad or the tearing of a ligament may result in a painful condition that persists over a long period, since these poorly vascularized structures heal so slowly.

Sprains and dislocations are other types of joint problems. In a **sprain,** the ligaments reinforcing a joint are damaged by excessive stretching or are torn away from the bony attachment. Since both ligaments and tendons are cords of dense connective tissue with a poor blood supply, sprains heal slowly and are quite painful. **Dislocations** occur when bones are forced out of their normal position in the joint cavity. They are normally accompanied by torn or stressed ligaments and considerable inflammation. The process of returning the bone to its proper position, called reduction, should be done only by a physician. Attempts by the untrained person to "snap the bone back into its socket" are often more harmful than helpful.

Advancing years also take their toll on joints. Weight-bearing joints in particular eventually begin to degenerate. *Adhesions* (fibrous bands) may form between the surfaces where bones join, and extraneous bone tissue (*spurs*) may grow along the joint edges. Such degenerative changes lead to the complaint so often heard from the elderly: "My joints are getting so stiff. . . ."

• If possible compare an X ray of an arthritic joint to one of a normal joint. ∎

Illustrations: 1–6: Precision Graphics. 7 and 8: Barbara Cousins. Photographs: 2: © Dr. Robert A. Chase. 7c: © Benjamin/Cummings Publishing Company. Photo by Stephen Spector, courtesy of Dr. Charles Thomas, Kansas University Medical Center. 8b: From *A Stereoscopic Atlas of Human Anatomy,* by David L. Bassett.

Articulations and Body Movements

Types of Joints

1. Use key responses to identify the joint types described below.

Key: a. cartilaginous   b. fibrous   c. synovial

_____ 1. typically allows a slight degree of movement

_____ 2. includes joints between the vertebral bodies and the pubic symphysis

_____ 3. essentially immovable joints

_____ 4. sutures are the most remembered examples

_____ 5. characterized by cartilage connecting the bony portions

_____ 6. all characterized by a fibrous articular capsule lined with a synovial membrane surrounding a joint cavity

_____ 7. all are freely movable or diarthrotic

_____ 8. bone regions are united by fibrous connective tissue

_____ 9. include the hip, knee, and elbow joints

2. Match the joint subcategories in column B with their descriptions in column A, and place an asterisk (*) beside all choices that are examples of synovial joints.

Column A	Column B
_____ 1. joint between skull bones	a. ball and socket
_____ 2. joint between the axis and atlas	b. condyloid
_____ 3. hip joint	c. gliding
_____ 4. intervertebral joints (between articular processes)	d. hinge
_____ 5. joint between forearm bones and wrist	e. pivot
_____ 6. elbow	f. saddle
_____ 7. interphalangeal joints	g. suture
_____ 8. intercarpal joints	h. symphysis
_____ 9. joint between tarsus and tibia/fibula	i. synchondrosis
_____ 10. joint between skull and vertebral column	j. syndesmosis

_____ 11. joint between jaw and skull

_____ 12. joints between proximal phalanges and metacarpal bones

_____ 13. epiphyseal plate of a child's long bone

_____ 14. a multiaxial joint

_____, _____ 15. biaxial joints

_____, _____ 16. uniaxial joints

3. What characteristics do all joints have in common? _____

_____

4. Describe the structure and function of the following structures or tissues in relation to a synovial joint and label the structures indicated by leader lines in the diagram.

ligament _____

_____

tendon _____

_____

hyaline cartilage _____

_____

synovial membrane _____

_____

_____

bursa _____

5. Which joint, the hip or the knee, is more stable? _____

Name two important factors that contribute to the stability of the hip joint.

_____ and _____

Name two important factors that contribute to the stability of the knee.

_____ and _____

6. The diagram shows a frontal section of the hip joint. Identify its major structural elements by using the key letters.

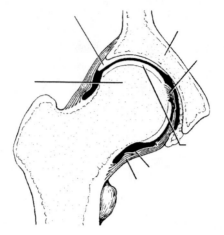

Key:

a. acetabular labrum

b. articular capsule

c. articular cartilage

d. coxal bone

e. head of femur

f. ligamentum teres

g. synovial cavity

Movements Allowed by Synovial Joints

1. Label the *origin* and *insertion* points on the diagram below and complete the following statement:

During muscle contraction, the _____

moves toward the _____.

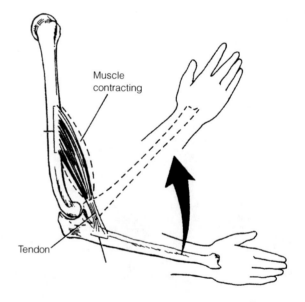

Muscle contracting

Tendon

2. Complete the statements below the stick diagrams by inserting the missing words in the answer blanks.

1. _____

2. _____

(continues on next page)

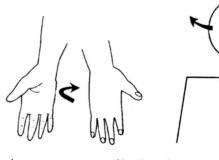

1. _____ of hand   2. _____ of head

3. _____

4. _____

5. _____

6. _____

7. _____

8. _____

9. _____

10. _____

11. _____

3. _____ of the arm

4. _____ of hip
5. _____ of knee

6. _____ of thigh
7. _____ of arm

8. _____ of hip

9. _____ of foot

10. _____ of elbow

11. _____ of foot

Joint Disorders

1. What structural joint changes are common to the elderly? _____

_____

2. Define:

   sprain _____

   dislocation _____

Review Sheet

99

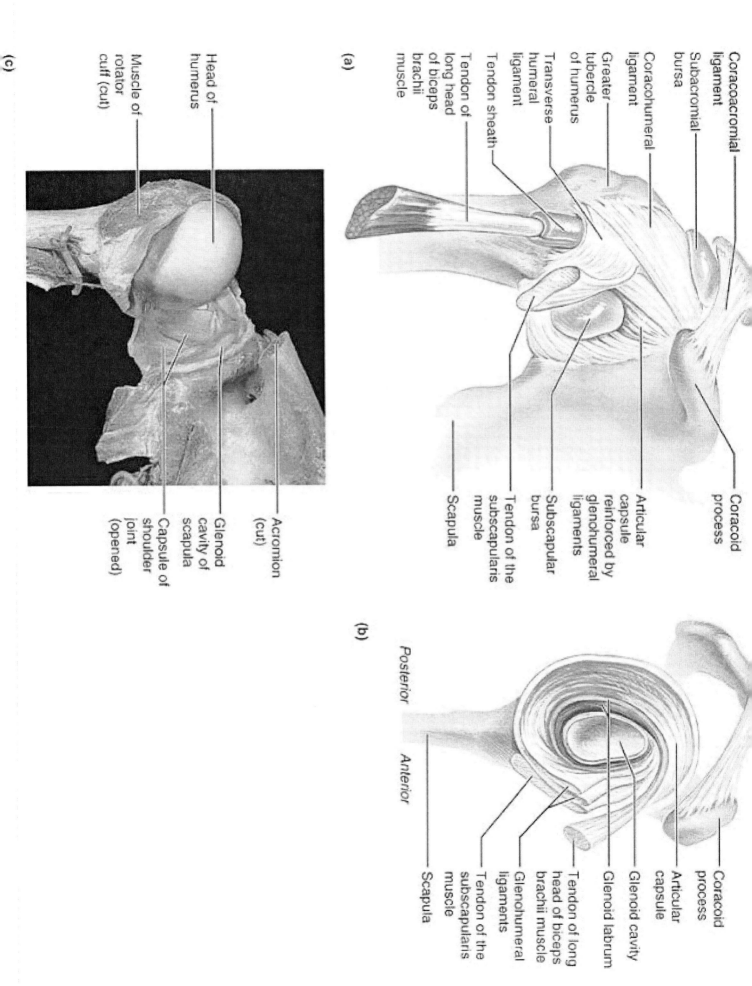

(a)

Coracoacromial
ligament

Subacromial
bursa

Coracohumeral
ligament

Greater
tubercle
of humerus

Transverse
humeral
ligament

Tendon sheath

Tendon of
long head
of biceps
brachii
muscle

Coracoid
process

Articular
capsule
reinforced by
glenohumeral
ligaments

Subscapular
bursa

Tendon of the
subscapularis
muscle

Scapula

(b)

Posterior

Anterior

Coracoid
process

Articular
capsule

Glenoid cavity

Glenoid labrum

Tendon of long
head of biceps
brachii muscle

Glenohumeral
ligaments

Tendon of the
subscapularis
muscle

Scapula

(c)

Muscle of
rotator
cuff (cut)

Head of
humerus

Capsule of
shoulder
joint
(opened)

Glenoid
cavity of
scapula

Acromion
(cut)

101

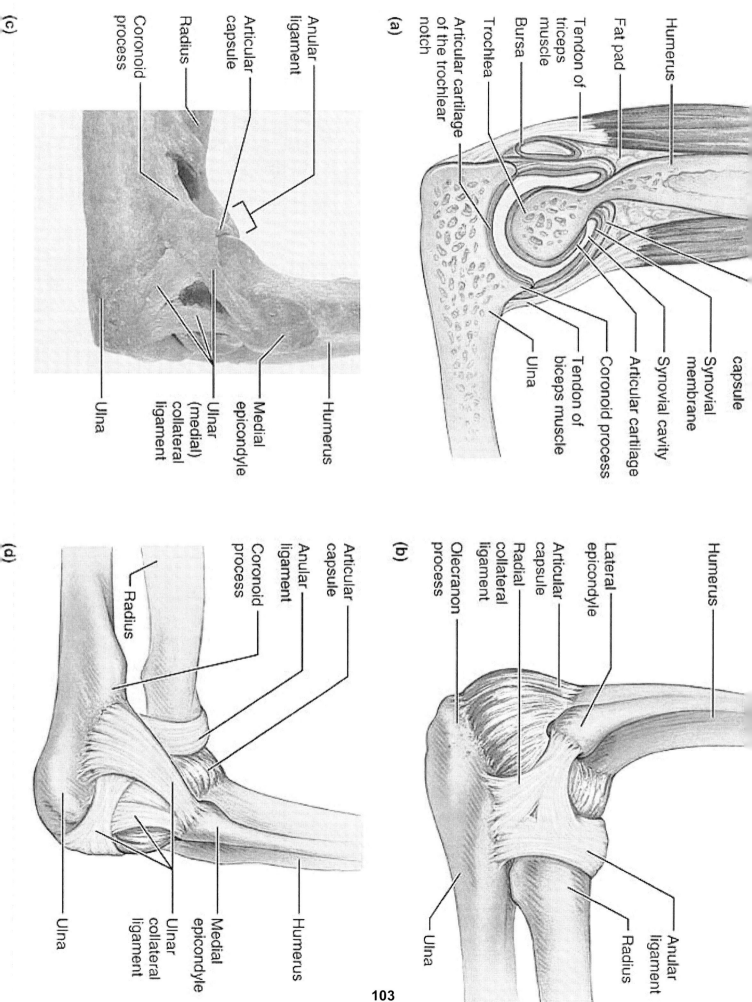

(a)

Humerus

Fat pad

Tendon of triceps muscle

Bursa

Trochlea

Articular cartilage of the trochlear notch

Ulna

Tendon of biceps muscle

Coronoid process

Articular cartilage

Synovial membrane

Synovial cavity

capsule

(b)

Humerus

Lateral epicondyle

Articular capsule

Radial collateral ligament

Olecranon process

Ulna

Radius

Anular ligament

(c)

Anular ligament

Articular capsule

Radius

Coronoid process

Ulna

Ulnar (medial) collateral ligament

Medial epicondyle

Humerus

(d)

Radius

Coronoid process

Anular ligament

Articular capsule

Ulna

Ulnar collateral ligament

Medial epicondyle

Humerus

103

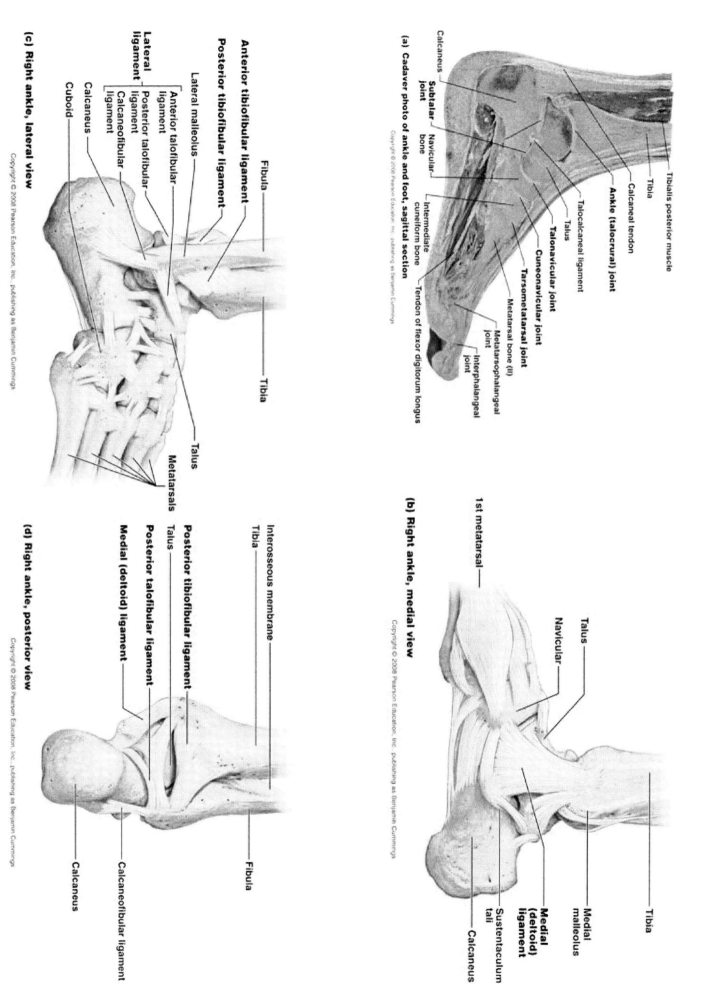

(a) Cadaver photo of ankle and foot, sagittal section

Calcaneus
Subtalar joint
Navicular bone
Intermediate cuneiform bone
Tendon of flexor digitorum longus
Tibialis posterior muscle
Tibia
Calcaneal tendon
Ankle (talocrural) joint
Talocalcaneal ligament
Talus
Talonavicular joint
Cuneonavicular joint
Tarsometatarsal joint
Metatarsal bone (II)
Metatarsophalangeal joint
Interphalangeal joint

Copyright © 2008 Pearson Education, Inc., publishing as Benjamin Cummings

(b) Right ankle, medial view

1st metatarsal
Navicular
Talus
Medial malleolus
Tibia
Sustentaculum tali
Medial (deltoid) ligament
Calcaneus

Copyright © 2008 Pearson Education, Inc. publishing as Benjamin Cummings

(c) Right ankle, lateral view

Posterior tibiofibular ligament
Anterior tibiofibular ligament
Fibula
Tibia
Lateral malleolus
Lateral ligament
Anterior talofibular ligament
Posterior talofibular ligament
Calcaneofibular ligament
Calcaneus
Cuboid
Talus
Metatarsals

Copyright © 2008 Pearson Education, Inc., publishing as Benjamin Cummings

(d) Right ankle, posterior view

Interosseous membrane
Tibia
Posterior tibiofibular ligament
Talus
Posterior talofibular ligament
Medial (deltoid) ligament
Fibula
Calcaneofibular ligament
Calcaneus

Copyright © 2008 Pearson Education, Inc. publishing as Benjamin Cummings

105

Articulations and Body Movement

Activity: Dance Nation

As a group: using the actions described in your manual, make up a dance/exercise routine and demonstrate it for the rest of the class. Describe the actions as you do each part (rotation, extension, flexion etc).

Activity: Types of cartilage
In the back of the room there are 3 types of cartilage.

Identify the following:
   a. the type of cartilage
   b. from what part of the body do you think the specimen came from
   c. what are the characteristics of this type of cartilage?

Sample #1
   a.
   b.
   c.

Sample #2
   a.
   b.
   c.

Sample #3
   a.
   b.
   c.

Microscopic Anatomy, Organization, and Classification of Skeletal Muscle

Objectives

1. To describe the structure of skeletal muscle from gross to microscopic levels.

2. To define and explain the role of the following:

   actin   myofilament   tendon
   myosin   perimysium   endomysium
   fiber   aponeurosis   epimysium
   myofibril

3. To describe the structure of a neuromuscular junction and to explain its role in muscle function.

4. To define: *agonist* (prime mover), *antagonist*, *synergist*, *fixator*, *origin*, and *insertion*.

5. To cite criteria used in naming skeletal muscles.

Materials

❑ Three-dimensional model of skeletal muscle cells (if available)

❑ Forceps

❑ Dissecting needles

❑ Microscope slides and coverslips

❑ 0.9% saline solution in dropper bottles

❑ Chicken breast or thigh muscle (freshly obtained from the meat market)

❑ Compound microscope

❑ Histologic slides of skeletal muscle (longitudinal and cross-sectional) and skeletal muscle showing neuromuscular junctions

❑ Three-dimensional model of skeletal muscle showing neuromuscular junction (if available)

The bulk of the body's muscle is called **skeletal muscle** because it is attached to the skeleton (or associated connective tissue structures). Skeletal muscle influences body contours and shape, allows you to grin and frown, provides a means of locomotion, and enables you to manipulate the environment. The balance of the body's muscle—smooth and cardiac muscle—as the major component of the walls of hollow organs and the heart, respectively, is involved with the transport of materials within the body.

Each of the three muscle types has a structure and function uniquely suited to its task in the body. However, because the term *muscular system* applies specifically to skeletal muscle, the primary objective of this unit is to investigate the structure and function of skeletal muscle.

Skeletal muscle is also known as *voluntary muscle* (because it can be consciously controlled) and as *striated muscle* (because it appears to be striped). As you might guess from both of these alternative names, skeletal muscle has some very special characteristics. Thus an investigation of skeletal muscle should begin at the cellular level.

The Cells of Skeletal Muscle

Skeletal muscle is composed of relatively large, long cylindrical cells ranging from 10 to 100 μm in diameter and up to 6 cm in length. However, the cells of large, hard-working muscles like the antigravity muscles of the hip are extremely coarse, ranging up to 25 cm in length, and can be seen with the naked eye.

Skeletal muscle cells (Figure 1a) are multinucleate: Multiple oval nuclei can be seen just beneath the plasma membrane (called the *sarcolemma* in these cells). The nuclei are pushed peripherally by the longitudinally arranged **myofibrils,** which nearly fill the sarcoplasm (Figure 1b). Alternating light (I) and dark (A) bands along the length of the perfectly aligned myofibrils give the muscle fiber as a whole its striped appearance.

Electron microscope studies have revealed that the myofibrils are made up of even smaller threadlike structures called **myofilaments** (Figure 1c and d). The myofilaments are composed largely of two varieties of contractile proteins—**actin** and **myosin**—which slide past each other during muscle activity to bring about shortening or contraction of the muscle cells. It is the highly specific arrangement of the myofilaments within the myofibrils that is responsible for the banding pattern in skeletal muscle. The actual contractile units of muscle, called **sarcomeres,** extend from the middle of one I band (its Z disc) to the middle of the next along the length of the myofibrils. (See Figure 1c and d.)

From *Human Anatomy & Physiology Laboratory Manual*, Main Version, Fifth Edition, Elaine N. Marieb.

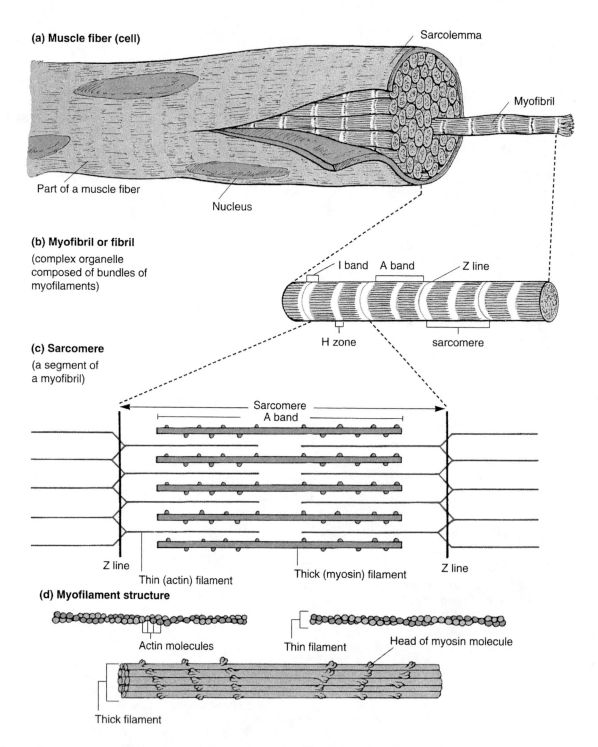

(a) Muscle fiber (cell)

Sarcolemma

Myofibril

Part of a muscle fiber

Nucleus

(b) Myofibril or fibril

(complex organelle
composed of bundles of
myofilaments)

I band   A band   Z line

H zone   sarcomere

(c) Sarcomere

(a segment of
a myofibril)

Sarcomere
A band

Z line

Thin (actin) filament

Thick (myosin) filament

Z line

(d) Myofilament structure

Actin molecules

Thin filament

Head of myosin molecule

Thick filament

Figure 1   Anatomy of a skeletal muscle cell (fiber). (a) A muscle fiber.
One myofibril has been extended. **(b)** Enlarged view of a myofibril showing its banding
pattern. **(c)** Enlarged view of one sarcomere (contractile unit) of a myofibril showing its
banding pattern. **(d)** Structure of the thick and thin myofilaments found in the sarcomeres.

Activity:
Examining Skeletal Muscle Cell Anatomy

1. Look at the three-dimensional model of skeletal muscle cells, noting the relative shape and size of the cells. Identify the nuclei, myofibrils, and light and dark bands.

2. Obtain forceps, two dissecting needles, slide and cover-slip, and a dropper bottle of saline solution. With forceps, re-move a very small piece of muscle from the chicken breast (or thigh). Place the tissue on a clean microscope slide, and add a drop of the saline solution.

3. Pull the muscle fibers apart with the dissecting needles (tease them) until you have a fluffy-looking mass of tissue. Cover the teased tissue with a coverslip, and observe under the high-power lens of a microscope. Look for the banding pattern. Regulate the light carefully to obtain the highest pos-sible contrast.

4. Now compare your observations with Figure 2 and with what can be seen with professionally prepared muscle tissue. Obtain a slide of skeletal muscle (longitudinal section), and view it under high power. From your observations, draw a small section of a muscle fiber in the space provided here. Label the nuclei, sarcolemma, and A and I bands.

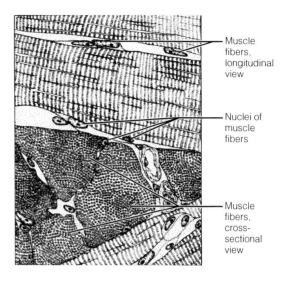

Muscle fibers, longitudinal view

Nuclei of muscle fibers

Muscle fibers, cross-sectional view

Figure 2 Muscle fibers, longitudinal and transverse views. (See also Plate 2 in the Histology Atlas.)

What structural details become apparent with the prepared slide?

_____

_____ ■

Organization of Skeletal Muscle Cells into Muscles

Muscle fibers are soft and surprisingly fragile. Thus thou-sands of muscle fibers are bundled together with connective tissue to form the organs we refer to as skeletal muscles (Fig-ure 3). Each muscle fiber is enclosed in a delicate, areolar connective tissue sheath called **endomysium.** Several sheathed muscle fibers are wrapped by a collagenic mem-brane called **perimysium,** forming a bundle of fibers called a **fascicle,** or **fasciculus.** A large number of fascicles are bound together by a substantially coarser "overcoat" of dense con-nective tissue called an **epimysium,** which sheathes the en-tire muscle. These epimysia blend into the **deep fascia,** still coarser sheets of dense connective tissue that bind muscles into functional groups, and into strong cordlike **tendons** or sheetlike **aponeuroses,** which attach muscles to each other or indirectly to bones. A muscle's more movable attachment is called its *insertion* whereas its fixed (or immovable) attach-ment is the *origin.*

Tendons perform several functions, two of the most im-portant being to provide durability and to conserve space. Be-cause tendons are tough collagenic connective tissue, they can span rough bony prominences that would destroy the more delicate muscle tissues. Because of their relatively small size, more tendons than fleshy muscles can pass over a joint.

In addition to supporting and binding the muscle fibers, and providing strength to the muscle as a whole, the connec-tive tissue wrappings provide a route for the entry and exit of nerves and blood vessels that serve the muscle fibers. The larger, more powerful muscles have relatively more connec-tive tissue than muscles involved in fine or delicate move-ments.

As we age, the mass of the muscle fibers decreases, and the amount of connective tissue increases; thus the skeletal muscles gradually become more sinewy, or "stringier." ■

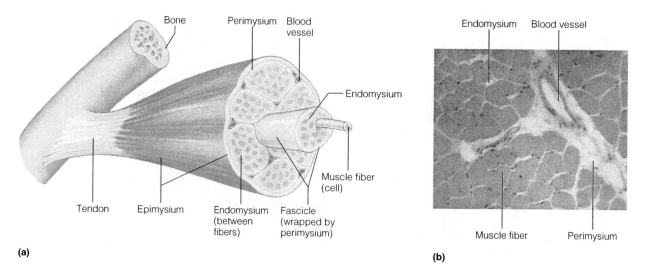

(a)

(b)

Figure 3   Connective tissue coverings of skeletal muscle.
(a) Diagrammatic view. **(b)** Photomicrograph of a cross section of skeletal muscle (90×).

Activity:
Observing the Structure of Skeletal Muscle Tissue

Obtain a slide showing a cross section of skeletal muscle tissue. Using Figure 3 as a reference, identify the muscle fibers, endomysium, perimysium, and epimysium (if visible). ■

The Neuromuscular Junction

The voluntary skeletal muscle cells are always stimulated by motor neurons via nerve impulses. The junction between a nerve fiber (axon) and a muscle cell is called a **neuromuscular, or myoneural, junction** (Figure 4).

Each motor axon breaks up into many branches called *axonal terminals* as it approaches the muscle, and each of these branches participates in forming a neuromuscular junction with a single muscle cell. Thus a single neuron may stimulate many muscle fibers. Together, a neuron and all the muscle cells it stimulates make up the functional structure called the **motor unit.** Part of a motor unit is shown in Figure 5.

The neuron and muscle fiber membranes, close as they are, do not actually touch. They are separated by a small fluid-filled gap called the **synaptic cleft** (see Figure 4).

Within the axonal terminals are many mitochondria and vesicles containing a neurotransmitter chemical called acetylcholine. When a nerve impulse reaches the axonal endings, some of these vesicles release their contents into the synaptic cleft. The acetylcholine rapidly diffuses across the junction and combines with the receptors on the sarcolemma. If sufficient acetylcholine has been released, a transient change in the permeability of the sarcolemma briefly allows more sodium ions to diffuse into the muscle fiber. The result is depolarization of the sarcolemma and subsequent contraction of the muscle fiber.

Activity:
Studying the Structure of a Neuromuscular Junction

1.   If possible, examine a three-dimensional model of skeletal muscle cells that illustrates the neuromuscular junction. Identify the structures just described.

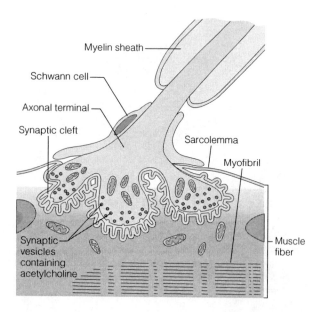

Figure 4   The neuromuscular junction.

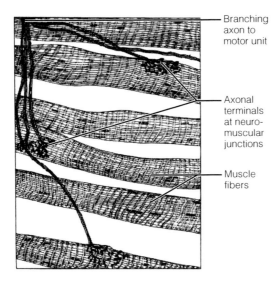

Branching axon to motor unit

Axonal terminals at neuro-muscular junctions

Muscle fibers

Figure 5   A portion of a motor unit.

2.   Obtain a slide of skeletal muscle stained to show a portion of a motor unit. Examine the slide under high power to identify the axonal fibers extending leashlike to the muscle cells. Follow one of the axonal fibers to its terminus to identify the oval-shaped axonal terminal. Compare your observations to Figure 5. Sketch a small section in the space provided, labeling the motor axon, its terminal branches, and muscle fibers. ∎

Classification of Skeletal Muscles

Naming Skeletal Muscles

Remembering the names of the skeletal muscles is a monumental task, but certain clues help. Muscles are named on the basis of the following criteria:

• **Direction of muscle fibers:** Some muscles are named in reference to some imaginary line, usually the midline of the body or the longitudinal axis of a limb bone. A muscle with

fibers (and fascicles) running parallel to that imaginary line will have the term *rectus* (straight) in its name. For example, the rectus abdominis is the straight muscle of the abdomen. Likewise, the terms *transverse* and *oblique* indicate that the muscle fibers run at right angles and obliquely (respectively) to the imaginary line.

• **Relative size of the muscle:** Terms such as *maximus* (largest), *minimus* (smallest), *longus* (long), and *brevis* (short) are often used in naming muscles—as in gluteus maximus and gluteus minimus.

• **Location of the muscle:** Some muscles are named for the bone with which they are associated. For example, the frontalis muscle overlies the frontal bone.

• **Number of origins:** When the term *biceps, triceps,* or *quadriceps* forms part of a muscle name, you can generally assume that the muscle has two, three, or four origins (respectively). For example, the biceps muscle of the arm has two heads, or origins.

• **Location of the muscle's origin and insertion:** For example, the sternocleidomastoid muscle has its origin on the sternum (*sterno*) and clavicle (*cleido*), and inserts on the mastoid process of the temporal bone.

• **Shape of the muscle:** For example, the deltoid muscle is roughly triangular (*deltoid* = triangle), and the trapezius muscle resembles a trapezoid.

• **Action of the muscle:** For example, all the adductor muscles of the anterior thigh bring about its adduction, and all the extensor muscles of the wrist extend the wrist.

Types of Muscles

Most often, body movements are not a result of the contraction of a single muscle but instead reflect the coordinated action of several muscles acting together. Muscles that are primarily responsible for producing a particular movement are called **prime movers,** or **agonists.**

Muscles that oppose or reverse a movement are called **antagonists.** When a prime mover is active, the fibers of the antagonist are stretched and in the relaxed state. The antagonist can also regulate the prime mover by providing some resistance, to prevent overshoot or to stop its action.

It should be noted that antagonists can be prime movers in their own right. For example, the biceps muscle of the arm (a prime mover of elbow flexion) is antagonized by the triceps (a prime mover of elbow extension).

Synergists aid the action of agonists by reducing undesirable or unnecessary movement. Contraction of a muscle crossing two or more joints would cause movement at all joints spanned if the synergists were not there to stabilize them. For example, you can make a fist without bending your wrist only because synergist muscles stabilize the wrist joint and allow the prime mover to exert its force at the finger joints.

Fixators, or fixation muscles, are specialized synergists. They immobilize the origin of a prime mover so that all the tension is exerted at the insertion. Muscles that help maintain posture are fixators; so too are muscles of the back that stabilize or "fix" the scapula during arm movements.

Illustrations: 2, 4, and 5: Precision Graphics. 3: Raychel Ciemma. **Photographs:** 3b: Courtesy of Marian Rice.

NAME ______________________ LAB TIME/DATE ______________________

REVIEW SHEET

Microscopic Anatomy, Organization, and Classification of Skeletal Muscle

Skeletal Muscle Cells and Their Packaging into Muscles

1. What capability is most highly expressed in muscle tissue? ______________________

2. Use the items on the right to correctly identify the structures described on the left.

______________ 1. connective tissue ensheathing a bundle of muscle cells

______________ 2. bundle of muscle cells

______________ 3. contractile unit of muscle

______________ 4. a muscle cell

______________ 5. thin reticular connective tissue investing each muscle cell

______________ 6. plasma membrane of the muscle fiber

______________ 7. a long filamentous organelle with a banded appearance found within muscle cells

______________ 8. actin- or myosin-containing structure

______________ 9. cord of collagen fibers that attaches a muscle to a bone

a. endomysium
b. epimysium
c. fascicle
d. fiber
e. myofilament
f. myofibril
g. perimysium
h. sarcolemma
i. sarcomere
j. sarcoplasm
k. tendon

3. Why are the connective tissue wrappings of skeletal muscle important? (Give at least three reasons.)

____

____

____

____

4. Why are indirect—that is, tendinous—muscle attachments to bone seen more often than direct attachments?

____

____

____

5. How does an aponeurosis differ from a tendon? ______________________

____

____

6. The diagram illustrates a small portion of a muscle myofibril. Using letters from the key, correctly identify each structure indicated by a leader line or a bracket. Below the diagram make a sketch of how this segment of the myofibril would look if contracted.

Key: a. actin filament   d. myosin filament
       b. A band   e. sarcomere
       c. I band   f. Z disc

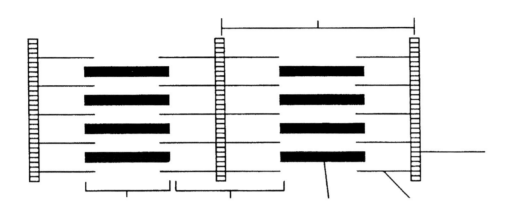

The Neuromuscular Junction

Complete the following statements:

The junction between a motor neuron's axon and the muscle cell membrane is called a neuromuscular junction or a __1__ junction. A motor neuron and all of the skeletal muscle cells it stimulates is called a __2__. The actual gap between the axonal terminal and the muscle cell is called a __3__. Within the axonal terminal are many small vesicles containing a neurotransmitter substance called__4__. When the __5__ reaches the ends of the axon, the neurotransmitter is released and diffuses to the muscle cell membrane to combine with receptors there. The combining of the neurotransmitter with the muscle membrane receptors causes the membrane to become permeable to sodium, which results in the influx of sodium ions and__6__ of the membrane. Then contraction of the muscle cell occurs. Before a muscle cell can be stimulated to contract again, __7__ must occur.

1. _____

2. _____

3. _____

4. _____

5. _____

6. _____

7. _____

Classification of Skeletal Muscles

1. Several criteria were given relative to the naming of muscles. Match the criteria (column B) to the muscle names (column A). Note that more than one criterion may apply in some cases.

Column A

_____ 1. gluteus maximus

_____ 2. adductor magnus

_____ 3. biceps femoris

_____ 4. abdominis transversus

_____ 5. extensor carpi ulnaris

_____ 6. trapezius

_____ 7. rectus femoris

_____ 8. external oblique

Column B

a. action of the muscle

b. shape of the muscle

c. location of the origin and/or insertion of the muscle

d. number of origins

e. location of the muscle relative to a bone or body region

f. direction in which the muscle fibers run relative to some imaginary line

g. relative size of the muscle

2. When muscles are discussed relative to the manner in which they interact with other muscles, the terms shown in the key are often used. Match the key terms with the appropriate definitions.

Key: a. antagonist   b. fixator   c. prime mover   d. synergist

_____ 1. agonist

_____ 2. postural muscles, for the most part

_____ 3. reverses and/or opposes the action of a prime mover

_____ 4. stabilizes a joint so that the prime mover may act at more distal joints

_____ 5. performs the same movement as the prime mover

_____ 6. immobilizes the origin of a prime mover

Muscle Physiology

Animations for Skeletal Muscle
Log in to www.myaandp.com
On the left side menu, choose "Tutorials: Interactive Physiology"
Complete the Chapter 9 modules: **Neuromuscular Junction**
                                                         Sliding Filament Theory

The Making of a Muscle and Neuromuscular Junction Structures
Using the materials provided, create a model of a muscle specifically identifying the following structures:

- Actin filaments   thin spaghetti
- Myosin filaments   linguine
- Sarcoplasmic reticulum   screen material
- Transverse (T) tubules   athletic tape
- Neuromuscular junction   electrical tape
- Nerve   cord
- Epi/peri/endomysium   saran wrap

Wrap the sarcoplasmic reticulum around some actin and myosin (make 4 of these). Use the athletic tape as your Transverse (T) tubules, then use 1 color of saran wrap and wrap around each structure, like a cigar. Take two structures (Myofibrils) and wrap them together using a different color of saran wrap, now you have created 2 fascicles. Take those 2 fascicles and wrap them together once more in a different color of saran wrap to create the epimysium. Finally take the cord and attach it to the structure with electrical tape to create your neuromuscular junction.

A group of myofilaments (the myofibril) is covered by areolar connective tissue called the *endomysium.* On your model, what color is the endomysium?

A group of myofibrils (the fascicle) is surrounded by another connective tissue sheath called the *perimysium*. On your model, what color is the perimysium?

A group of fascicles are joined by still another connective tissue called the *epimysium*. On your model, what color is the epimysium?

Here is how it works…

1. An electrochemical nerve impulse travels down the nerve to where it meets the muscle. This connection is called the __Neuromuscular junction__.

2. Here, the chemical mediator _____ACH_____ is released causing an action potential that runs the length of the muscle.

3. When this action potential reaches a T tubule, __calcium__ is released by the sarcoplasmic reticulum. This is referred to as the ___latent___ phase of muscle contraction.

4. This causes the actin and myosin to join together (some refer to it as sliding) and the muscle shortens. This is referred to as the __contraction__ phase of muscle contraction.

5. Finally, the muscle returns to a resting state, this is referred to as the __relaxation__ phase of muscle contraction.

Muscle Physiology - Let's Get Fired Up!!

With specific instruction and assistance from the instructor, you will experience electrical stimulation.

a. What part of your body was receiving electrical stimulation?

Right thigh

b. Where were your pads located?

quads

c. Describe the different sensations/motor movements you experienced with the stimulation.

Pins/needles

d. Nerves are being stimulated to release what?
→

ACH

e. This causes the sarcoplasmic reticulum to release what?

calcium

f. This molecule attaches to troponin which then moves what out of the way?

tropomyosin

g. What is now able to attach to the actin myofilament?

myosin

h. This attachment is called a what?

actin myosin theory

i. This will cause the two myofilaments to what?

slide

j. This causes the muscle to do what?

contract

Muscle Tissue Specimens

Look at the muscle tissue specimens. Remember to use gloves when picking up the tissue.

How does the muscle tissue feel?

a steak

How does this tissue differ from the skin and cartilage we looked at earlier in the semester?

its stretch and can move it

Can you determine where on the body the specimens are from?

stomach

Determine the muscle type (pennate, circular, etc.) of each specimen.

Gross Anatomy of the Muscular System

Identification of Human Muscles

Muscles of the Head and Neck

The muscles of the head serve many specific functions. For instance, the muscles of facial expression differ from most skeletal muscles because they insert into the skin (or other muscles) rather than into bone. As a result, they move the facial skin, allowing a wide range of emotions to be shown on the face. Other muscles of the head are the muscles of mastication, which manipulate the mandible during chewing, and the six extrinsic eye muscles located within the orbit, which aim the eye.

Activity:
Identifying Head and Neck Muscles

Neck muscles are primarily concerned with the movement of the head and shoulder girdle. Figures 1 and 2 are summary figures illustrating the superficial musculature of the body as a whole. Head and neck muscles are discussed in Tables 1 and 2 and shown in Figures 3 and 4.

While reading the tables and identifying the head and neck muscles in the figures, try to visualize what happens when the muscle contracts. Then, use a torso model or an anatomical chart to again identify as many of these muscles as possible. (If a human cadaver is available for observation, specific instructions for muscle examination will be provided by your instructor.) Then carry out the following palpations on yourself:

• To demonstrate the temporalis, clench your teeth. The masseter can also be palpated now at the angle of the jaw. ∎

Muscles of the Trunk

The trunk musculature includes muscles that move the vertebral column; anterior thorax muscles that act to move ribs, head, and arms; and muscles of the abdominal wall that play a role in the movement of the vertebral column but more importantly form the "natural girdle," or the major portion of the abdominal body wall.

Activity:
Identifying Muscles of the Trunk

The trunk muscles are described in Tables 3 and 4 and shown in Figures 5 through 8. As before, identify the muscles in the figure as you read the tabular descriptions and then identify them on the torso or laboratory chart. ∎

Objectives

1. To name and locate the major muscles of the human body (on a torso model, a human cadaver, lab chart, or diagram) and state the action of each.

2. To explain how muscle actions are related to their location.

3. To name muscle origins and insertions as required by the instructor.

4. To identify antagonists of the major prime movers.

Materials

❑ Human torso model or large anatomical chart showing human musculature

❑ Human cadaver for demonstration (if available)

❑ Disposable gloves or protective skin cream

❑ *Human Musculature* videotape*

 See Appendix C, Exercise 15 for links to A.D.A.M. Interactive Anatomy.

 For instructions on animal dissections, see the dissection exercises in the cat and fetal pig editions of this manual.

*Available to qualified adopters from Benjamin/Cummings.

Activity:
Demonstrating Operation of Trunk Muscles

Now, work with a partner to demonstrate the operation of the following muscles. One of you can demonstrate the movement (the following steps are addressed to this partner). The other can supply resistance and palpate the muscle being tested.

1. Fully abduct the arm and extend the elbow. Now adduct the arm against resistance. You are using the *latissimus dorsi*.

2. To observe the *deltoid*, attempt to abduct your arm against resistance. Now attempt to elevate your shoulder against resistance; you are contracting the upper portion of the *trapezius*.

3. The *pectoralis major* is used when you press your hands together at chest level with your elbows widely abducted. ∎

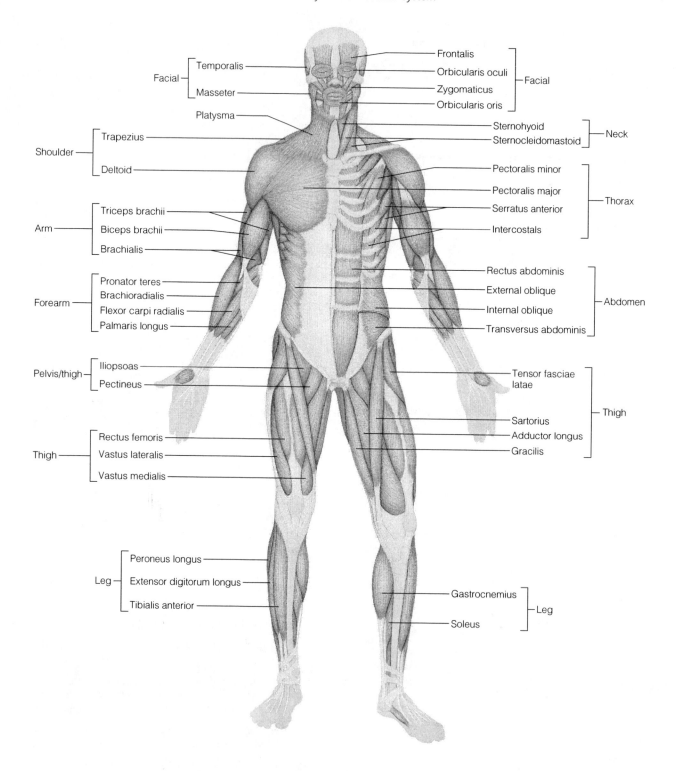

Figure 1 Anterior view of superficial muscles of the body.
The abdominal surface has been partially dissected on the left side of the body
to show somewhat deeper muscles.

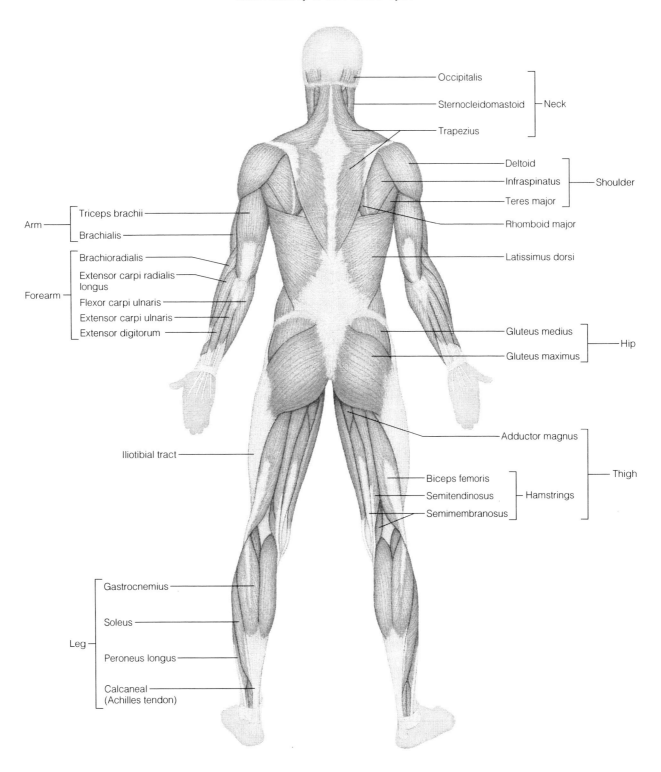

Figure 2   Posterior view of superficial muscles of the body.

Table 1	Major Muscles of Human Head (see Figure 3)			
Muscle	**Comments**	**Origin**	**Insertion**	**Action**
Facial Expression (Figure 3a)				
Epicranius— frontalis and occipitalis	Bipartite muscle consisting of frontalis and occipitalis, which covers dome of skull	Frontalis: cranial aponeurosis (galea aponeurotica); occipitalis: occipital bone	Frontalis: skin of eyebrows and root of nose; occipitalis: cranial aponeurosis	With aponeurosis fixed, frontalis raises eyebrows; occipitalis fixes aponeurosis and pulls scalp posteriorly
Orbicularis oculi	Sphincter muscle of eyelids	Frontal and maxillary bones and ligaments around orbit	Encircles orbit and inserts in tissue of eyelid	Various parts can be activated individually; closes eyes, produces blinking, squinting, and draws eyebrows downward
Corrugator supercilii	Small muscle; activity associated with that of orbicularis oculi	Arch of frontal bone above nasal bone	Skin of eyebrow	Draws eyebrows medially; wrinkles skin of forehead vertically
Levator labii superioris	Thin muscle between orbicularis oris and inferior eye margin	Zygomatic bone and infraorbital margin of maxilla	Skin and muscle of upper lip and border of nostril	Raises and furrows upper lip; flares nostril (as in disgust)
Zygomaticus— major and minor	Extends diagonally from corner of mouth to cheekbone	Zygomatic bone	Skin and muscle at corner of mouth	Raises lateral corners of mouth upward (smiling muscle)
Risorius	Slender muscle; runs laterally to zygomaticus	Fascia of masseter muscle	Skin at corner of mouth	Draws corner of lip laterally; tenses lip; zygomaticus synergist
Depressor labii inferioris	Small muscle from lower lip to jawbone	Body of mandible lateral to its midline	Skin and muscle of lower lip	Draws lower lip downward
Depressor anguli oris	Small muscle lateral to depressor labii inferioris	Body of mandible below incisors	Skin and muscle at angle of mouth below insertion of zygomaticus	Zygomaticus antagonist; draws corners of mouth downward and laterally
Orbicularis oris	Multilayered sphincter muscle of lips with fibers that run in many different directions	Arises indirectly from maxilla and mandible; fibers blended with fibers of other muscles associated with lips	Encircles mouth; inserts into muscle and skin at angles of mouth	Closes mouth; purses and protrudes lips (kissing muscle)
Mentalis	One of muscle pair forming V-shaped muscle mass on chin	Mandible below incisors	Skin of chin	Protrudes lower lip; wrinkles chin
Buccinator	Principal muscle of cheek; runs horizontally, deep to the masseter	Molar region of maxilla and mandible	Orbicularis oris	Draws corner of mouth laterally; compresses cheek (as in whistling); holds food between teeth during chewing

(continued on page after next)

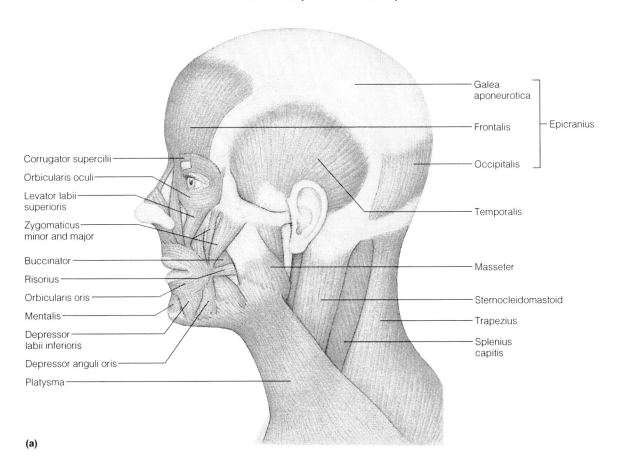

Galea
aponeurotica

Frontalis ⎤ Epicranius

Occipitalis ⎦

Corrugator supercilii

Orbicularis oculi

Levator labii
superioris

Zygomaticus
minor and major

Buccinator

Risorius

Orbicularis oris

Mentalis

Depressor
labii inferioris

Depressor anguli oris

Platysma

Temporalis

Masseter

Sternocleidomastoid

Trapezius

Splenius
capitis

(a)

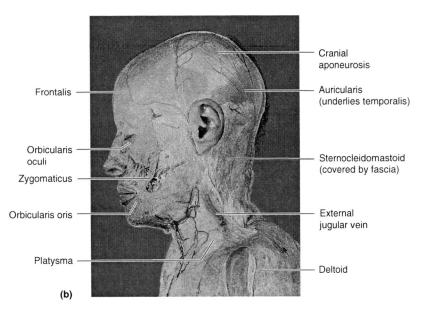

Frontalis

Orbicularis
oculi

Zygomaticus

Orbicularis oris

Platysma

Cranial
aponeurosis

Auricularis
(underlies temporalis)

Sternocleidomastoid
(covered by fascia)

External
jugular vein

Deltoid

(b)

Figure 3 Muscles of the scalp, face, and neck; left lateral view.
(a) Superficial muscles. (b) Photo of superficial structures of head and neck.

Table 1	Major Muscles of Human Head *(continued)*			
Muscle	**Comments**	**Origin**	**Insertion**	**Action**
Mastication (Figure 3c,d)				
Masseter	Extends across jawbone; can be palpated on forcible closure of jaws	Zygomatic process and arch	Angle and ramus of mandible	Closes jaw and elevates mandible
Temporalis	Fan-shaped muscle over temporal bone	Temporal fossa	Coronoid process of mandible	Closes jaw; elevates and retracts mandible
Buccinator	(See muscles of facial expression.)			
Pterygoid—medial	Runs along internal (medial) surface of mandible (thus largely concealed by that bone)	Sphenoid, palatine, and maxillary bones	Medial surface of mandibular ramus and angle	Synergist of temporalis and masseter; closes and elevates mandible; in conjunction with lateral pterygoid, aids in grinding movements
Pterygoid—lateral	Superior to medial pterygoid	Greater wing of sphenoid bone	Mandibular condyle	Protracts jaw (moves it anteriorly); in conjunction with medial pterygoid, aids in grinding movements of teeth

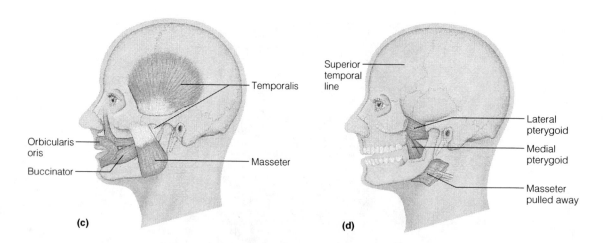

Figure 3 (*continued*) Muscles promoting mastication.
(c) Lateral view of the temporalis, masseter, and buccinator muscles. **(d)** Lateral view of the deep chewing muscles, the medial and lateral pterygoid muscles.

Table 2	Anterolateral Muscles of Human Neck (see Figure 4)			
Muscle	Comments	Origin	Insertion	Action
Superficial				
Platysma	Unpaired muscle: thin, sheetlike superficial neck muscle, not strictly a head muscle but plays role in facial expression (see also Fig. 3a)	Fascia of chest (over pectoral muscles) and deltoid	Lower margin of mandible, skin, and muscle at corner of mouth	Depresses mandible; pulls lower lip back and down; i.e., produces downward sag of the mouth
Sternocleidomastoid	Two-headed muscle located deep to platysma on anterolateral surface of neck; fleshy parts on either side indicate limits of anterior and posterior triangles of neck	Manubrium of sternum and medial portion of clavicle	Mastoid process of temporal bone	Simultaneous contraction of both muscles of pair causes flexion of neck forward, generally against resistance (as when lying on the back); acting independently, rotate head toward shoulder on opposite side
Scalenes—anterior, middle, and posterior	Located more on lateral than anterior neck; deep to platysma (see Fig. 4c)	Transverse processes of cervical vertebrae	Anterolaterally on first two ribs	Flex and slightly rotate neck; elevate first two ribs (aid in inspiration)

(continued)

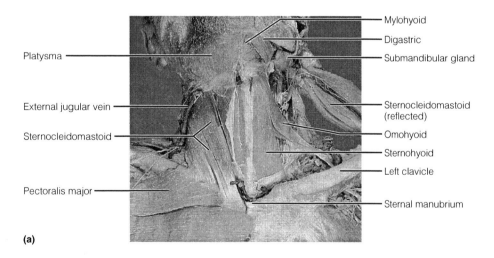

(a)

Figure 4 Muscles of the anterolateral neck and throat.
(a) Photo of the anterior and lateral regions of the neck. The fascia has been partially removed (left side of the photo) to expose the sternocleidomastoid muscle. On the right side of the photo, the sternocleidomastoid muscle is reflected to expose the sternohyoid and omohyoid muscles.

| Table 2 | Anterolateral Muscles of Human Neck *(continued)* | | | |

Muscle	Comments	Origin	Insertion	Action
Deep (Figure 4a,b)				
Digastric	Consists of two bellies united by an intermediate tendon; assumes a V-shaped configuration under chin	Lower margin of mandible (anterior belly) and mastoid process (posterior belly)	By a connective tissue loop to hyoid bone	Acting in concert, elevate hyoid bone; open mouth and depress mandible
Stylohyoid	Slender muscle parallels posterior border of digastric	Styloid process of temporal	Hyoid bone	Elevates and retracts hyoid bone
Mylohyoid	Just deep to digastric; forms floor of mouth	Medial surface of mandible	Hyoid bone	Elevates hyoid bone and base of tongue during swallowing
Sternohyoid	Runs most medially along neck; straplike	Posterior surface of manubrium	Lower margin of body of hyoid bone	Acting with sternothyroid and omohyoid (all inferior to hyoid bone), depresses larynx and hyoid bone if mandible is fixed; may also flex skull
Sternothyroid	Lateral to sternohyoid; straplike	Manubrium and medial end of clavicle	Thyroid cartilage of larynx	(See Sternohyoid above)
Omohyoid	Straplike with two bellies; lateral to sternohyoid	Superior surface of scapula	Hyoid bone	(See Sternohyoid above)
Thyrohyoid	Appears as a slender continuation of sternothyroid muscle	Thyroid cartilage	Hyoid bone	Depresses hyoid bone; elevates thyroid cartilage

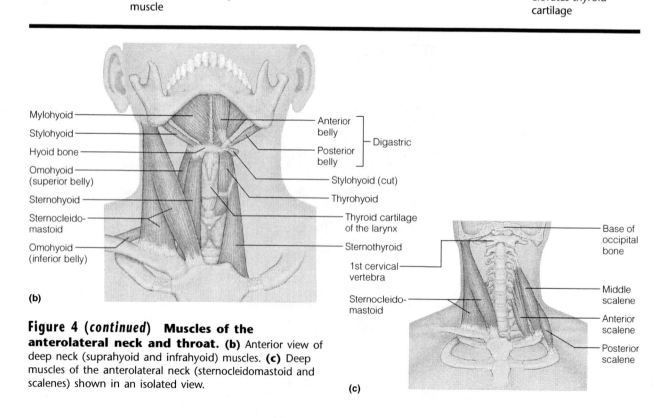

Figure 4 (*continued*) Muscles of the anterolateral neck and throat. (b) Anterior view of deep neck (suprahyoid and infrahyoid) muscles. **(c)** Deep muscles of the anterolateral neck (sternocleidomastoid and scalenes) shown in an isolated view.

Table 3	Anterior Muscles of Human Thorax, Shoulder, and Abdominal Wall (see Figures 5, 6, and 7)			
Muscle	**Comments**	**Origin**	**Insertion**	**Action**
Thorax and Shoulder, Superficial (Figure 5)				
Pectoralis major	Large fan-shaped muscle covering upper portion of chest	Clavicle, sternum, cartilage of first six ribs, and aponeurosis of external oblique muscle	Fibers converge to insert by short tendon into greater tubercle of humerus	Prime mover of arm flexion; adducts, medially rotates arm; with arm fixed, pulls chest upward (thus also acts in forced inspiration)
Serratus anterior	Deep and superficial portions; beneath and inferior to pectoral muscles on lateral rib cage	Lateral aspect of first to eighth (or ninth) ribs	Vertebral border of anterior surface of scapula	Moves scapula forward toward chest wall; rotates scapula causing inferior angle to move laterally and upward
Deltoid	Fleshy triangular muscle forming shoulder muscle mass	Lateral third of clavicle; acromion and spine of scapula	Deltoid tuberosity of humerus	Acting as a whole, prime mover of arm abduction; when only specific fibers are active, can aid in flexion, extension, and rotation of humerus
Pectoralis minor	Flat, thin muscle directly beneath and obscured by pectoralis major	Anterior surface of third, fourth, and fifth ribs, near their costal cartilages	Coracoid process of scapula	With ribs fixed, draws scapula forward and inferiorly; with scapula fixed, draws rib cage superiorly
Thorax, Deep: Muscles of Respiration (Figure 6)				
Intercostals—external	11 pairs lie between ribs; fibers run obliquely downward and forward toward sternum	Inferior border of rib above (not shown in figure)	Superior border of rib below	Pulls ribs toward one another to elevate rib cage; aids in inspiration

(continued)

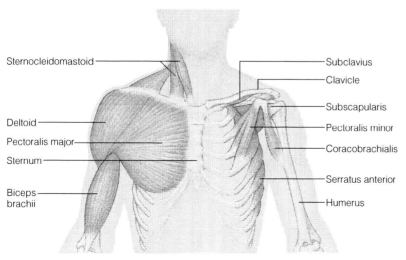

Figure 5 Superficial muscles of the thorax and shoulder acting on the scapula and arm, anterior view. The superficial muscles, which effect arm movements, are shown on the left. These muscles have been removed on the right side of the figure to show the muscles that stabilize or move the pectoral girdle.

Table 3		Anterior Muscles of Human Thorax, Shoulder, and Abdominal Wall *(continued)*		
Muscle	**Comments**	**Origin**	**Insertion**	**Action**
Intercostals—internal	11 pairs lie between ribs; fibers run deep and at right angles to those of external intercostals	Superior border of rib below	Inferior border of rib above (not shown in figure)	Draws ribs together to depress rib cage; aids in forced expiration; antagonistic to external intercostals
Diaphragm	Broad muscle; forms floor of thoracic cavity; dome shaped in relaxed state; fibers converge from margins of thoracic cage toward a central tendon	Inferior border of rib and sternum, costal cartilages of last six ribs and lumbar vertebrae	Central tendon	Prime mover of inspiration flattens on contraction increasing vertical dimensions of thorax; increases intra-abdominal pressure

(continued)

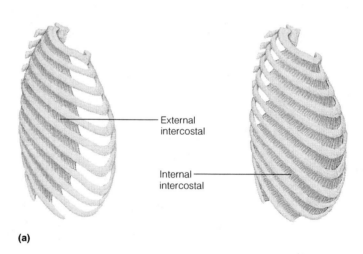

External intercostal

Internal intercostal

(a)

Figure 6 Deep muscles of the thorax: muscles of respiration.
(a) The external intercostals (inspiratory muscles) are shown on the left and the internal intercostals (expiratory muscles) are shown on the right. These two muscle layers run obliquely and at right angles to each other. (b) Inferior view of the diaphragm, the prime mover of inspiration. Notice that its muscle fibers converge toward a central tendon, an arrangement that causes the diaphragm to flatten and move inferiorly as it contracts. The diaphragm and its tendon are pierced by the great vessels (aorta and inferior vena cava) and the esophagus.

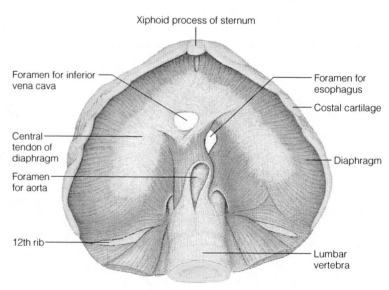

Xiphoid process of sternum

Foramen for inferior vena cava

Foramen for esophagus

Costal cartilage

Central tendon of diaphragm

Diaphragm

Foramen for aorta

12th rib

Lumbar vertebra

(b)

Table 3	(continued)			
Muscle	**Comments**	**Origin**	**Insertion**	**Action**
Abdominal Wall (Figure 7a and b)				
Rectus abdominis	Medial superficial muscle, extends from pubis to rib cage; ensheathed by aponeuroses of oblique muscles; segmented	Pubic crest and symphysis	Xiphoid process and costal cartilages of fifth through seventh ribs	Flexes vertebral column; increases abdominal pressure; fixes and depresses ribs; stabilizes pelvis during walking
External oblique	Most superficial lateral muscle; fibers run downward and medially; ensheathed by an aponeurosis	Anterior surface of last eight ribs	Linea alba,* pubic tubercles, and iliac crest	See Rectus abdominis, above; also aids muscles of back in trunk rotation and lateral flexion
Internal oblique	Fibers run at right angles to those of external oblique, which it underlies	Lumbodorsal fascia, iliac crest, and inguinal ligament	Linea alba, pubic crest, and costal cartilages of last three ribs	As for External oblique
Transversus abdominis	Deepest muscle of abdominal wall; fibers run horizontally	Inguinal ligament, iliac crest, and cartilages of last five or six ribs	Linea alba and pubic crest	Compresses abdominal contents

*The linea alba ("white line") is a narrow, tendinous sheath that runs along the middle of the abdomen from the sternum to the pubic symphysis. It is formed by the fusion of the aponeurosis of the external oblique and transversus muscles.

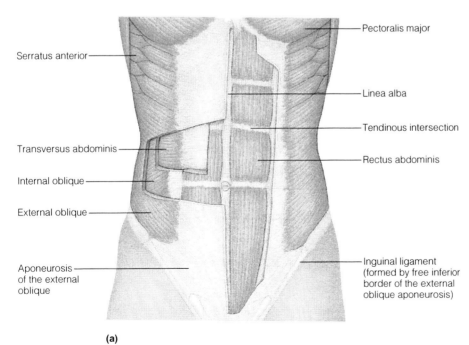

Serratus anterior

Transversus abdominis

Internal oblique

External oblique

Aponeurosis of the external oblique

Pectoralis major

Linea alba

Tendinous intersection

Rectus abdominis

Inguinal ligament (formed by free inferior border of the external oblique aponeurosis)

(a)

Figure 7 Anterior view of the muscles forming the anterolateral abdominal wall. (a) The superficial muscles have been partially cut away on the left side of the diagram to reveal the deeper internal oblique and transversus abdominis muscles.

129

Table 4	Posterior Muscles of Human Trunk (see Figure 8)			
Muscle	**Comments**	**Origin**	**Insertion**	**Action**
Muscles of the Neck, Shoulder, and Thorax (Figure 8a)				
Trapezius	Most superficial muscle of posterior neck and thorax; very broad origin and insertion	Occipital bone; ligamentum nuchae; spines of C_7 and all thoracic vertebrae	Acromion and spinous process of scapula; lateral third of clavicle	Extends head; retracts (adducts) scapula and stabilizes it; upper fibers elevate scapula; lower fibers depress it
Latissimus dorsi	Broad flat muscle of lower back (lumbar region); extensive superficial origins	Indirect attachment to spinous processes of lower six thoracic vertebrae, lumbar vertebrae, lower 3 to 4 ribs, and iliac crest	Floor of intertubercular groove of humerus	Prime mover of arm extension; adducts and medially rotates arm; depresses scapula; brings arm down in power stroke, as in striking a blow
Infraspinatus	Partially covered by deltoid and trapezius; a rotator cuff muscle	Infraspinous fossa of scapula	Greater tubercle of humerus	Lateral rotation of humerus; helps hold head of humerus in glenoid cavity
Teres minor	Small muscle inferior to infraspinatus; a rotator cuff muscle	Lateral margin of scapula	Greater tuberosity of humerus	As for infraspinatus
Teres major	Located inferiorly to teres minor	Posterior surface at inferior angle of scapula	Crest of lesser tubercle of humerus	Extends, medially rotates, and adducts humerus; synergist of latissimus dorsi

(continued)

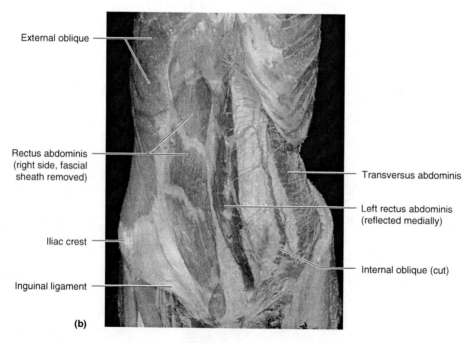

(b)

Figure 7 (*continued*) Anterior view of the muscles forming the anterolateral abdominal wall. (b) Photo of the anterolateral abdominal wall.

Table 4 (continued)

Muscle	Comments	Origin	Insertion	Action
Supraspinatus	Obscured by trapezius and deltoid; a rotator cuff muscle	Supraspinous fossa of scapula	Greater tubercle of humerus	Assists abduction of humerus; stabilizes shoulder joint
Levator scapulae	Located at back and side of neck, deep to trapezius	Transverse processes of C_1 through C_4	Superior vertebral border of scapula	Raises and adducts scapula; with fixed scapula, flexes neck to the same side
Rhomboids— major and minor	Beneath trapezius and inferior to levator scapulae; run from vertebral column to scapula	Spinous processes of C_7 and T_1 through T_5	Vertebral border of scapula	Pull scapula medially (retraction) and elevate it

Muscles Associated with the Vertebral Column (Figure 15.8b)

Muscle	Comments	Origin	Insertion	Action
Semispinalis	Deep composite muscle of the back— thoracis, cervicis, and capitis portions	Transverse processes of C_7–T_{12}	Occipital bone and spinous processes of cervical vertebrae and T_1–T_4	Acting together, extend head and vertebral column; acting independently (right vs. left) causes rotation toward the opposite side

(continued)

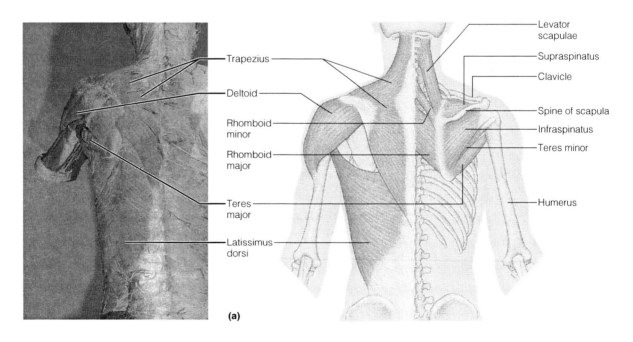

(a)

Figure 8   Muscles of the neck, shoulder, and thorax, posterior view. **(a)** The superficial muscles of the back are shown for the left side of the body, with a corresponding photograph. The superficial muscles are removed on the right side of the illustration to reveal the deeper muscles acting on the scapula and the rotator cuff muscles that help to stabilize the shoulder joint.

131

Table 4	Posterior Muscles of Human Trunk *(continued)*			
Muscle	**Comments**	**Origin**	**Insertion**	**Action**
Erector spinae	A long tripartite muscle composed of iliocostalis (lateral), longissimus, and spinalis (medial) muscle columns; superficial to semispinalis muscles; extends from pelvis to head	Sacrum, iliac crest, transverse processes of lumbar, thoracic, and cervical vertebrae, and/or ribs 3–12 depending on specific part	Ribs and transverse processes of vertebrae about six segments above origin. Longissimus also inserts into mastoid process	All act to extend and abduct the vertebral column; fibers of the longissimus also extend head

(continued)

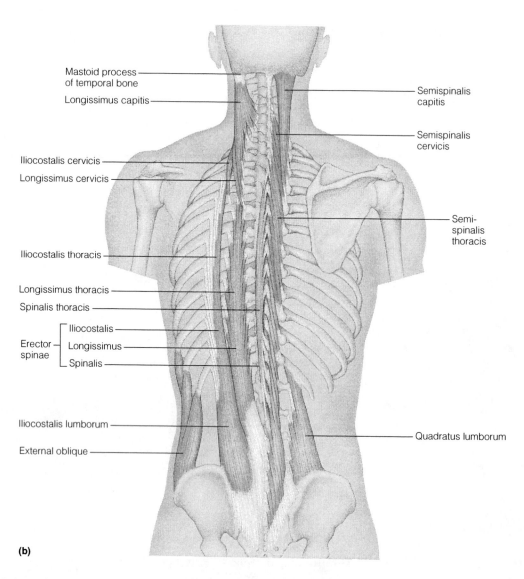

(b)

Figure 8 (*continued*) **Muscles of the neck, shoulder, and thorax, posterior view. (b)** The erector spinae and semispinalis muscles which respectively form the intermediate and deep muscle layers of the back associated with the vertebral column.

Table 4 (continued)

Muscle	Comments	Origin	Insertion	Action
Splenius (see Figure 8c)	Superficial muscle (capitis and cervicis parts) just deep to levator scapulae and superficial to erector spinae	Ligamentum nuchae and spinous processes of C_7–T_6	Mastoid process, occipital bone, and transverse processes of C_2–C_4	As a group, extend or hyperextend head; when only one side is active, head is rotated and bent toward the same side
Quadratus lumborum	Forms greater portion of posterior abdominal wall	Iliac crest and iliolumbar fascia	Inferior border twelfth rib; transverse processes of lumbar vertebrae	Each flexes vertebral column laterally; together extend the lumbar spine and fix the twelfth rib

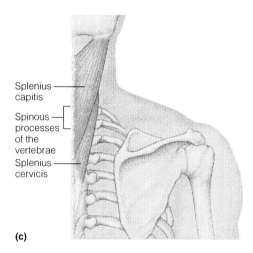

Splenius capitis

Spinous processes of the vertebrae

Splenius cervicis

(c)

Figure 8 (continued) Muscles of the neck, shoulder, and thorax, posterior view. (c) Deep (splenius) muscles of the posterior neck. Superficial muscles have been removed.

Muscles of the Upper Limb

The muscles that act on the upper limb fall into three groups: those that move the arm, those causing movement at the elbow, and those effecting movements of the wrist and hand.

The muscles that cross the shoulder joint to insert on the humerus and move the arm (subscapularis, supraspinatus and infraspinatus, deltoid, and so on) are primarily trunk muscles that originate on the axial skeleton or shoulder girdle. These muscles are included with the trunk muscles.

The second group of muscles, which cross the elbow joint and move the forearm, consists of muscles forming the musculature of the humerus. These muscles arise primarily from the humerus and insert in forearm bones. They are responsible for flexion, extension, pronation, and supination. The origins, insertions, and actions of these muscles are summarized in Table 5 and the muscles are shown in Figure 9.

The third group composes the musculature of the forearm. For the most part, these muscles insert on the digits and produce movements at the wrist and fingers. In general, muscles acting on the wrist and hand are more easily identified if their insertion tendons are located first. These muscles are described in Table 6 and illustrated in Figure 10.

Activity:
Identifying Muscles of the Upper Limb

First study the tables and figures, then see if you can identify these muscles on a torso model, anatomical chart, or cadaver. Complete this portion of the exercise with palpation demonstrations as outlined next.

• To observe the *biceps brachii*, attempt to flex your forearm (hand supinated) against resistance. The insertion tendon of this biceps muscle can also be felt in the lateral aspect of the antecubital fossa (where it runs toward the radius to attach).

• If you acutely flex your elbow and then try to extend it against resistance, you can demonstrate the action of your *triceps brachii*.

• Strongly flex your wrist and make a fist. Palpate your contracting wrist flexor muscles (which originate from the medial epicondyle of the humerus) and their insertion tendons, which can be easily felt at the anterior aspect of the wrist.

• Flare your fingers to identify the tendons of the *extensor digitorum* muscle on the dorsum of your hand. ■

133

Table 5	Muscles of Human Humerus That Act on the Forearm (see Figure 9)			
Muscle	**Comments**	**Origin**	**Insertion**	**Action**
Triceps brachii	Sole, large fleshy muscle of posterior humerus; three-headed origin	Long head: inferior margin of glenoid cavity; lateral head: posterior humerus; medial head: distal radial groove on posterior humerus	Olecranon process of ulna	Powerful forearm extensor; antagonist of forearm flexors (brachialis and biceps brachii)
Biceps brachii	Most familiar muscle of anterior humerus because this two-headed muscle bulges when forearm is flexed	Short head: coracoid process; tendon of long head runs in intertubercular groove and within capsule of shoulder joint	Radial tuberosity	Flexion (powerful) of elbow and supination of forearm; "it turns the corkscrew and pulls the cork"; weak arm flexor
Brachioradialis	Superficial muscle of lateral forearm; forms lateral boundary of antecubital fossa	Lateral ridge at distal end of humerus	Base of styloid process of radius	Forearm flexor (weak)
Brachialis	Immediately deep to biceps brachii	Distal portion of anterior humerus	Coronoid process of ulna	A major flexor of forearm

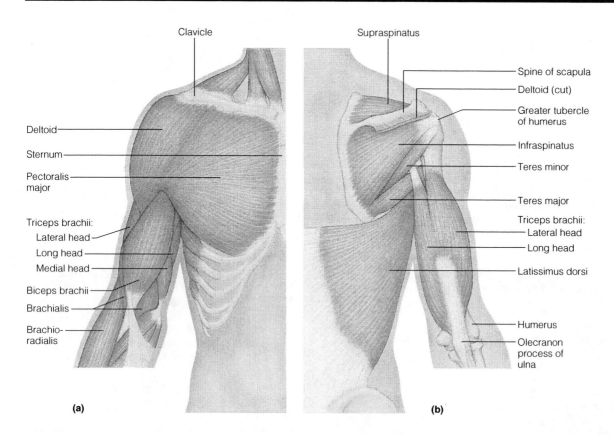

Figure 9 Muscles causing movements of the forearm.
(a) Superficial muscles of the anterior thorax, shoulder, and arm, anterior view.
(b) Posterior aspect of the arm showing the lateral and long heads of the triceps brachii muscle.

Table 6		Muscles of Human Forearm That Act on Hand and Fingers (see Figure 10)		
Muscle	**Comments**	**Origin**	**Insertion**	**Action**
Anterior Compartment (Figure 10a, b, c)				
Superficial				
Pronator teres	Seen in a superficial view between proximal margins of brachioradialis and flexor carpi ulnaris	Medial epicondyle of humerus and coronoid process of ulna	Midshaft of radius	Acts synergistically with pronator quadratus to pronate forearm; weak forearm flexor
Flexor carpi radialis	Superficial; runs diagonally across forearm	Medial epicondyle of humerus	Base of second and third metacarpals	Powerful flexor of wrist; abducts hand
Palmaris longus	Small fleshy muscle with a long tendon; medial to flexor carpi radialis	Medial epicondyle of humerus	Palmar aponeurosis	Flexes wrist (weak)
Flexor carpi ulnaris	Superficial; medial to palmaris longus	Medial epicondyle of humerus and olecranon process of ulna	Base of fifth metacarpal	Powerful flexor of wrist; adducts hand

(continued)

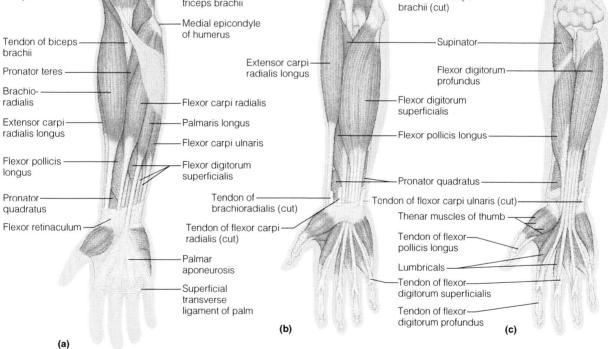

(a)

(b)

(c)

Figure 10 Muscles of the forearm and wrist. (a) Superficial anterior view of right forearm and hand. **(b)** The brachioradialis, flexors carpi radialis and ulnaris, and palmaris longus muscles have been removed to reveal the position of the somewhat deeper flexor digitorum superficialis. **(c)** Deep muscles of the anterior compartment. Superficial muscles have been removed. Note: The thenar muscles of the thumb and the lumbricals that help move the fingers are illustrated here but are not described in Table 6.

Table 6	Muscles of Human Forearm That Act on Hand and Fingers *(continued)*			
Muscle	**Comments**	**Origin**	**Insertion**	**Action**
Flexor digitorum superficialis	Deeper muscle; overlain by muscles named above; visible at distal end of forearm	Medial epicondyle of humerus, medial surface of ulna, and anterior border of radius	Middle phalanges of second through fifth fingers	Flexes wrist and middle phalanges of second through fifth fingers
Deep				
Flexor pollicis longus	Deep muscle of anterior forearm; distal to and paralleling lower margin of flexor digitorum superficialis	Anterior surface of radius, and interosseous membrane	Distal phalanx of thumb	Flexes thumb (*pollix* is Latin for "thumb"); weak flexor of wrist
Flexor digitorum profundus	Deep muscle; overlain entirely by flexor digitorum superficialis	Anteromedial surface of ulna and interosseous membrane	Distal phalanges of second through fifth fingers	Sole muscle that flexes distal phalanges; assists in wrist flexion
Pronator quadratus	Deepest muscle of distal forearm	Distal portion of anterior ulnar surface	Anterior surface of radius, distal end	Pronates forearm
Posterior Compartment (Figure 10d, e, f)				
Superficial				
Extensor carpi radialis longus	Superficial; parallels brachioradialis on lateral forearm	Lateral supracondylar ridge of humerus	Base of second metacarpal	Extends and abducts wrist
Extensor carpi radialis brevis	Posterior to extensor carpi radialis longus	Lateral epicondyle of humerus	Base of third metacarpal	Extends and abducts wrist; steadies wrist during finger flexion
Extensor digitorum	Superficial; between extensor carpi ulnaris and extensor carpi radialis brevis	Lateral epicondyle of humerus	By four tendons into distal phalanges of second through fifth fingers	Prime mover of finger extension; extends wrist; can flare (abduct) fingers
Extensor carpi ulnaris	Superficial; medial posterior forearm	Lateral epicondyle of humerus	Base of fifth metacarpal	Extends and adducts wrist
Deep				
Extensor pollicis longus and brevis	Deep muscle pair with a common origin and action; overlain by extensor carpi ulnaris	Dorsal shaft of ulna and radius, interosseous membrane	Base of distal phalanx of thumb (longus) and proximal phalanx of thumb (brevis)	Extends thumb
Abductor pollicis longus	Deep muscle; lateral and parallel to extensor pollicis longus	Posterior surface of radius and ulna; interosseous membrane	First metacarpal	Abducts and extends thumb
Supinator	Deep muscle at posterior aspect of elbow	Lateral epicondyle of humerus	Proximal end of radius	Acts with biceps brachii to supinate forearm; antagonist of pronator muscles

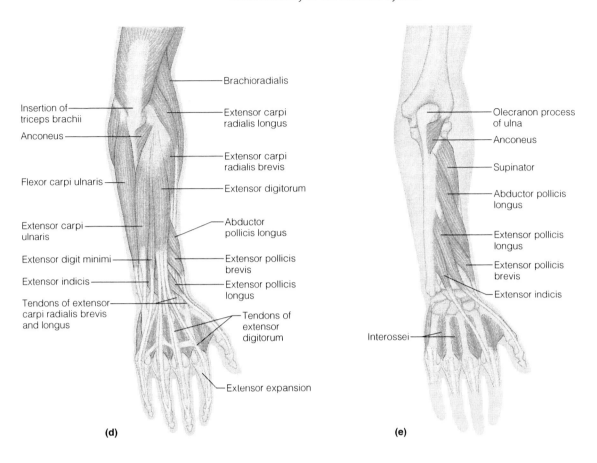

Brachioradialis

Insertion of triceps brachii

Anconeus

Flexor carpi ulnaris

Extensor carpi ulnaris

Extensor digit minimi

Extensor indicis

Tendons of extensor carpi radialis brevis and longus

Extensor carpi radialis longus

Extensor carpi radialis brevis

Extensor digitorum

Abductor pollicis longus

Extensor pollicis brevis

Extensor pollicis longus

Tendons of extensor digitorum

Extensor expansion

(d)

Olecranon process of ulna

Anconeus

Supinator

Abductor pollicis longus

Extensor pollicis longus

Extensor pollicis brevis

Extensor indicis

Interossei

(e)

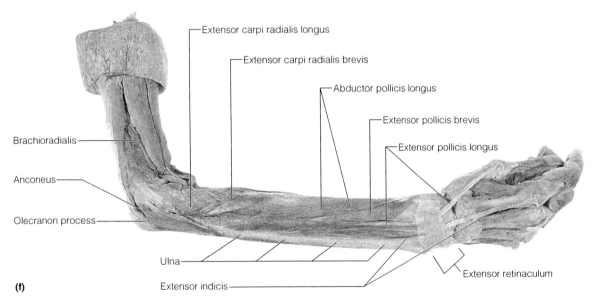

Extensor carpi radialis longus

Extensor carpi radialis brevis

Abductor pollicis longus

Extensor pollicis brevis

Extensor pollicis longus

Brachioradialis

Anconeus

Olecranon process

Ulna

Extensor indicis

Extensor retinaculum

(f)

Figure 10 (*continued*)   Muscles of the forearm and wrist.
(d) Superficial muscles, posterior view. **(e)** Deep posterior muscles; superficial muscles have been removed. The interossei, the deepest layer of intrinsic hand muscles, are also illustrated. **(f)** Photo of deep posterior muscles of the right forearm. The superficial muscles have been removed.

Muscles of the Lower Limb

Muscles that act on the lower limb cause movement at the hip, knee, and foot joints. Since the human pelvic girdle is composed of heavy fused bones that allow very little movement, no special group of muscles is necessary to stabilize it. This is unlike the shoulder girdle, where several muscles (mainly trunk muscles) are needed to stabilize the scapulae.

Muscles acting on the thigh (femur) cause various movements at the multiaxial hip joint (flexion, extension, rotation, abduction, and adduction). These include the iliopsoas, the adductor group, and other muscles summarized in Tables 7 and 8 and illustrated in Figures 11 and 12.

Muscles acting on the leg form the major musculature of the thigh. (Anatomically the term *leg* refers only to that portion between the knee and the ankle.) The thigh muscles cross

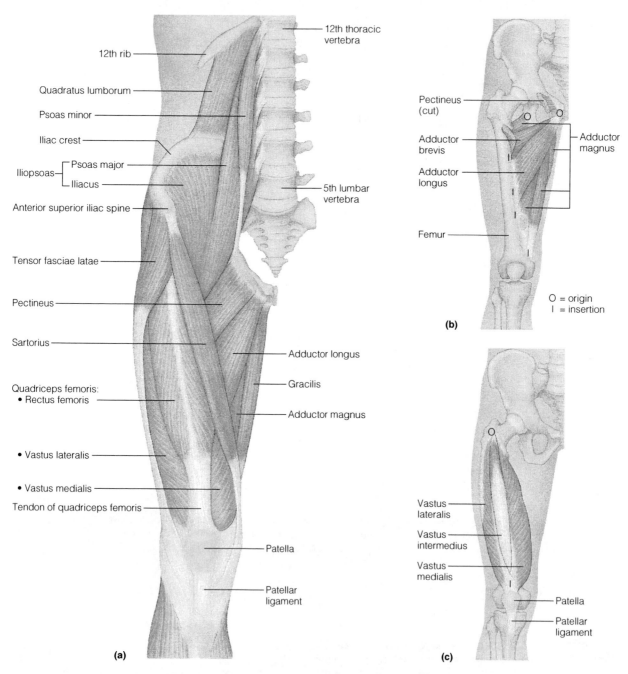

Figure 11 Anterior and medial muscles promoting movements of the thigh and leg. (a) Anterior view of the deep muscles of the pelvis and superficial muscles of the right thigh. **(b)** Adductor muscles of the medial compartment of the thigh. **(c)** The vastus muscles (isolated) of the quadriceps group.

Table 7	Muscles Acting on Human Thigh and Leg, Anterior and Medial Aspects (see Figure 11)			
Muscle	**Comments**	**Origin**	**Insertion**	**Action**
Origin on the Pelvis				
Iliopsoas—iliacus and psoas major	Two closely related muscles; fibers pass under inguinal ligament to insert into femur via a common tendon	Iliacus: iliac fossa; psoas major: transverse processes, bodies, and discs of T_{12} and lumbar vertebrae	Lesser trochanter of femur	Flex trunk on thigh; major flexor of hip (or thigh on pelvis when pelvis is fixed)
Sartorius	Straplike superficial muscle running obliquely across anterior surface of thigh to knee	Anterior superior iliac spine	By an aponeurosis into medial aspect of proximal tibia	Flexes and laterally rotates thigh; flexes knee; known as "tailor's muscle" because it helps bring about cross-legged position in which tailors are often depicted
Medial Compartment				
Adductors—magnus, longus, and brevis	Large muscle mass forming medial aspect of thigh; arise from front of pelvis and insert at various levels on femur	Magnus: ischial and pubic rami; longus: pubis near pubic symphysis; brevis: body and inferior ramus of pubis	Magnus: linea aspera and adductor tubercle of femur; longus and brevis: linea aspera	Adduct and laterally rotate and flex thigh; posterior part of magnus is also a synergist in thigh extension
Pectineus	Overlies adductor brevis on proximal thigh	Pectineal line of pubis	Inferior to lesser trochanter of femur	Adducts, flexes, and laterally rotates thigh
Gracilis	Straplike superficial muscle of medial thigh	Inferior ramus and body of pubis	Medial surface of head of tibia	Adducts thigh; flexes and medially rotates leg, especially during walking
Anterior Compartment				
Quadriceps*				
Rectus femoris	Superficial muscle of thigh; runs straight down thigh; only muscle of group to cross hip joint; arises from two heads	Anterior inferior iliac spine and superior margin of acetabulum	Tibial tuberosity	Extends knee and flexes thigh at hip
Vastus lateralis	Forms lateral aspect of thigh	Greater trochanter and linea aspera	Tibial tuberosity	Extends knee
Vastus medialis	Forms medial aspect of thigh	Linea aspera	Tibial tuberosity	Extends knee
Vastus intermedius	Obscured by rectus femoris; lies between vastus lateralis and vastus medialis on anterior thigh	Anterior and lateral surface of femur (not shown in figure)	Tibial tuberosity	Extends knee
Tensor fasciae latae	Enclosed between fascia layers of thigh	Anterior aspect of iliac crest and anterior superior iliac spine	Iliotibial band of fascia lata	Flexes, abducts, and medially rotates thigh

*The quadriceps form the flesh of the anterior thigh and have a common insertion in the tibial tuberosity via the patellar tendon. They are powerful leg extensors, enabling humans to kick a football, for example.

Table 8	Muscles Acting on Human Thigh and Leg, Posterior Aspect (see Figure 12)			
Muscle	**Comments**	**Origin**	**Insertion**	**Action**
Origin on the Pelvis				
Gluteus maximus	Largest and most superficial of gluteal muscles (which form buttock mass)	Dorsal ilium, sacrum, and coccyx	Gluteal tuberosity of femur and iliotibial tract*	Complex, powerful hip extensor (most effective when hip is flexed, as in climbing stairs—but not as in walking); antagonist of iliopsoas; laterally rotates thigh
Gluteus medius	Partially covered by gluteus maximus	Upper lateral surface of ilium	Greater trochanter of femur	Abducts and medially rotates thigh; steadies pelvis during walking
Gluteus minimus (not shown in figure)	Smallest and deepest gluteal muscle	Inferior surface of ilium	Greater trochanter of femur	Abducts and medially rotates thigh
Posterior Compartment				
Hamstrings†				
Biceps femoris	Most lateral muscle of group; arises from two heads	Ischial tuberosity (long head); linea aspera and distal femur (short head)	Tendon passes laterally to insert into head of fibula and lateral condyle of tibia	Extends thigh; laterally rotates leg on thigh; flexes knee
Semitendinosus	Medial to biceps femoris	Ischial tuberosity	Medial aspect of upper tibial shaft	Extends thigh; flexes knee; medially rotates leg
Semimembranosus	Deep to semitendinosus	Ischial tuberosity	Medial condyle of tibia	Extends thigh; flexes knee; medially rotates leg

*The iliotibial tract, a thickened lateral portion of the fascia lata, ensheathes all the muscles of the thigh. It extends as a tendinous band from the iliac crest to the knee.

†The hamstrings are the fleshy muscles of the posterior thigh. The name comes from the butchers' practice of using the tendons of these muscles to hang hams for smoking. As a group, they are strong extensors of the hip; they counteract the powerful quadriceps by stabilizing the knee joint when standing.

the knee to allow its flexion and extension. They include the hamstrings and the quadriceps and, along with the muscles acting on the thigh, are described in Tables 7 and 8 and illustrated in Figures 11 and 12. Since some of these muscles also have attachments on the pelvic girdle, they can cause movement at the hip joint.

The muscles originating on the leg and acting on the foot and toes are described in Table 9 and shown in Figures 13 and 14.

Activity:
Identifying Muscles of the Lower Limb

Identify the muscles acting on the thigh, leg, foot, and toes as instructed previously for other muscle groups. ∎

Activity:
Palpating Muscles of the Hip and Lower Limb

Complete this exercise by performing the following palpation demonstrations with your lab partner.

• Go into a deep knee bend and palpate your own *gluteus maximus* muscle as you extend your hip to resume the upright posture.

• Demonstrate the contraction of the anterior *quadriceps femoris* by trying to extend your knee against resistance. Do this while seated and note how the patellar tendon reacts. The *biceps femoris* of the posterior thigh comes into play when you flex your knee against resistance.

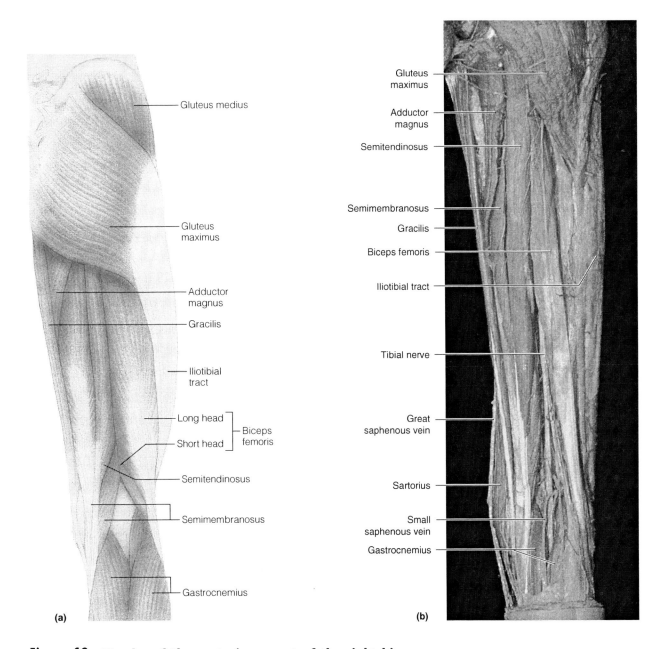

Figure 12 Muscles of the posterior aspect of the right hip and thigh. (a) Superficial view showing the gluteus muscles of the buttock and hamstring muscles of the thigh. **(b)** Photo of muscles of the posterior thigh.

• Now stand on your toes. Have your partner palpate the lateral and medial heads of the *gastrocnemius* and follow it to its insertion in the calcaneal tendon.

• Dorsiflex and invert your foot while palpating your *tibialis anterior* muscle (which parallels the sharp anterior crest of the tibia laterally). ∎

Table 9	Muscles Acting on Human Foot and Ankle (see Figures 13 and 14)			
Muscle	**Comments**	**Origin**	**Insertion**	**Action**
Posterior Compartment				
Superficial (Figure 13a, b)				
Triceps surae	Muscle pair that shapes posterior calf		Via common tendon (calcaneal or Achilles) into heel	Plantar flex foot
Gastrocnemius	Superficial muscle of pair; two prominent bellies	By two heads from medial and lateral condyles of femur	Calcaneus via calcaneal tendon	Crosses knee joint; thus also can flex knee (when foot is dorsiflexed)

(continued)

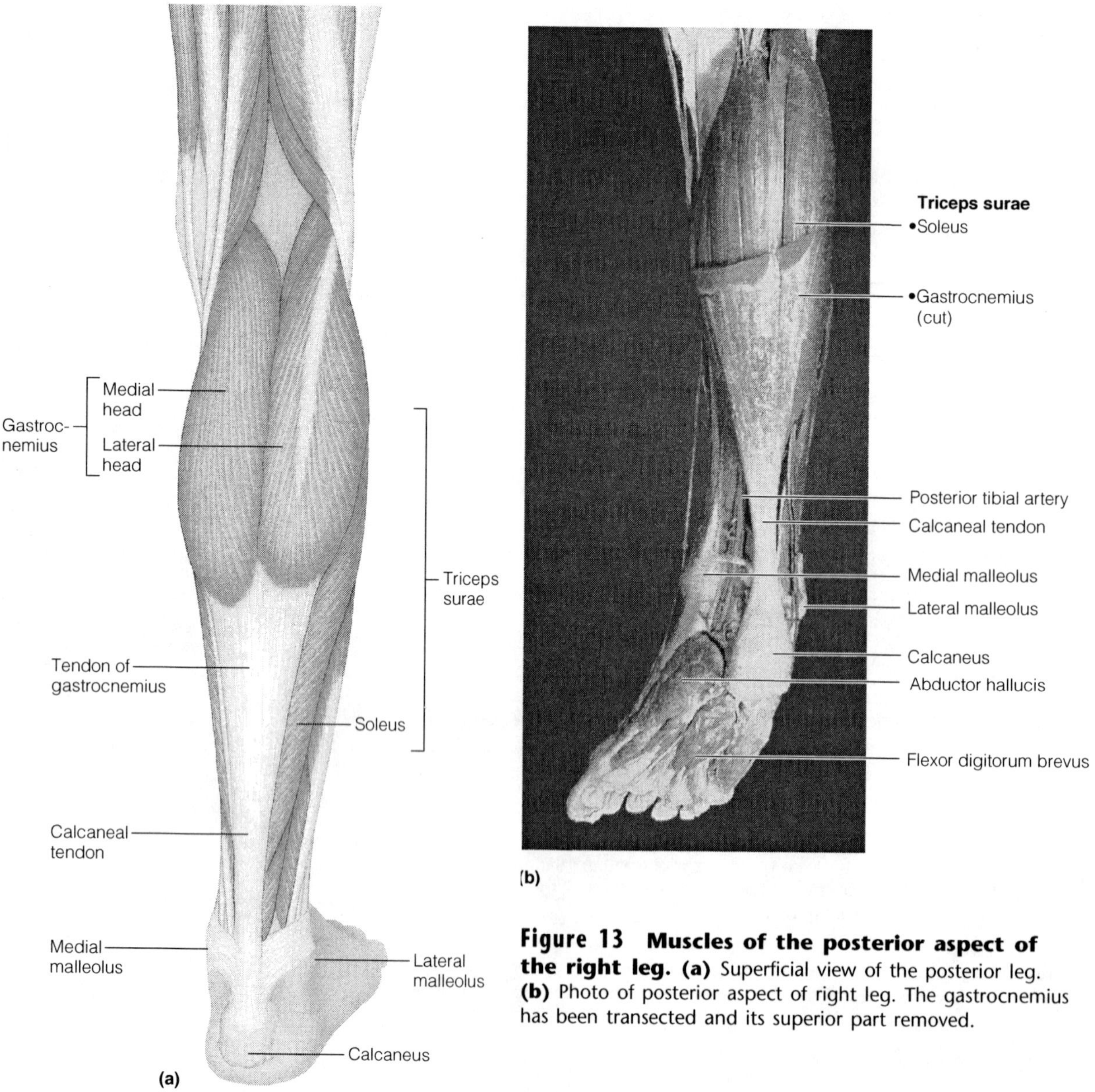

(b)

Figure 13 Muscles of the posterior aspect of the right leg. (a) Superficial view of the posterior leg. **(b)** Photo of posterior aspect of right leg. The gastrocnemius has been transected and its superior part removed.

Table 9	(continued)			
Muscle	**Comments**	**Origin**	**Insertion**	**Action**
Soleus	Deep to gastrocnemius	Proximal portion of tibia and fibula	Calcaneus via calcaneal tendon	Plantar flexion; is an important muscle for locomotion
Deep (Figure 13c, d)				
Popliteus	Thin muscle at posterior aspect of knee	Lateral condyle of femur	Proximal tibia	Flexes and rotates leg medially to "unlock" extended knee when knee flexion begins

(continued)

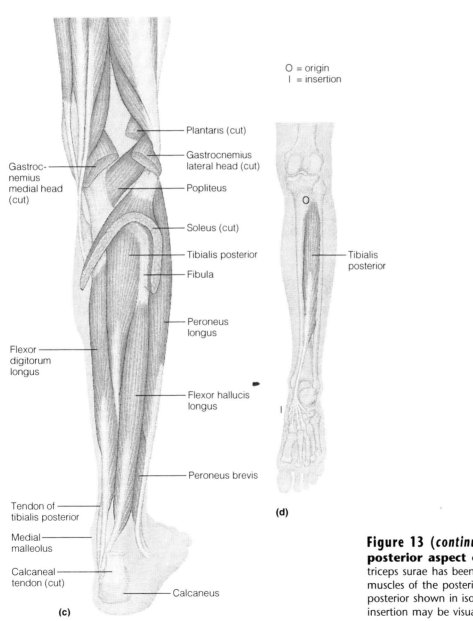

O = origin
I = insertion

Gastroc-
nemius
medial head
(cut)

Flexor
digitorum
longus

Tendon of
tibialis posterior

Medial
malleolus

Calcaneal
tendon (cut)

Calcaneus

(c)

Plantaris (cut)

Gastrocnemius
lateral head (cut)

Popliteus

Soleus (cut)

Tibialis posterior

Fibula

Peroneus
longus

Flexor hallucis
longus

Peroneus brevis

Tibialis
posterior

(d)

Figure 13 (continued) Muscles of the posterior aspect of the right leg. (c) The triceps surae has been removed to show the deep muscles of the posterior compartment. **(d)** Tibialis posterior shown in isolation so that its origin and insertion may be visualized.

143

Table 9	Muscles Acting on Human Foot and Ankle *(continued)*			

Muscle	Comments	Origin	Insertion	Action
Tibialis posterior	Thick muscle deep to soleus	Superior portion of tibia and fibula and interosseous membrane	Tendon passes obliquely behind medial malleolus and under arch of foot; inserts into several tarsals and metatarsals 2–4	Prime mover of foot inversion; plantar flexes foot
Flexor digitorum longus	Runs medial to and partially overlies tibialis posterior	Posterior surface of tibia	Distal phalanges of second through fifth toes	Flexes toes; plantar flexes and inverts foot
Flexor hallucis longus (see also Figure 14)	Lies lateral to inferior aspect of tibialis posterior	Middle portion of fibula shaft	Tendon runs under foot to insert on distal phalanx of great toe	Flexes great toe; plantar flexes and inverts foot; the "push-off muscle" during walking

Lateral Compartment (Figure 13c and Figure 14a, b)

Muscle	Comments	Origin	Insertion	Action
Peroneus longus	Superficial lateral muscle; overlies fibula	Head and upper portion of fibula	By long tendon under foot to first metatarsal and medial cuneiform	Plantar flexes and everts foot; helps keep foot flat on ground
Peroneus brevis	Smaller muscle; deep to peroneus longus	Distal portion of fibula shaft	By tendon running behind lateral malleolus to insert on proximal end of fifth metatarsal	Plantar flexes and everts foot, as part of peronei group

Anterior Compartment (Figure14a, b)

Muscle	Comments	Origin	Insertion	Action
Tibialis anterior	Superficial muscle of anterior leg; parallels sharp anterior margin of tibia	Lateral condyle and upper 2/3 of tibia; interosseous membrane	By tendon into inferior surface of first cuneiform and metatarsal 1	Prime mover of dorsiflexion; inverts foot
Extensor digitorum longus	Anterolateral surface of leg; lateral to tibialis anterior	Lateral condyle of tibia; proximal 3/4 of fibula; interosseous membrane	Tendon divides into four parts; insert into middle and distal phalanges of toes 2–5	Prime mover of toe extension; dorsiflexes foot
Peroneus tertius	Small muscle; often fused to distal part of extensor digitorum longus	Distal anterior surface of fibula	Tendon passes anterior to lateral malleolus and inserts on dorsum of fifth metatarsal	Dorsiflexes and everts foot
Extensor hallucis longus	Deep to extensor digitorum longus and tibialis anterior	Anteromedial shaft of fibula and interosseous membrane	Tendon inserts on distal phalanx of great toe	Extends great toe; dorsiflexes foot

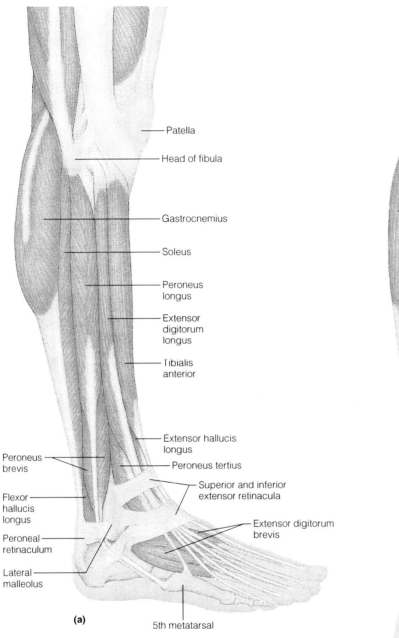

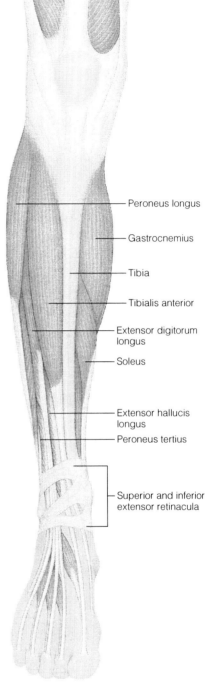

(a)

Patella

Head of fibula

Gastrocnemius

Soleus

Peroneus longus

Extensor digitorum longus

Tibialis anterior

Extensor hallucis longus

Peroneus tertius

Superior and inferior extensor retinacula

Extensor digitorum brevis

Peroneus brevis

Flexor hallucis longus

Peroneal retinaculum

Lateral malleolus

5th metatarsal

Peroneus longus

Gastrocnemius

Tibia

Tibialis anterior

Extensor digitorum longus

Soleus

Extensor hallucis longus

Peroneus tertius

Superior and inferior extensor retinacula

(b)

Figure 14 Muscles of the anterolateral aspect of the right leg. (a) Superficial view of lateral aspect of the leg, illustrating the positioning of the lateral compartment muscles (peroneus longus and brevis) relative to anterior and posterior leg muscles. **(b)** Superficial view of anterior leg muscles.

Illustrations: 1–11: Raychel Ciemma. 12: Wendy Hiller-Gee. 13 and 14: Raychel Ciemma. **Photographs:** 3b, 7b, 12b, and 13b: © Dr. Robert A. Chase. 4a and 8a: From *A Stereoscopic Atlas of Human Anatomy,* by David L. Bassett. 10f: © Benjamin/Cummings Publishing Company. Photo by Stephen Spector, courtesy of Dr. Charles Thomas, Kansas University Medical Center.

Gross Anatomy of the Muscular System

Muscles of the Head and Neck

1. Using choices from the list at the right, correctly identify muscles provided with leader lines on the diagram.

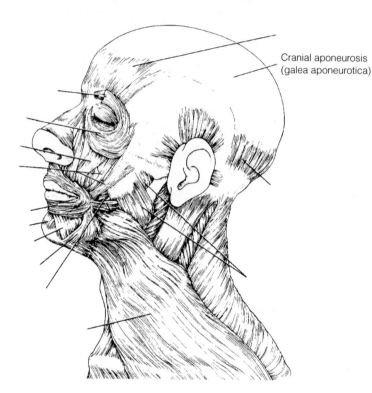

Cranial aponeurosis
(galea aponeurotica)

a.   buccinator

b.   corrugator supercilii

c.   depressor anguli oris

d.   depressor labii inferioris

e.   epicranius frontalis

f.   epicranius occipitalis

g.   levator labii superioris

h.   masseter

i.   mentalis

j.   platysma

k.   orbicularis oculi

l.   orbicularis oris

m.   zygomaticus

2. Using the terms provided above, identify the muscles described next.

_____ 1. used in smiling

_____ 2. used to suck in your cheeks

_____ 3. used in blinking and squinting

_____ 4. used to pout (pulls the corners of the mouth downward)

_____ 5. raises your eyebrows for a questioning expression

_____ 6. used to form the vertical frown crease on the forehead

_____ 7. your "kisser"

_____ 8. prime mover to raise the lower jawbone

_____ 9. tenses skin of the neck during shaving

Muscles of the Trunk

1. Correctly identify both intact and transected (cut) muscles depicted in the diagram, using the terms given at the right. (Not all terms will be used in this identification.)

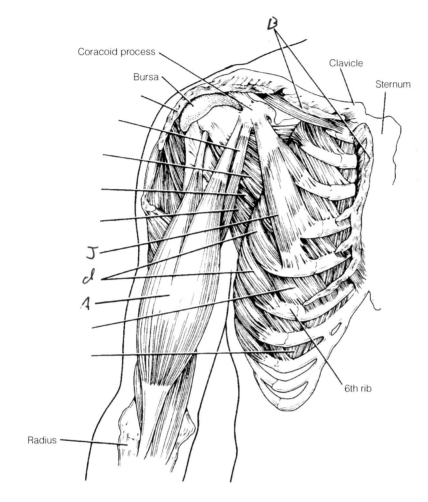

Coracoid process

Bursa

B

Clavicle

Sternum

J

d

1

Radius

6th rib

a. biceps brachii

b. coracobrachialis

c. deltoid (cut)

d. external intercostals

e. external oblique

f. internal intercostals

g. internal oblique

h. latissimus dorsi

i. pectoralis major (cut)

j. pectoralis minor

k. rectus abdominis

l. rhomboids

m. serratus anterior

n. subscapularis

o. teres major

p. teres minor

q. transversus abdominis

r. trapezius

2. Using choices from the terms provided in question 1 above, identify the major muscles described next:

___Q___ 1. a major spine flexor

___H___ 2. prime mover for pulling the arm posteriorly

___R___ 3. prime mover for shoulder flexion

___Q, K, G___ 4. assume major responsibility for forming the abdominal girdle (three pairs of muscles)

___H___ 5. pulls the shoulder backward and downward

___H___ 6. prime mover of shoulder abduction

___C P___ 7. important in shoulder adduction; antagonists of the shoulder abductor (two muscles)

___n___ 8. moves the scapula forward and downward

___D___ 9. small, inspiratory muscles between the ribs; elevate the ribs

___B___ 10. extends the head

___m___ 11. pull the scapulae medially

Muscles of the Upper Limb

1. Using terms from the list on the right, correctly identify all muscles provided with leader lines in the diagram. Note that not all the listed terms will be used in this exercise.

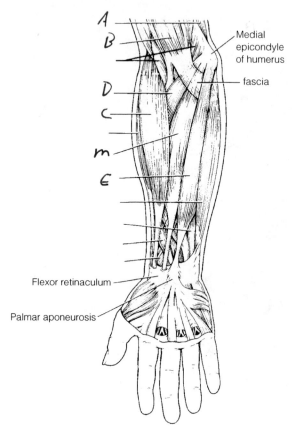

A
B
Medial
epicondyle
of humerus
fascia
D
C
m
E

Flexor retinaculum
Palmar aponeurosis

a. biceps brachii

b. brachialis

c. brachioradialis

d. extensor carpi radialis longus

e. extensor digitorum

f. flexor carpi radialis

g. flexor carpi ulnaris

h. flexor digitorum superficialis

i. flexor pollicis longus

j. palmaris longus

k. pronator quadratus

l. pronator teres

m. supinator

n. triceps brachii

2. Use the terms provided in question 1 to identify the muscles described next.

_m, B_ 1. places the palm upward (two muscles)

_l_ 2. flexes the forearm and supinates the hand

_H, I_ 3. forearm flexors; no role in supination (two muscles)

_h_ 4. elbow extensor

_J_ 5. power wrist flexor and abductor

_H_ 6. flexes wrist and middle phalanges

_K, L_ 7. pronate the hand (two muscles)

_I_ 8. flexes the thumb

_C_ 9. extends and abducts the wrist

_E_ 10. extends the wrist and digits

_B_ 11. flat muscle that is a weak wrist flexor

Review Sheet

Muscles of the Lower Limb

1. Using the terms listed to the right, correctly identify all muscles provided with leader lines in the diagram below. Not all listed terms will be used in this exercise.

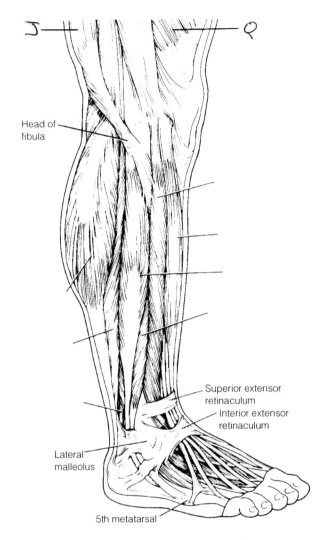

Head of fibula

Superior extensor retinaculum

Interior extensor retinaculum

Lateral malleolus

5th metatarsal

a. adductor group

b. biceps femoris

c. extensor digitorum longus

d. flexor hallucis longus

e. gastrocnemius

f. gluteus maximus

g. gluteus medius

h. peroneus brevis

i. peroneus longus

j. rectus femoris

k. semimembranosus

l. semitendinosus

m. soleus

n. tensor fasciae latae

o. tibialis anterior

p. tibialis posterior

q. vastus muscles

2. Use the key terms in exercise 1 to respond to the descriptions below.

___D___ 1. flexes the great toe and inverts the ankle

___E, M___ 2. lateral compartment muscles that plantar flex and evert the ankle (two muscles)

___G___ 3. move the thigh laterally to take the "at ease" stance (two muscles)

___F___ 4. used to extend the hip when climbing stairs

___n___ 5. prime movers of ankle plantar flexion (two muscles)

___A___ 6. major foot inverter

___O___ 7. prime mover of ankle dorsiflexion

___Q___ 8. allow you to draw your legs to the midline of your body, as when standing at attention

___C___ 9. extends the toes

___(Q, J___ 10. extend thigh and flex knee (three muscles)

___Q, J___ 11. extends knee and flexes thigh

Review Sheet

General Review: Muscle Recognition

1. Identify the lettered muscles in the diagram of the human anterior superficial musculature by matching the letter with one of the following muscle names:

_____ 1. orbicularis oris

_____ 2. pectoralis major

_____ 3. external oblique

_____ 4. sternocleidomastoid

_____ 5. biceps brachii

_____ 6. deltoid

_____ 7. vastus lateralis

_____ 8. brachioradialis

_____ 9. frontalis

_____ 10. rectus femoris

_____ 11. pronator teres

_____ 12. rectus abdominis

_____ 13. sartorius

_____ 14. gracilis

_____ 15. flexor carpi ulnaris

_____ 16. adductor longus

_____ 17. palmaris longus

_____ 18. flexor carpi radialis

_____ 19. latissimus dorsi

_____ 20. orbicularis oculi

_____ 21. gastrocnemius

_____ 22. masseter

_____ 23. trapezius

_____ 24. tibialis anterior

_____ 25. extensor digitorum longus

_____ 26. tensor fasciae latae

_____ 27. pectineus

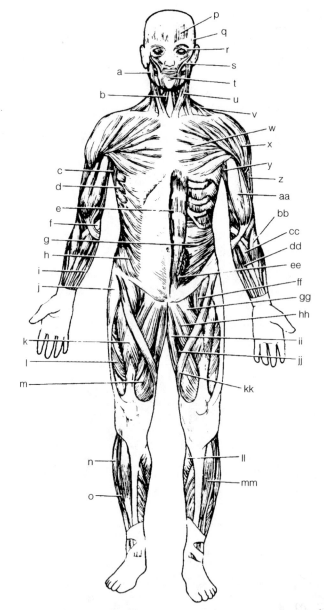

_____ 28. sternohyoid

_____ 29. serratus anterior

_____ 30. adductor magnus

_____ 31. vastus medialis

_____ 32. transversus abdominis

_____ 33. peroneus longus

_____ 34. iliopsoas

_____ 35. temporalis

_____ 36. zygomaticus

_____ 37. coracobrachialis

_____ 38. triceps brachii

_____ 39. internal oblique

Review Sheet

150

2. Identify each of the lettered muscles in this diagram of the human posterior superficial musculature by matching its letter to one of the following muscle names:

_____ 1. gluteus maximus

_____ 2. semimembranosus

_____ 3. gastrocnemius

_____ 4. latissimus dorsi

_____ 5. deltoid

_____ 6. iliotibial tract (tendon)

_____ 7. teres major

_____ 8. semitendinosus

_____ 9. trapezius

_____ 10. biceps femoris

_____ 11. triceps brachii

_____ 12. external oblique

_____ 13. gluteus medius

_____ 14. gracilis

_____ 15. flexor carpi ulnaris

_____ 16. extensor carpi ulnaris

_____ 17. extensor digitorum communis

_____ 18. extensor carpi radialis longus

_____ 19. occipitalis

_____ 20. extensor carpi radialis brevis

_____ 21. sternocleidomastoid

_____ 22. adductor magnus

_____ 23. anconeus

Review Sheet

General Review: Muscle Descriptions

1. Identify the muscles described below by completing the statements:

_____, _____, and _____

are commonly used for intramuscular injections (three muscles).

The insertion tendon of the _____ group contains a large sesamoid bone, the patella.

The triceps surae insert in common into the _____ tendon.

The bulk of the tissue of a muscle tends to lie _____ to the part of the body it causes to move.

The extrinsic muscles of the hand originate on the _____.

Most flexor muscles are located on the _____ aspect of the body; most extensors are

located _____. An exception to this generalization is the extensor-flexor musculature

of the _____.

Gross Anatomy of Skeletal Muscle

Muscle Tissue Specimens
Look at the muscle tissue specimens. Remember to use gloves when picking up the tissue.

How does the muscle tissue feel?

How does this tissue differ from the skin and cartilage we looked at earlier in the semester?

Can you determine where on the body the specimens are from?

Determine the muscle type (pennate, circular, etc.) of each specimen.

Histology of Nervous Tissue

The nervous system is the master integrating and coordinating system, continuously monitoring and processing sensory information both from the external environment and from within the body. Every thought, action, and sensation is a reflection of its activity. Like a computer, it processes and integrates new "inputs" with information previously fed into it ("programmed") to produce an appropriate response ("readout"). However, no computer can possibly compare in complexity and scope to the human nervous system.

Despite its complexity, nervous tissue is made up of just two principal cell populations: **neurons** and their **supporting cells.** The supporting cells in the CNS (central nervous system: brain and spinal cord) are usually referred to as **neuroglia** or **glial cells**. The *neuroglia*, literally "nerve glue," include *astrocytes, oligodendrocytes, microglia,* and *ependymal cells* (Figure 1). The most important supporting cells in the PNS (peripheral nervous system), that is, in the neural structures outside the CNS, are *Schwann cells* and *satellite cells.* Supporting cells serve the needs of the neurons by acting as phagocytes and by bracing, protecting, and myelinating the delicate neurons. In addition, they probably serve some nutritive function by acting as a selective barrier between the capillary blood supply and the neurons. Although neuroglia resemble neurons in some ways (they have fibrous cellular extensions), they are not capable of generating and transmitting nerve impulses, a capability that is highly developed in neurons. Our focus in this exercise is the highly irritable neurons.

Neuron Anatomy

Neurons are the structural units of nervous tissue. They are highly specialized to transmit messages (nerve impulses) from one part of the body to another. Although neurons differ structurally, they have many identifiable features in common (Figure 2a). All have a **cell body** from which slender processes or fibers extend. Although neuron cell bodies are typically found in the CNS in clusters called **nuclei,** occasionally they reside in **ganglia** (collections of neuron cell bodies outside the CNS). They make up the gray matter of the nervous system. Neuron processes running through the CNS form **tracts** of white matter; in the PNS they form the peripheral **nerves.**

Objectives

1. To differentiate between the functions of neurons and neuroglia.
2. To list four types of neuroglia cells.
3. To identify the important anatomical characteristics of a neuron on an appropriate diagram or projected slide.
4. To state the functions of axons, dendrites, axonal terminals, neurofibrils, and myelin sheaths.
5. To explain how a nerve impulse is transmitted from one neuron to another.
6. To explain the role of Schwann cells in the formation of the myelin sheath.
7. To classify neurons according to structure and function.
8. To distinguish between a nerve and a tract and between a ganglion and a nucleus.
9. To describe the structure of a nerve, identifying the connective tissue coverings (endoneurium, perineurium, and epineurium) and citing their functions.

Materials

- ☐ Model of a "typical" neuron (if available)
- ☐ Compound microscope
- ☐ Histologic slides of an ox spinal cord smear and teased myelinated nerve fibers
- ☐ Prepared slides of Purkinje cells (cerebellum), pyramidal cells (cerebrum), and a dorsal root ganglion
- ☐ Prepared slide of a nerve (cross section)

From *Human Anatomy & Physiology Laboratory Manual,* Main Version, Fifth Edition, Elaine N. Marieb.

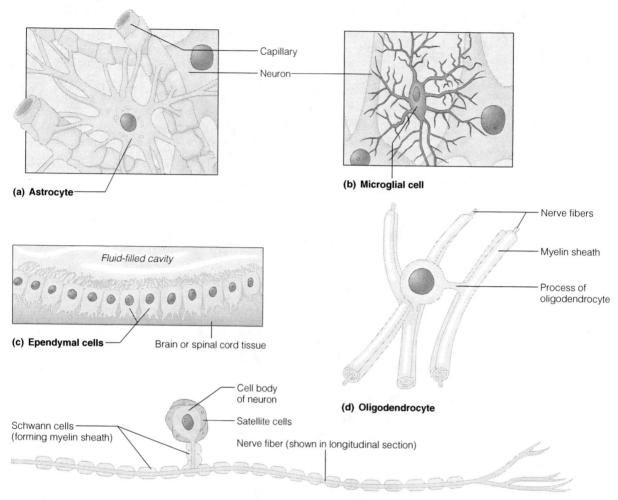

Figure 1 Supporting cells of nervous tissue. (a) Astrocyte.
(b) Microglial cell. **(c)** Ependymal cells. **(d)** Oligodendrocyte. **(e)** Neuron with
Schwann cells and satellite cells.

The neuron cell body contains a large round nucleus surrounded by cytoplasm (*neuroplasm*). The cytoplasm is riddled with neurofibrils and with darkly staining structures called Nissl bodies. **Neurofibrils,** the cytoskeletal elements of the neuron, have a support and intracellular transport function. **Nissl bodies,** an elaborate type of rough endoplasmic reticulum, are involved in the metabolic activities of the cell.

According to the older, traditional scheme, neuron processes that conduct electrical currents *toward* the cell body are called **dendrites;** and those that carry impulses away *from* the nerve cell body are called **axons.** When it was discovered that this functional scheme had pitfalls (some axons carry impulses *both* toward and away from the cell body), a newer functional definition of neuron processes was adopted. According to this scheme, dendrites are *receptive regions* (they bear receptors for neurotransmitters released by other neurons), whereas axons are *nerve impulse generators* and *transmitters.* Neurons have only one axon (which may branch into **collaterals**) but may have many dendrites, depending on the neuron type. Notice that the term *nerve fiber* is a synonym for axon and is, thus, quite specific.

In general, a neuron is excited by other neurons when their axons release neurotransmitters close to its dendrites or cell body. The electrical current produced travels across the cell body and (given a threshold stimulus) down the axon. As Figure 2a shows, the axon (in motor neurons) begins at a slightly enlarged cell body structure called the **axon hillock** and ends in many small structures called **axonal terminals,**

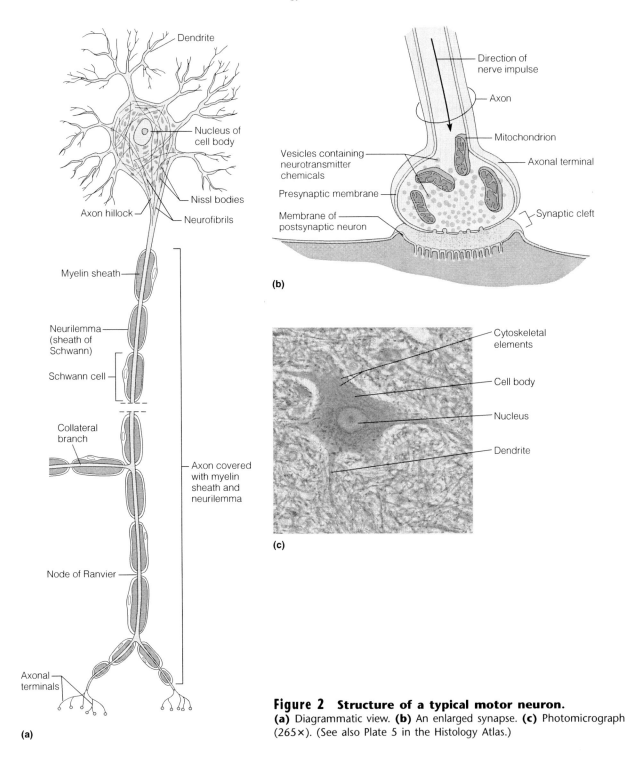

Figure 2 Structure of a typical motor neuron.
(a) Diagrammatic view. (b) An enlarged synapse. (c) Photomicrograph (265×). (See also Plate 5 in the Histology Atlas.)

or synaptic knobs. These terminals store the neurotransmitter chemical in tiny vesicles. Each axonal terminal is separated from the cell body or dendrites of the next (postsynaptic) neuron by a tiny gap called the **synaptic cleft** (Figure 2b). Thus, although they are close, there is no actual physical contact between neurons. When an impulse reaches the axonal terminals, some of the synaptic vesicles rupture and release

neurotransmitter into the synaptic cleft. The neurotransmitter then diffuses across the synaptic cleft to bind to membrane receptors on the next neuron, initiating the action potential.*

* Specialized synapses in skeletal muscle are called neuromuscular junctions.

157

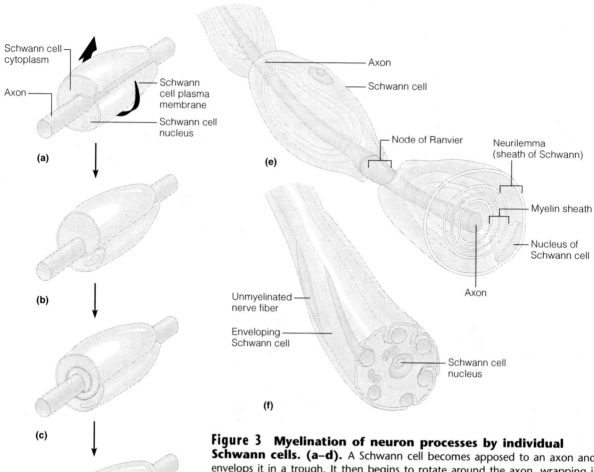

Figure 3   **Myelination of neuron processes by individual Schwann cells. (a–d).** A Schwann cell becomes apposed to an axon and envelops it in a trough. It then begins to rotate around the axon, wrapping it loosely in successive layers of its plasma membrane. Eventually, the Schwann cell cytoplasm is forced from between the membranes and comes to lie peripherally just beneath the exposed portion of the Schwann cell membrane. The tight membrane wrappings surrounding the axon form the myelin sheath. The area of Schwann cell cytoplasm and its exposed membrane are referred to as the neurilemma or sheath of Schwann. **(e)** Longitudinal view of myelinated axon showing portions of adjacent Schwann cells and the node of Ranvier between them. **(f)** Unmyelinated fibers. Schwann cells may associate loosely with several axons, which they partially invest. In such cases, Schwann cell coiling around the axons does not occur.

Most long nerve fibers are covered with a fatty material called *myelin,* and such fibers are referred to as **myelinated fibers.** Axons in the peripheral nervous system are typically heavily myelinated by special supporting cells called **Schwann cells,** which wrap themselves tightly around the axon jelly-roll fashion (Figure 3). During the wrapping process, the cytoplasm is squeezed from between adjacent layers of the Schwann cell membranes, so that when the process is completed a tight core of plasma membrane material (protein-lipoid material) encompasses the axon. This wrapping is the **myelin sheath.** The Schwann cell nucleus and the bulk of its cytoplasm ends up just beneath the outer-

most portion of its plasma membrane. This peripheral part of the Schwann cell and its plasma membrane is referred to as the **neurilemma.** Since the myelin sheath is formed by many individual Schwann cells, it is a discontinuous sheath. The gaps or indentations in the sheath are called **nodes of Ranvier** (see Figure 2).

Within the CNS, myelination is accomplished by glial cells called **oligodendrocytes** (see Figure 1d). These CNS sheaths do not exhibit the neurilemma seen in fibers myelinated by Schwann cells. Because of its chemical composition, myelin insulates the fibers and greatly increases the speed of neurotransmission by neuron fibers.

Activity:
Identifying Parts of a Neuron

1. Study the typical motor neuron shown in Figure 2, noting the structural details described above, and then identify these structures on a neuron model.

2. Obtain a prepared slide of the ox spinal cord smear, which has large, easily identifiable neurons. Study one representative neuron under oil immersion and identify the cell body; the nucleus; the large, prominent "owl's eye" nucleolus; and the granular Nissl bodies. If possible, distinguish the axon from the many dendrites. Sketch the cell in the space provided here, and label the important anatomical details you have observed. Compare your sketch to Plate 4 of the Histology Atlas. Also reexamine Figure 2a, which differentiates the neuronal processes more clearly.

3. Obtain a prepared slide of teased myelinated nerve fibers. Using Figure 4 as a guide, identify the following: nodes of Ranvier, neurilemma, axis cylinder (the axon itself), Schwann cell nuclei, and myelin sheath.

Sketch a portion of a myelinated nerve fiber in the space provided here, illustrating two or three nodes of Ranvier. Label the axon, myelin sheath, nodes, and neurilemma.

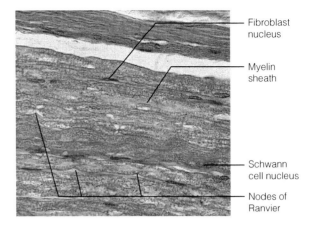

Fibroblast nucleus

Myelin sheath

Schwann cell nucleus

Nodes of Ranvier

Figure 4   Photomicrograph of a small portion of a peripheral nerve in longitudinal section.

Explain the significance of this finding: _____

_____

_____

_____

_____

_____

_____

_____ ■

Neuron Classification

Neurons may be classified on the basis of structure or of function.

Basis of Structure

Structurally, neurons may be differentiated according to the number of processes attached to the cell body (Figure 5a). In **unipolar neurons,** one very short process, which divides

Do the nodes seem to occur at consistent intervals, or are they irregularly distributed?

_____

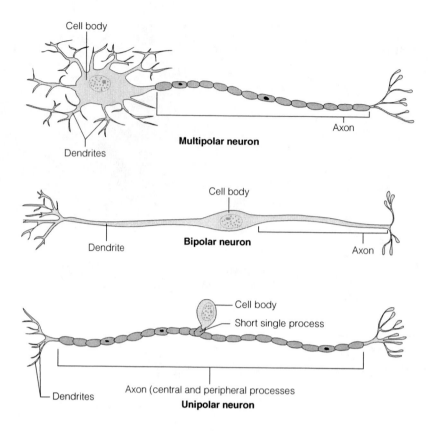

(a) **Classification of neurons based on structure (number of processes extending from the cell body).**

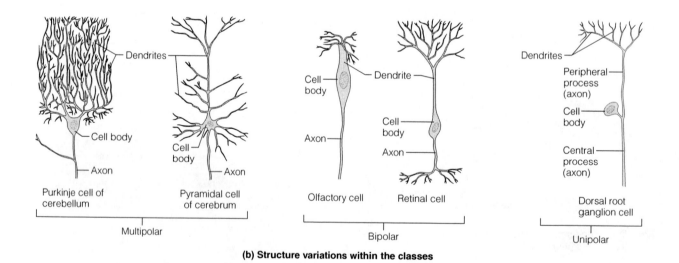

(b) **Structure variations within the classes**

Figure 5 Classification of neurons according to structure.
(a) Classification of neurons based on structure (number of processes extending from the cell body). (b) Structural variations within the classes.

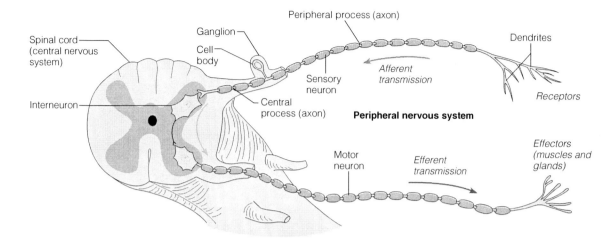

Figure 6 Classification of neurons on the basis of function. Sensory (afferent) neurons conduct impulses from the body's sensory receptors to the central nervous system; most are unipolar neurons with their nerve cell bodies in ganglia in the peripheral nervous system (PNS). Motor (efferent) neurons transmit impulses from the CNS to effectors such as muscles and glands. Association neurons (interneurons) complete the communication line between sensory and motor neurons. They are typically multipolar and their cell bodies reside in the CNS.

into *peripheral* and *central processes,* extends from the cell body. Functionally, only the most distal portions of the peripheral process act as dendrites; the rest acts as an axon along with the central process. Nearly all neurons that conduct impulses toward the CNS are unipolar.

Bipolar neurons have two processes—one axon and one dendrite—attached to the cell body. This neuron type is quite rare, typically found only as part of the receptor apparatus of the eye, ear, and olfactory mucosa.

Many processes issue from the cell body of **multipolar neurons,** all classified as dendrites except for a single axon. Most neurons in the brain and spinal cord (CNS neurons) and those whose axons carry impulses away from the CNS fall into this last category.

Activity:

Studying the Microscopic Structure of Selected Neurons

Obtain prepared slides of Purkinje cells of the cerebellar cortex, pyramidal cells of the cerebral cortex, and a dorsal root ganglion. As you observe them under the microscope, try to pick out the anatomical details depicted in Figure 5b, and in Plates 5 and 6 of the Histology Atlas. Notice that the neurons of the cerebral and cerebellar tissues (both brain tissues) are extensively branched; in contrast, the neurons of the dorsal root ganglion are more rounded. You may also be able to identify astrocytes (a type of neuroglia) in the brain tissue slides if you examine them closely, and satellite cells can be seen surrounding the neurons in the dorsal root ganglion.

Which of these neuron types would be classified as multipolar neurons?

_____

Which as unipolar?

_____ ∎

Basis of Function

In general, neurons carrying impulses from the sensory receptors in the internal organs (viscera) or in the skin are termed **sensory,** or **afferent, neurons** (see Figure 6). The dendritic endings of sensory neurons are often equipped with specialized receptors that are stimulated by specific changes in their immediate environment. The structure and function of these receptors is considered separately in another exercise (General Sensation). The cell bodies of sensory neurons are always found in a ganglion outside the CNS, and these neurons are typically unipolar.

Neurons carrying activating impulses from the CNS to the viscera and/or body muscles and glands are termed **motor,** or **efferent, neurons.** Motor neurons are most often multipolar and their cell bodies are almost always located in the CNS.

The third functional category of neurons is the **association neurons,** or **interneurons,** which are situated between and contribute to pathways that connect sensory and motor neurons. Their cell bodies are always located within the CNS and they are multipolar neurons structurally.

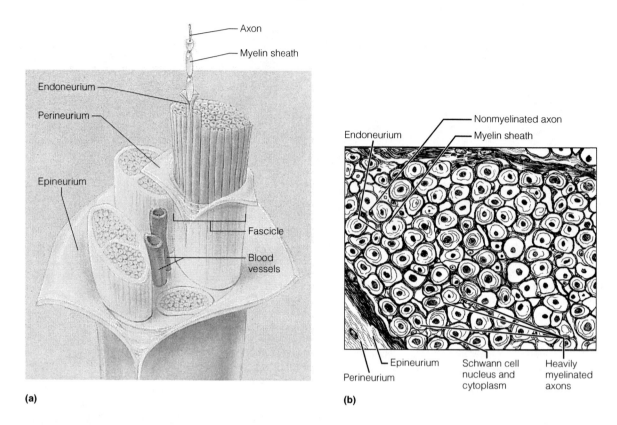

(a)

(b)

Figure 7   Structure of a nerve showing connective tissue wrappings. (a) Three-dimensional view of a portion of a nerve. **(b)** Cross-sectional view. (See also Plate 9 in the Histology Atlas.)

Structure of a Nerve

A nerve is a bundle of neuron fibers or processes wrapped in connective tissue coverings that extends to and/or from the CNS and visceral organs or structures of the body periphery (such as skeletal muscles, glands, and skin).

Within a nerve, each fiber is surrounded by a delicate connective tissue sheath called an **endoneurium,** which insulates it from the other neuron processes adjacent to it. The endoneurium is often mistaken for the myelin sheath; it is instead an additional sheath that surrounds the myelin sheath. Groups of fibers are bound by a coarser connective tissue, called the **perineurium,** to form bundles of fibers called **fascicles.** Finally, all the fascicles are bound together by a tough, white, fibrous connective tissue sheath called the **epineurium,** forming the cordlike nerve (Figure 7). In addition to the connective tissue wrappings, blood vessels and lymphatic vessels serving the fibers also travel within a nerve.

Like neurons, nerves are classified according to the direction in which they transmit impulses. Nerves carrying both sensory (afferent) and motor (efferent) fibers are called **mixed nerves;** all spinal nerves are mixed nerves. Nerves that carry only sensory processes and conduct impulses only toward the CNS are referred to as **sensory,** or **afferent, nerves.** A few of the cranial nerves are pure sensory nerves, but the majority are mixed nerves. The ventral roots of the spinal cord, which carry only motor fibers, can be considered **motor,** or **efferent, nerves.**

Activity:
Examining the Microscopic Structure of a Nerve

Examine under the compound microscope a prepared cross section of a peripheral nerve. Identify nerve fibers, myelin sheaths, fascicles, and endoneurium, perineurium, and epineurium sheaths. If desired, sketch the nerve in the space below. ■

Illustrations: 1–3, 5, 6, and 7b: Precision Graphics. 7a: Charles W. Hoffman. **Photographs:** 2c: © Benjamin/Cummings Publishing. Photo by Victor Eroschencko. 4: © Dennis Strete, Ph.D.

Histology of Nervous Tissue

1. The cellular unit of the nervous system is the neuron. What is the major function of this cell type?

    _____

2. Name four types of neuroglia and list at least four functions of these cells. (You will need to consult your textbook for this.)

    Types   **Functions**

    _____   _____

                                       _____

    _____   _____

                                       _____

    _____   _____

                                       _____

    _____   _____

                                       _____

3. Match each statement with a response chosen from the key.

    Key: a. afferent neuron   e. ganglion   i. nuclei
          b. association neuron   f. neuroglia   j. peripheral nervous system
          c. central nervous system   g. neurotransmitters   k. synapse
          d. efferent neuron   h. nerve   l. tract

    _____ 1. the brain and spinal cord collectively

    _____ 2. specialized supporting cells in the CNS

    _____ 3. junction or point of close contact between neurons

    _____ 4. a bundle of nerve processes inside the central nervous system

    _____ 5. neuron serving as part of the conduction pathway between sensory and motor neurons

    _____ 6. spinal and cranial nerves and ganglia

    _____ 7. collection of nerve cell bodies found outside the CNS

    _____ 8. neuron that conducts impulses away from the CNS to muscles and glands

    _____ 9. neuron that conducts impulses toward the CNS from the body periphery

    _____ 10. chemicals released by neurons that stimulate or inhibit other neurons or effectors

Review Sheet

Neuron Anatomy

1. Match the following anatomical terms (column B) with the appropriate description or function (column A).

   Column A

   _____ 1. region of the cell body from which the axon originates

   _____ 2. secretes neurotransmitters

   _____ 3. receptive region of a neuron

   _____ 4. insulates the nerve fibers

   _____ 5. is site of the nucleus and the most important metabolic area

   _____ 6. may be involved in the transport of substances within the neuron

   _____ 7. essentially rough endoplasmic reticulum, important metabolically

   _____ 8. impulse generator and transmitter

   Column B

   a. axon

   b. axonal terminal

   c. axon hillock

   d. dendrite

   e. myelin sheath

   f. neuronal cell body

   g. neurofibril

   h. Nissl bodies

2. Draw a "typical" neuron in the space below. Include and label the following structures on your diagram: cell body, nucleus, Nissl bodies, dendrites, axon, axon collaterals, myelin sheath, and nodes of Ranvier.

3. How is one-way conduction at synapses assured? _____

   _____

4. What anatomical characteristic determines whether a particular neuron is classified as unipolar, bipolar, or multipolar?

   _____

   Make a simple line drawing of each type here.

   Unipolar neuron   Bipolar neuron   Multipolar neuron

Review Sheet

5. Correctly identify the sensory (afferent) neuron, association neuron (interneuron), and motor (efferent) neuron in the figure below.

Which of these neuron types is/are unipolar? _____

Which is/are most likely multipolar? _____

Receptors (thermal and pain in the skin)

Effector (biceps brachii muscle)

6. Describe how the Schwann cells form the myelin sheath and the neurilemma encasing the nerve processes. (You may want to diagram the process.)

_____

_____

_____

Structure of a Nerve

1. What is a nerve? _____

_____

2. State the location of each of the following connective tissue coverings:

endoneurium _____

perineurium _____

epineurium _____

3. What is the value of the connective tissue wrappings found in a nerve? _____

_____

4. Define *mixed nerve:* _____

_____

5. Identify all indicated parts of the nerve section.

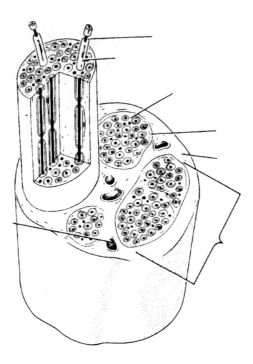

Nervous System
Build a neuron
1. Obtain six colors of play dough.
2. Use the following color code to build a nerve cell.
    a. Cell body: blue
    b. Dendrites: green
    c. Axon: yellow
    d. Schwann cells: red
    e. Synaptic bulb: black

3. With another group, place your nerve cells together to make a synapse.

Animations for Neurophysiology
Log in to www.myaandp.com
On the left side menu, choose "Tutorials: Interactive Physiology"
Complete the Chapter11 modules: **Nervous System I: The Membrane Potential**
                                Nervous System I: The Action Potential
                                Nervous System II: Anatomy Review
On the left side menu, choose "Tutorials: A&P Flix"
Complete **The Reflex Arc**

Be sure to use your P.A.L 2.0 to get a better look at the brain and other nervous system structures!!!

Gross Anatomy of the Brain and Cranial Nerves

Objectives

1. To identify the following brain structures on a dissected specimen, human brain model (or slices), or appropriate diagram, and to state their functions:

   - *Cerebral hemisphere structures:* lobes, important fissures, lateral ventricles, basal nuclei, corpus callosum, fornix, septum pellucidum
   - *Diencephalon structures:* thalamus, intermediate mass, hypothalamus, optic chiasma, pituitary gland, mammillary bodies, pineal body, choroid plexus of the third ventricle, interventricular foramen
   - *Brain stem structures:* corpora quadrigemina, cerebral aqueduct, cerebral peduncles of the midbrain, pons, medulla, fourth ventricle
   - *Cerebellum structures:* cerebellar hemispheres, vermis, arbor vitae

2. To describe the composition of gray and white matter.

3. To locate the well-recognized functional areas of the human cerebral hemispheres.

4. To define *gyri* and *fissures* (*sulci*).

5. To identify the three meningeal layers and state their function, and to locate the falx cerebri, falx cerebelli, and tentorium cerebelli.

6. To state the function of the arachnoid villi and dural sinuses.

7. To discuss the formation, circulation, and drainage of cerebrospinal fluid.

8. To identify at least four pertinent anatomical differences between the human brain and that of the sheep (or other mammal).

9. To identify the cranial nerves by number and name on an appropriate model or diagram, stating the origin and function of each.

Materials

- ❑ Human brain model (dissectible)
- ❑ 3-D model of ventricles
- ❑ Preserved human brain (if available)
- ❑ Coronally sectioned human brain slice (if available)
- ❑ Preserved sheep brain (meninges and cranial nerves intact)
- ❑ Dissecting tray and instruments
- ❑ Protective skin cream or disposable gloves
- ❑ Materials as needed for cranial nerve testing (see Table 1)
- ❑ *The Human Nervous System: The Brain and Cranial Nerves* videotape*

 See Appendix C, Exercise 19 for links to A.D.A.M. Interactive Anatomy.

*Available to qualified adopters from Benjamin/Cummings.

When viewed alongside all nature's animals, humans are indeed unique, and the key to their uniqueness is found in the brain. Only in humans has the brain region called the cerebrum become so elaborated and grown out of proportion that it overshadows other brain areas. Other animals are primarily concerned with informational input and response for the sake of survival and preservation of the species, but human beings devote considerable time to nonsurvival ends. They are the only animals who manipulate abstract ideas and search for knowledge for its own sake, who are capable of emotional response and artistic creativity, or who can anticipate the future and guide their lives according to ethical and moral values. For all this, humans can thank their overgrown cerebrum (cerebral hemispheres).

Each of us is a composite reflection of our brain's experience. If all past sensory input could mysteriously and suddenly be "erased," we would be unable to walk, talk, or communicate in any manner. Spontaneous movement would occur, as in a fetus, but no voluntary integrated function of any type would be possible. Clearly we would cease to be the same individuals.

Because of the complexity of the nervous system, its anatomical structures are usually considered in terms of two principal divisions: the **central nervous system (CNS)** and the **peripheral nervous system (PNS).** The central nervous system consists of the brain and spinal cord, which primarily interpret incoming sensory information and issue instructions based on past experience. The peripheral nervous system consists of the cranial and spinal nerves, ganglia, and sensory receptors. These structures serve as communication lines as they carry impulses—from the sensory receptors to the CNS and from the CNS to the appropriate glands or muscles.

In this exercise both CNS (brain) and PNS (cranial nerves) structures will be studied because of their close anatomical relationship.

From *Human Anatomy & Physiology Laboratory Manual*, Main Version, Fifth Edition, Elaine N. Marieb.

The Human Brain

During embryonic development of all vertebrates, the CNS first makes its appearance as a simple tubelike structure, the **neural tube,** that extends down the dorsal median plane. By the fourth week, the human brain begins to form as an expansion of the anterior or rostral end of the neural tube (the end toward the head). Shortly thereafter, constrictions appear, dividing the developing brain into three major regions—**forebrain, midbrain,** and **hindbrain** (Figure 1). The remainder of the neural tube becomes the spinal cord.

During fetal development, two anterior outpocketings extend from the forebrain and grow rapidly to form the cerebral hemispheres. Because of space restrictions imposed by the skull, the cerebral hemispheres are forced to grow posteriorly and inferiorly, and finally end up enveloping and obscuring the rest of the forebrain and most midbrain structures. Somewhat later in development, the dorsal part of the hindbrain also enlarges to produce the cerebellum. The central canal of the neural tube, which remains continuous throughout the brain and cord, becomes enlarged in four regions of the brain, forming chambers called **ventricles** (see Figure 8a and b).

Activity:
Identifying External Brain Structures

Identify external brain structures using the figures cited. Also use a model of the human brain and other learning aids as they are mentioned.

Generally, the brain is considered in terms of four major regions: the cerebral hemispheres, diencephalon, brain stem, and cerebellum. The relationship between these four anatomical regions and the structures of the forebrain, midbrain, and hindbrain is also outlined in Figure 1.

Cerebral Hemispheres

The **cerebral hemispheres** are the most superior portion of the brain (Figure 2). Their entire surface is thrown into elevated ridges of tissue called **gyri** that are separated by depressed areas called **fissures** or **sulci.** Of the two types of depressions, the fissures are deeper. Many of the fissures and gyri are important anatomical landmarks.

The cerebral hemispheres are divided by a single deep fissure, the **longitudinal fissure.** The **central sulcus** divides the **frontal lobe** from the **parietal lobe,** and the **lateral sulcus** separates the **temporal lobe** from the parietal lobe. The **parieto-occipital sulcus,** which divides the **occipital lobe** from the parietal lobe, is not visible externally. Notice that the cerebral hemisphere lobes are named for the cranial bones that lie over them.

Some important functional areas of the cerebral hemispheres have also been located (Figure 2d). The **primary somatosensory area** is located in the **postcentral gyrus** of the parietal lobe. Impulses traveling from the body's sensory receptors (such as those for pressure, pain, and temperature) are localized in this area of the brain. ("This information is from my big toe.") Immediately posterior to the primary somatosensory area is the **somatosensory association area,** in which the meaning of incoming stimuli is analyzed. ("Ouch! I have a *pain* there.") Thus, the somatosensory association

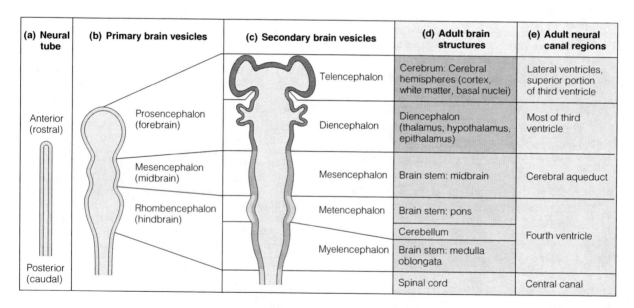

(a) Neural tube	(b) Primary brain vesicles	(c) Secondary brain vesicles	(d) Adult brain structures	(e) Adult neural canal regions
Anterior (rostral)	Prosencephalon (forebrain)	Telencephalon	Cerebrum: Cerebral hemispheres (cortex, white matter, basal nuclei)	Lateral ventricles, superior portion of third ventricle
		Diencephalon	Diencephalon (thalamus, hypothalamus, epithalamus)	Most of third ventricle
	Mesencephalon (midbrain)	Mesencephalon	Brain stem: midbrain	Cerebral aqueduct
	Rhombencephalon (hindbrain)	Metencephalon	Brain stem: pons	Fourth ventricle
			Cerebellum	Fourth ventricle
		Myelencephalon	Brain stem: medulla oblongata	
Posterior (caudal)			Spinal cord	Central canal

Figure 1 **Embryonic development of the human brain. (a)** The neural tube becomes subdivided into **(b)** the primary brain vesicles, which subsequently form **(c)** the secondary brain vesicles, which differentiate into **(d)** the adult brain structures. **(e)** The adult structures derived from the neural canal.

Figure 2 External structure (lobes and fissures) of the cerebral hemispheres. (a) Left lateral view of the brain. **(b)** Superior view. **(c)** Photograph of the superior aspect of the human brain. **(d)** Functional areas of the left cerebral cortex. The olfactory area, which is deep to the temporal lobe on the medial hemispheric surface, is not identified. Numbers indicate brain regions plotted by the Brodman system.

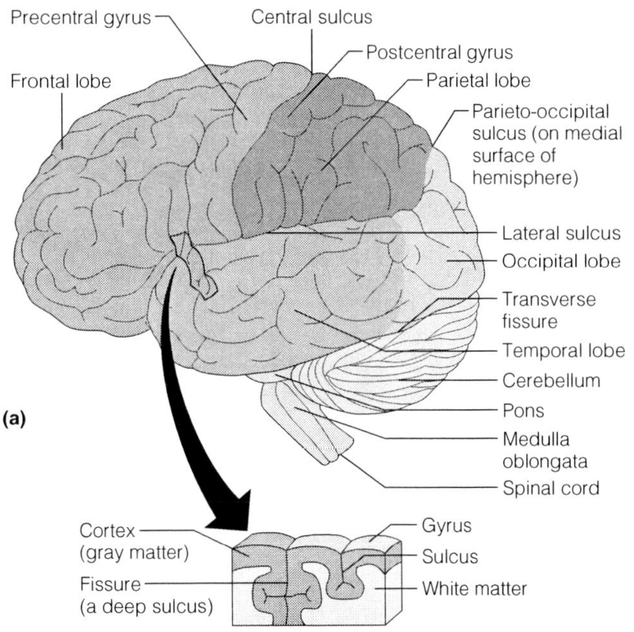

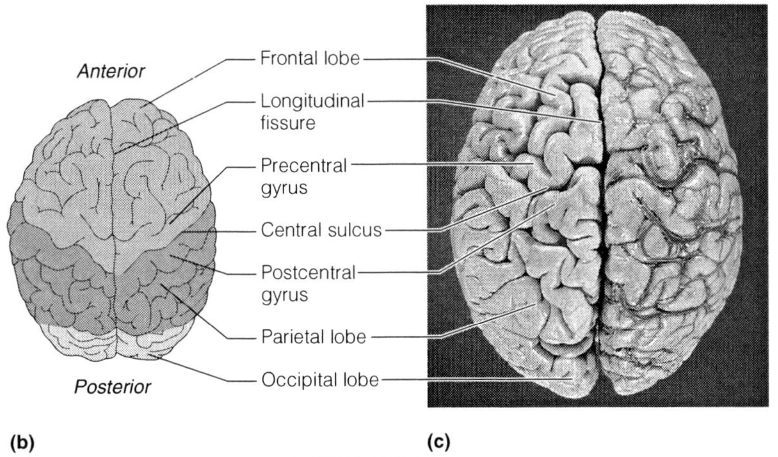

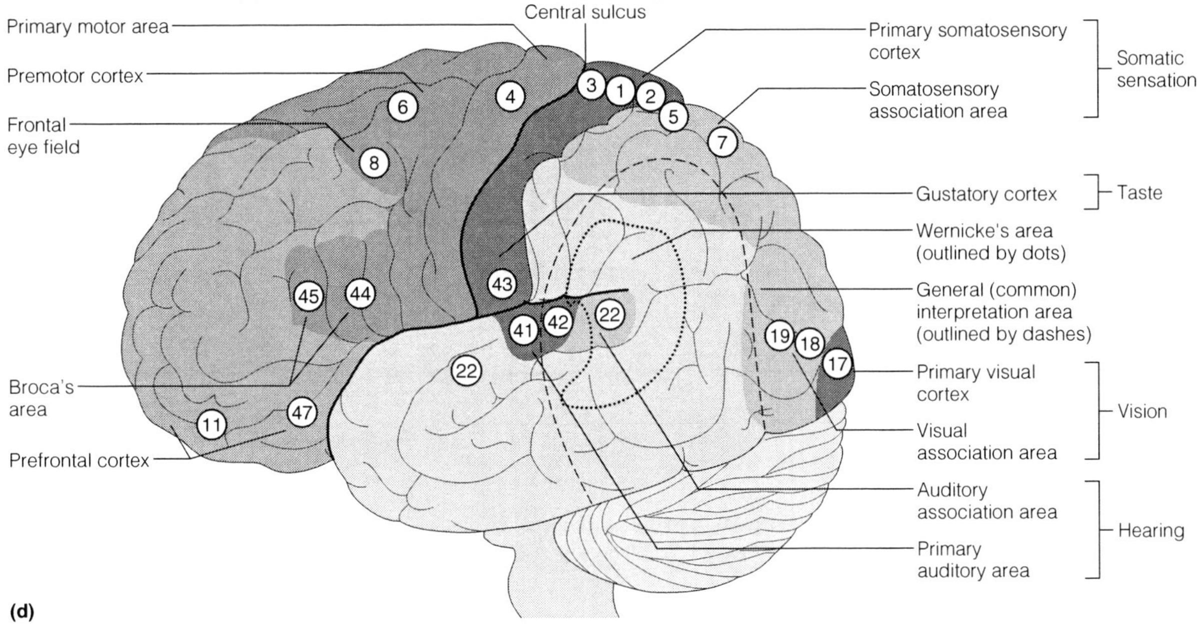

Precentral gyrus — Central sulcus
Frontal lobe
Postcentral gyrus
Parietal lobe
Parieto-occipital sulcus (on medial surface of hemisphere)
Lateral sulcus
Occipital lobe
Transverse fissure
Temporal lobe
Cerebellum
Pons
Medulla oblongata
Spinal cord

(a)

Cortex (gray matter)
Gyrus
Sulcus
Fissure (a deep sulcus)
White matter

Anterior
Frontal lobe
Longitudinal fissure
Precentral gyrus
Central sulcus
Postcentral gyrus
Parietal lobe
Occipital lobe
Posterior

(b)

(c)

Primary motor area
Premotor cortex
Frontal eye field
Central sulcus
Primary somatosensory cortex
Somatosensory association area
Somatic sensation
6
4
3 1 2
5
8
7
Gustatory cortex — Taste
Wernicke's area (outlined by dots)
General (common) interpretation area (outlined by dashes)
45 44
43
41 42 22
22
19 18
17
Primary visual cortex
Visual association area
Vision
Broca's area
11
47
Prefrontal cortex
Auditory association area
Primary auditory area
Hearing

(d)

area allows you to become aware of pain, coldness, a light touch, and the like.

Impulses from the special sense organs are interpreted in other specific areas also noted in Figure 2d. For example, the visual areas are in the posterior portion of the occipital lobe and the auditory area is located in the temporal lobe in the gyrus bordering the lateral sulcus. The olfactory area is deep within the temporal lobe along its medial surface, in a region called the **uncus** (see Figure 4a).

The **primary motor area,** which is responsible for conscious or voluntary movement of the skeletal muscles, is located in the **precentral gyrus** of the frontal lobe. A specialized motor speech area called **Broca's area** is found at the base of the precentral gyrus just above the lateral sulcus. Damage to this area (which is located only in one cerebral hemisphere, usually the left) reduces or eliminates the ability to articulate words. Areas involved in intellect, complex reasoning, and personality lie in the anterior portions of the frontal lobes, in a region called the **prefrontal cortex.**

A rather poorly defined region at the junction of the parietal and temporal lobes is **Wernicke's area,** an area in which unfamiliar words are sounded out. Like Broca's area, Wernicke's area is located in one cerebral hemisphere only, typically the left.

Although there are many similar functional areas in both cerebral hemispheres, such as motor and sensory areas, each hemisphere is also a "specialist" in certain ways. For example, the left hemisphere is the "language brain" in most of us, because it houses centers associated with language skills and speech. The right hemisphere is more specifically concerned with abstract, conceptual, or spatial processes—skills associated with artistic or creative pursuits.

The cell bodies of cerebral neurons involved in these functions are found only in the outermost gray matter of the cerebrum, the area called the **cerebral cortex.** Most of the balance of cerebral tissue—the deeper **cerebral white matter**—is composed of fiber tracts carrying impulses to or from the cortex.

Using a model of the human brain (and a preserved human brain, if available), identify the areas and structures of the cerebral hemispheres described above.

Then continue using the model and preserved brain along with the figures as you read about other structures.

Diencephalon

The **diencephalon,** sometimes considered the most superior portion of the brain stem, is embryologically part of the forebrain, along with the cerebral hemispheres.

Turn the brain model so the ventral surface of the brain can be viewed. Using Figure 3 as a guide, start superiorly and identify the externally visible structures that mark the

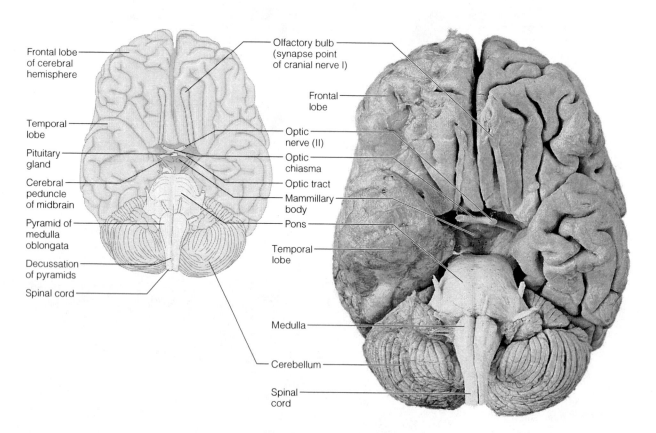

Figure 3   Ventral aspect of the human brain, showing the three regions of the brain stem. Only a small portion of the midbrain can be seen; the rest is surrounded by other brain regions. (See also Plate C in the Human Anatomy Atlas.)

Labels (left illustration): Frontal lobe of cerebral hemisphere; Temporal lobe; Pituitary gland; Cerebral peduncle of midbrain; Pyramid of medulla oblongata; Decussation of pyramids; Spinal cord; Olfactory bulb (synapse point of cranial nerve I); Frontal lobe; Optic nerve (II); Optic chiasma; Optic tract; Mammillary body; Pons; Temporal lobe; Medulla; Cerebellum; Spinal cord

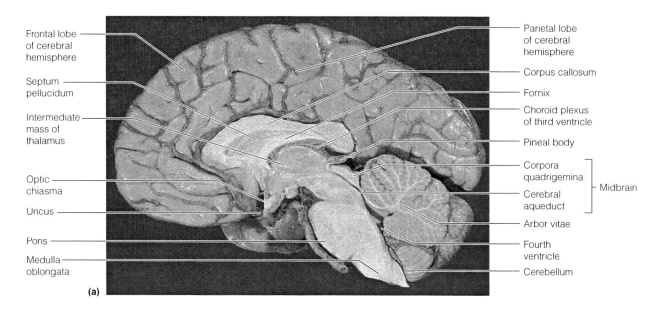

Frontal lobe of cerebral hemisphere

Septum pellucidum

Intermediate mass of thalamus

Optic chiasma

Uncus

Pons

Medulla oblongata

(a)

Parietal lobe of cerebral hemisphere

Corpus callosum

Fornix

Choroid plexus of third ventricle

Pineal body

Corpora quadrigemina

Cerebral aqueduct

⎤ Midbrain ⎦

Arbor vitae

Fourth ventricle

Cerebellum

Figure 4   Diencephalon and brain stem structures as seen in a midsagittal section of the brain. (a) Photograph.

position of the floor of the diencephalon. These are the **olfactory bulbs** and **tracts, optic nerves, optic chiasma** (where the fibers of the optic nerves partially cross over), **optic tracts, pituitary gland,** and **mammillary bodies.**

Brain Stem

Continue inferiorly to identify the **brain stem** structures—the **cerebral peduncles** (fiber tracts in the **midbrain** connecting the pons below with cerebrum above), the pons, and the medulla oblongata. *Pons* means "bridge," and the **pons** consists primarily of motor and sensory fiber tracts connecting the brain with lower CNS centers. The lowest brain stem region, the **medulla,** is also composed primarily of fiber tracts. You can see the **decussation of pyramids,** a crossover point for the major motor tract (pyramidal tract) descending from the motor areas of the cerebrum to the cord, on the medulla's anterior surface. The medulla also houses many vital autonomic centers involved in the control of heart rate, respiratory rhythm, and blood pressure as well as involuntary centers involved in the initiation of vomiting, swallowing, and so on.

Cerebellum

1.   Turn the brain model so you can see the dorsal aspect. Identify the large cauliflowerlike **cerebellum,** which projects dorsally from under the occipital lobe of the cerebrum. Notice that, like the cerebrum, the cerebellum has two major hemispheres and a convoluted surface (see Figure 6). It also has an outer cortex made up of gray matter with an inner region of white matter.

2.   Remove the cerebellum to view the **corpora quadrigemina,** located on the posterior aspect of the midbrain, a

brain stem structure. The two superior prominences are the **superior colliculi** (visual reflex centers); the two smaller inferior prominences are the **inferior colliculi** (auditory reflex centers). ■

Activity:
Identifying Internal Brain Structures

The deeper structures of the brain have also been well mapped. Like the external structures, these can be studied in terms of the four major regions. As the internal brain areas are described, identify them on the figures cited. Also, use the brain model as indicated to help you in this study.

Cerebral Hemispheres

1.   Take the brain model apart so you can see a median sagittal view of the internal brain structures (Figure 4). Observe the model closely to see the extent of the outer cortex (gray matter), which contains the cell bodies of cerebral neurons. (The pyramidal cells of the cerebral motor cortex are representative of the neurons seen in the precentral gyrus.)

2.   Observe the deeper area of white matter, which is composed of fiber tracts. The fiber tracts found in the cerebral hemisphere white matter are called *association tracts* if they connect two portions of the same hemisphere, *projection tracts* if they run between the cerebral cortex and the lower brain or spinal cord, and *commissures* if they run from one hemisphere to another. Observe the large **corpus callosum,** the major commissure connecting the cerebral hemispheres. The corpus callosum arches above the structures of the diencephalon and roofs over the lateral ventricles. Note also the **fornix,** a bandlike fiber tract concerned with olfaction as well

173

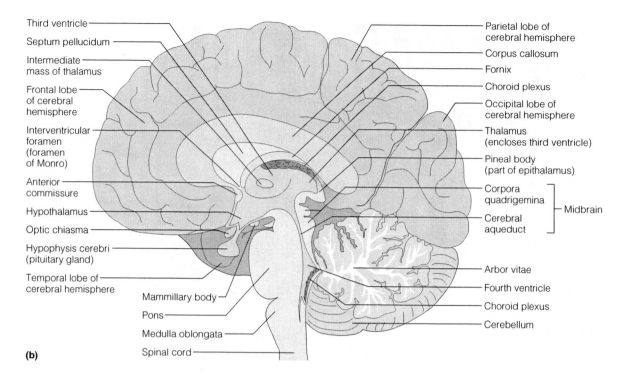

(b)

Figure 4 *(continued)* **Diencephalon and brain stem structures as seen in a midsagittal section of the brain.** **(b)** Diagrammatic view.

as limbic system functions, and the membranous **septum pellucidum,** which separates the lateral ventricles of the cerebral hemispheres.

3. In addition to the gray matter of the cerebral cortex, there are several "islands" of gray matter (clusters of neuron cell bodies) called **nuclei** buried deep within the white matter of the cerebral hemispheres. One important group of cerebral nuclei, called the **basal nuclei,*** flank the lateral and third ventricles. You can see the basal nuclei if you have an appropriate dissectible model or a coronally or cross-sectioned human brain slice. Otherwise, Figure 5 will suffice.

The basal nuclei, which are important subcortical motor nuclei (and part of the so-called *extrapyramidal system*), are involved in regulating voluntary motor activities. The most important of them are the arching, comma-shaped **caudate nucleus,** the **claustrum,** the **amygdaloid nucleus** (located at the tip of the caudate nucleus), and the **lentiform nucleus,** which is composed of the **putamen** and **globus pallidus nuclei.** The **corona radiata,** a spray of projection fibers coursing down from the precentral (motor) gyrus, combines with sensory fibers traveling to the sensory cortex to form a broad band of fibrous material called the **internal capsule.** The internal capsule passes between the diencephalon and the basal

nuclei, and gives these basal nuclei a striped appearance. This is why the caudate nucleus and the lentiform nucleus are sometimes referred to collectively as the **corpus striatum,** or "striped body."

4. Examine the relationship of the lateral ventricles and corpus callosum to the diencephalon structures; that is, hypothalamus, thalamus, and third ventricle—from the cross-sectional viewpoint (see Figure 5b).

Diencephalon

1. The major internal structures of the diencephalon are the thalamus, hypothalamus, and epithalamus (Figure 4). The **thalamus** consists of two large lobes of gray matter that laterally enclose the shallow third ventricle of the brain. A slender stalk of thalamic tissue, the **intermediate mass,** or **massa intermedia,** connects the two thalamic lobes and bridges the ventricle. The thalamus is a major integrating and relay station for sensory impulses passing upward to the cortical sensory areas for localization and interpretation. Locate also the **interventricular foramen** *(foramen of Monro),* a tiny orifice connecting the third ventricle with the lateral ventricle on the same side.

2. The **hypothalamus** makes up the floor and the inferolateral walls of the third ventricle. It is an important autonomic center involved in regulation of body temperature, water balance, and fat and carbohydrate metabolism as well as in many other activities and drives (sex, hunger, thirst). Locate again

---

*The historical term for these nuclei is *basal ganglia,* a misleading term because ganglia are PNS structures.

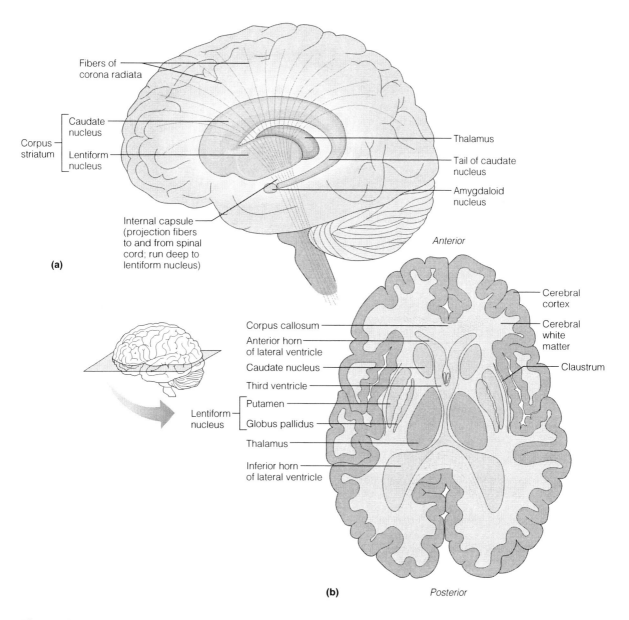

Figure 5 Basal nuclei. (a) Three-dimensional view of the basal nuclei showing their positions within the cerebrum. **(b)** A transverse section of the cerebrum and diencephalon showing the relationship of the basal nuclei to the thalamus and the lateral and third ventricles.

the pituitary gland, or **hypophysis,** which hangs from the anterior floor of the hypothalamus by a slender stalk, the **infundibulum.** (The pituitary gland is usually not present in preserved brain specimens.) In life, the pituitary rests in the hypophyseal fossa of the sella turcica of the sphenoid bone.

Anterior to the pituitary, identify the optic chiasma portion of the optic pathway to the brain. The **mammillary bodies,** relay stations for olfaction, bulge exteriorly from the floor of the hypothalamus just posterior to the pituitary gland.

3. The **epithalamus** forms the roof of the third ventricle and is the most dorsal portion of the diencephalon. Important structures in the epithalamus are the **pineal body,** or **gland** (a neuroendocrine structure), and the **choroid plexus** of the third ventricle. The choroid plexuses, knotlike collections of capillaries within each ventricle, form the cerebrospinal fluid.

175

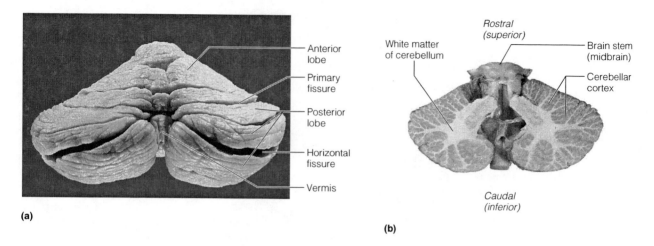

(a)

(b)

Figure 6 Cerebellum. (a) Posterior (dorsal) view. **(b)** The cerebellum, sectioned to reveal its cortex and medullary regions. (Note that the cerebellum is sectioned frontally and the brain stem is sectioned horizontally in this posterior view.)

Brain Stem

1. Now trace the short midbrain from the mammillary bodies to the rounded pons below. Continue to refer to Figure 4. The **cerebral aqueduct** is a slender canal traveling through the midbrain; it connects the third ventricle to the fourth ventricle in the hindbrain below. The cerebral peduncles and the rounded corpora quadrigemina make up the midbrain tissue anterior and posterior (respectively) to the cerebral aqueduct.

2. Locate the hindbrain structures. Trace the rounded pons to the medulla oblongata below, and identify the fourth ventricle posterior to these structures. Attempt to identify the single median aperture and the two lateral apertures, three orifices found in the walls of the fourth ventricle. These apertures serve as conduits for cerebrospinal fluid to circulate into the subarachnoid space from the fourth ventricle.

Cerebellum

Examine the cerebellum. Notice that it is composed of two lateral hemispheres each with three lobes (*anterior, posterior,* and a deep *flocculonodular*) connected by a midline lobe called the **vermis** (Figure 6). As in the cerebral hemispheres, the cerebellum has an outer cortical area of gray matter and an inner area of white matter. The treelike branching of the cerebellar white matter is referred to as the **arbor vitae,** or "tree of life." The cerebellum is concerned with unconscious coordination of skeletal muscle activity and control of bal-

ance and equilibrium. Fibers converge on the cerebellum from the equilibrium apparatus of the inner ear, visual pathways, proprioceptors of the tendons and skeletal muscles, and from many other areas. Thus the cerebellum remains constantly aware of the position and state of tension of the various body parts. ■

Meninges of the Brain

The brain (and spinal cord) are covered and protected by three connective tissue membranes called **meninges** (Figure 7). The outermost meninx is the leathery **dura mater,** a double-layered membrane. One of its layers (the *periosteal layer*) is attached to the inner surface of the skull, forming the periosteum. The other (the *meningeal layer*) forms the outermost brain covering and is continuous with the dura mater of the spinal cord.

The dural layers are fused together except in three places where the inner membrane extends inward to form a septum that secures the brain to structures inside the cranial cavity. One such extension, the **falx cerebri,** dips into the longitudinal fissure between the cerebral hemispheres to attach to the crista galli of the ethmoid bone of the skull. The cavity created at this point is the large **superior sagittal sinus,** which collects blood draining from the brain tissue. The **falx cerebelli,** separating the two cerebellar hemispheres, and the **tentorium cerebelli,** separating the cerebrum from the cerebellum below, are two other important inward folds of the inner dural membrane.

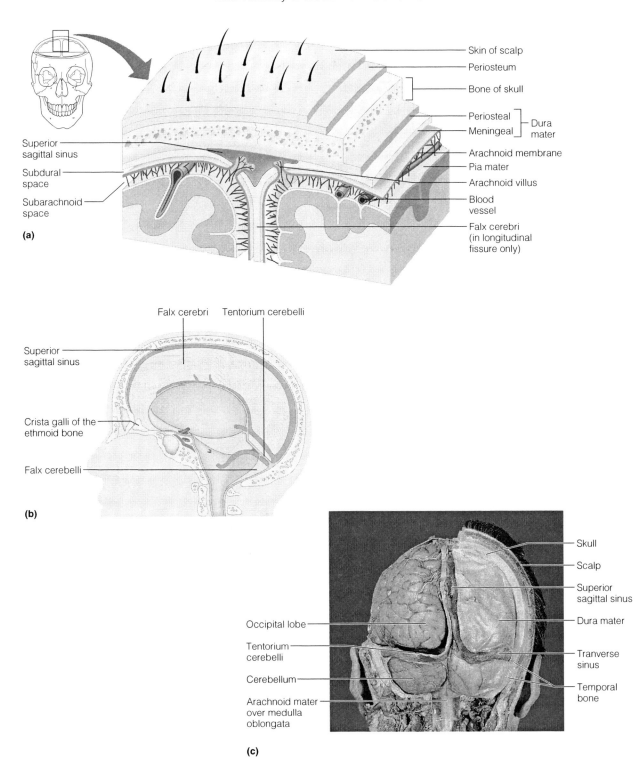

Figure 7   Meninges of the brain. (a) Three-dimensional frontal section showing the relationship of the dura mater, arachnoid mater, and pia mater. The meningeal dura forms the falx cerebri fold, which extends into the longitudinal fissure and attaches the brain to the ethmoid bone of the skull. A dural sinus, the superior sagittal sinus, is enclosed by the dural membranes superiorly. Arachnoid villi, which return cerebrospinal fluid to the dural sinus, are also shown. **(b)** Position of the dural folds, the falx cerebri, tentorium cerebelli, and falx cerebelli. **(c)** Posterior view of the brain in place, surrounded by the dura mater.

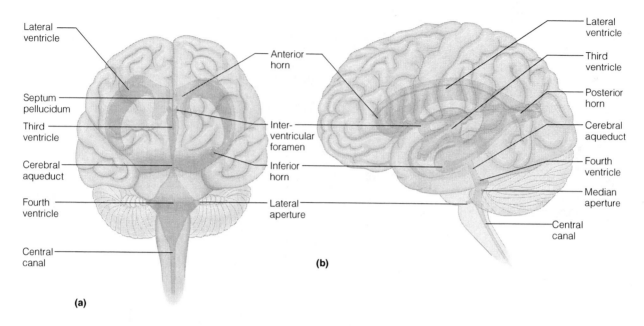

Figure 8 Location and circulatory pattern of cerebro-spinal fluid. **(a)** Anterior view; note that different regions of the large lateral ventricles are indicated by the terms *anterior horn, posterior horn,* and *inferior horn.* **(b)** Lateral view.

The middle meninx, the weblike **arachnoid mater,** or simply the **arachnoid,** underlies the dura mater and is partially separated from it by the **subdural space.** Threadlike projections bridge the **subarachnoid space** to attach the arachnoid to the innermost meninx, the **pia mater.** The delicate pia mater is highly vascular and clings tenaciously to the surface of the brain, following its convolutions.

In life, the subarachnoid space is filled with cerebrospinal fluid. Specialized projections of the arachnoid tissue called **arachnoid villi** protrude through the dura mater to allow the cerebrospinal fluid to drain back into the venous circulation via the superior sagittal sinus and other dural sinuses.

Meningitis, inflammation of the meninges, is a serious threat to the brain because of the intimate association between the brain and meninges. Should infection spread to the neural tissue of the brain itself, life-threatening **encephalitis** may occur. Meningitis is often diagnosed by taking a sample of cerebrospinal fluid from the subarachnoid space. ∎

Cerebrospinal Fluid

The cerebrospinal fluid, much like plasma in composition, is continually formed by the **choroid plexuses,** small capillary knots hanging from the roof of the ventricles of the brain. The cerebrospinal fluid in and around the brain forms a watery cushion that protects the delicate brain tissue against blows to the head.

Within the brain, the cerebrospinal fluid circulates from the two lateral ventricles (in the cerebral hemispheres) into the third ventricle via the **interventricular foramina,** and then through the cerebral aqueduct of the midbrain into the fourth ventricle in the hindbrain (Figure 8). Some of the fluid reaching the fourth ventricle continues down the central canal of the spinal cord, but the bulk of it circulates into the subarachnoid space, exiting through the three foramina in the walls of the fourth ventricle (the two lateral and the single median apertures). The fluid returns to the blood in the dural sinuses via the arachnoid villi.

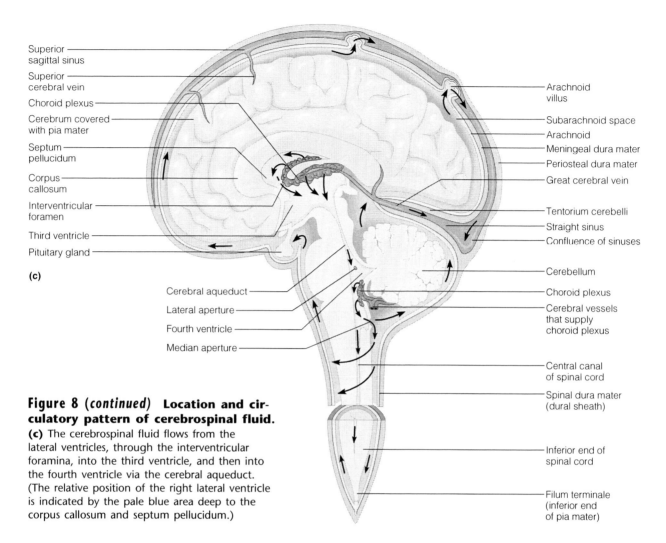

Superior sagittal sinus
Superior cerebral vein
Choroid plexus
Cerebrum covered with pia mater
Septum pellucidum
Corpus callosum
Interventricular foramen
Third ventricle
Pituitary gland

(c)

Arachnoid villus
Subarachnoid space
Arachnoid
Meningeal dura mater
Periosteal dura mater
Great cerebral vein
Tentorium cerebelli
Straight sinus
Confluence of sinuses
Cerebellum
Choroid plexus
Cerebral vessels that supply choroid plexus
Central canal of spinal cord
Spinal dura mater (dural sheath)
Inferior end of spinal cord
Filum terminale (inferior end of pia mater)

Cerebral aqueduct
Lateral aperture
Fourth ventricle
Median aperture

Figure 8 (*continued*) Location and circulatory pattern of cerebrospinal fluid.
(c) The cerebrospinal fluid flows from the lateral ventricles, through the interventricular foramina, into the third ventricle, and then into the fourth ventricle via the cerebral aqueduct. (The relative position of the right lateral ventricle is indicated by the pale blue area deep to the corpus callosum and septum pellucidum.)

Ordinarily, cerebrospinal fluid forms and drains at a constant rate. However, under certain conditions—for example, obstructed drainage or circulation resulting from tumors or anatomical deviations—the cerebrospinal fluid accumulates and exerts increasing pressure on the brain which, uncorrected, causes neurological damage in adults. In infants, **hydrocephalus** (literally, "water on the brain") is indicated by a gradually enlarging head. Since the infant's skull is still flexible and contains fontanels, it can expand to accommodate the increasing size of the brain. ∎

Cranial Nerves

The **cranial nerves** are part of the peripheral nervous system and not part of the brain proper, but they are most appropriately identified in conjunction with the study of brain anatomy. The 12 pairs of cranial nerves primarily serve the head and neck. Only one pair, the vagus nerves, extends into the thoracic and abdominal cavities. All but the first two pairs (olfactory and optic nerves) arise from the brain stem and pass through foramina in the base of the skull to reach their destination.

The cranial nerves are numbered consecutively, and in most cases their names reflect the major structures they control. The cranial nerves are described by name, number (Roman numeral), origin, course, and function in Table 1. This information should be committed to memory. A mnemonic device that might be helpful for remembering the cranial nerves in order is "*On occasion, our trusty truck acts funny—very good vehicle anyhow.*" The first letter of each word and the "a" and "h" of the final word "anyhow" will remind you of the first letter of the cranial nerve name.

Most cranial nerves are mixed nerves (containing both motor and sensory fibers). But close scrutiny of Table 1 will reveal that three pairs of cranial nerves (optic, olfactory, and vestibulocochlear) are purely sensory in function.

You may recall that the cell bodies of neurons are always located within the central nervous system (cortex or nuclei) or in specialized collections of cell bodies (ganglia) outside the CNS. Neuron cell bodies of the sensory cranial nerves are located in ganglia; those of the mixed cranial nerves are found both within the brain and in peripheral ganglia.

Table 1	The Cranial Nerves (see Figure 9)		
Number and name	**Origin and course**	**Function**	**Testing**
I. Olfactory	Fibers arise from olfactory mucosa and run through cribriform plate of ethmoid bone to synapse with olfactory bulbs.	Purely sensory–carries impulses associated with sense of smell.	Person is asked to sniff aromatic substances, such as oil of cloves and vanilla, and to identify each.
II. Optic	Fibers arise from retina of eye and pass through optic foramen in sphenoid bone. Fibers of the two optic nerves then take part in forming optic chiasma (with partial crossover of fibers) after which they continue on to thalamus as the optic tracts. Final fibers of this pathway travel from the thalamus to the optic cortex as the optic radiation.	Purely sensory—carries impulses associated with vision.	Vision and visual field are determined with eye chart and by testing the point at which the person first sees an object (finger) moving into the visual field. Fundus of eye viewed with ophthalmoscope to detect papilledema (swelling of optic disc, or point at which optic nerve leaves the eye) and to observe blood vessels.
III. Oculomotor	Fibers emerge from midbrain and exit from skull via superior orbital fissure to run to eye.	Mixed—somatic motor fibers to inferior oblique and superior, inferior, and medial rectus muscles, which direct eyeball, and to levator palpebrae muscles of eyelid; parasympathetic fibers to iris and smooth muscle controlling lens shape (reflex responses to varying light intensity and focusing of eye for near vision); contains proprioceptive sensory fibers carrying impulses from extrinsic eye muscles.	Pupils are examined for size, shape, and equality. Pupillary reflex is tested with penlight (pupils should constrict when illuminated). Convergence for near vision is tested, as is subject's ability to follow objects up, down, side to side, and diagonally.
IV. Trochlear	Fibers emerge from midbrain and exit from skull via superior orbital fissure to run to eye.	Mixed—provides somatic motor fibers to superior oblique muscle (an extrinsic eye muscle); conveys proprioceptive impulses from same muscle to brain.	Tested in common with cranial nerve III.
V. Trigeminal	Fibers emerge from pons and form three divisions, which exit separately from skull: mandibular division through foramen ovale in sphenoid bone, maxillary division via foramen rotundum in sphenoid bone, and ophthalmic division through superior orbital fissure of eye socket.	Mixed—major sensory nerve of face; conducts sensory impulses from skin of face and anterior scalp, from mucosae of mouth and nose, and from surface of eyes; mandibular division also contains motor fibers that innervate muscles of mastication and muscles of floor of mouth.	Sensations of pain, touch, and temperature are tested with safety pin and hot and cold objects. Corneal reflex tested with wisp of cotton. Motor branch assessed by asking person to clench his teeth, open mouth against resistance, and move jaw side to side.
VI. Abducens	Fibers leave inferior region of pons and exit from skull via superior orbital fissure to run to eye.	Carries motor fibers to lateral rectus muscle of eye and proprioceptive fibers from same muscle to brain.	Tested in common with cranial nerve III.

Table 1	The Cranial Nerves (see Figure 9) (continued)		
Number and name	**Origin and course**	**Function**	**Testing**
VII. Facial	Fibers leave pons and travel through temporal bone via internal acoustic meatus, exiting via stylomastoid foramen to reach the face.	Mixed—supplies somatic motor fibers to muscles of facial expression and parasympathetic motor fibers to lacrimal and salivary glands; carries sensory fibers from taste receptors of anterior portion of tongue.	Anterior two-thirds of tongue is tested for ability to taste sweet (sugar), salty, sour (vinegar), and bitter (quinine) substances. Symmetry of face is checked. Subject is asked to close eyes, smile, whistle, and so on. Tearing is assessed with ammonia fumes.
VIII. Vestibulo-cochlear	Fibers run from inner-ear equilibrium and hearing apparatus, housed in temporal bone, through internal acoustic meatus to enter pons.	Purely sensory—vestibular branch transmits impulses associated with sense of equilibrium from vestibular apparatus and semicircular canals; cochlear branch transmits impulses associated with hearing from cochlea.	Hearing is checked by air and bone conduction using tuning fork.
IX. Glosso-pharyngeal	Fibers emerge from medulla and leave skull via jugular foramen to run to throat.	Mixed—somatic motor fibers serve pharyngeal muscles, and parasympathetic motor fibers serve salivary glands; sensory fibers carry impulses from pharynx, tonsils, posterior tongue (taste buds), and pressure receptors of carotid artery.	Position of the uvula is checked. Gag and swallowing reflexes are checked. Subject is asked to speak and cough. Posterior third of tongue may be tested for taste.
X. Vagus	Fibers emerge from medulla and pass through jugular foramen and descend through neck region into thorax and abdomen.	Mixed—fibers carry somatic motor impulses to pharynx and larynx and sensory fibers from same structures; very large portion is composed of parasympathetic motor fibers, which supply heart and smooth muscles of abdominal visceral organs; transmits sensory impulses from viscera.	As for cranial nerve IX (IX and X are tested in common, since they both innervate muscles of throat and mouth).
XI. Accessory	Fibers arise from medulla and superior aspect of spinal cord and travel through jugular foramen to reach muscles of neck and back.	Mixed—provides somatic motor fibers to sternocleido-mastoid and trapezius muscles and to muscles of soft palate, pharynx, and larynx (spinal and medullary fibers respectively); proprioceptive impulses are conducted from these muscles to brain.	Sternocleidomastoid and trapezius muscles are checked for strength by asking person to rotate head and shoulders against resistance.
XII. Hypoglossal	Fibers arise from medulla and exit from skull via hypoglossal canal to travel to tongue.	Mixed—carries somatic motor fibers to muscles of tongue and proprioceptive impulses from tongue to brain.	Person is asked to protrude and retract tongue. Any deviations in position are noted.

181

Activity:
Identifying and Testing the Cranial Nerves

1. Observe the anterior surface of the brain model to identify the cranial nerves. Figure 9 may also aid you in this study. Notice that the first (olfactory) cranial nerves are not visible on the model because they consist only of short axons that run from the nasal mucosa through the cribriform plate of the ethmoid bone. (However, the synapse points of the first cranial nerves, the *olfactory bulbs,* are visible on the model.)

2. The last column of Table 1 describes techniques for testing cranial nerves, which is an important part of any neurologic examination. This information may help you understand cranial nerve function, especially as it pertains to some aspects of brain function. Conduct tests of cranial nerve function following directions given in the "testing" column of the table.

3. Several cranial nerve ganglia are named here. *Using your textbook or an appropriate reference,* name the cranial nerve the ganglion is associated with and state its location.

Cranial nerve ganglion	Cranial nerve	Site of ganglion
trigeminal		
geniculate		
inferior		
superior		
spiral		
vestibular		

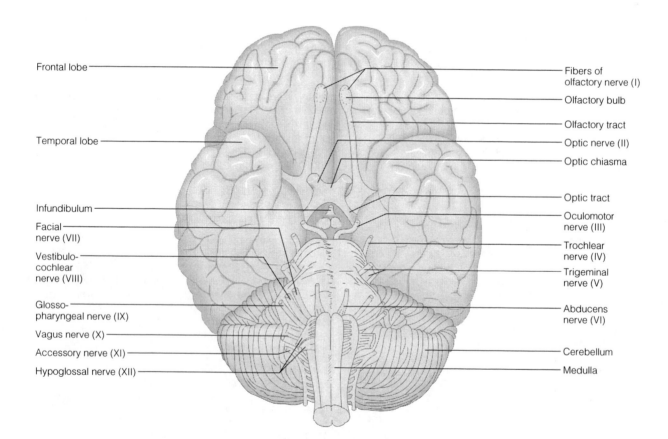

Figure 9 Ventral aspect of the human brain, showing the cranial nerves. (See also Plate C in the Human Anatomy Atlas.)

182

Dissection:
The Sheep Brain

The brain of any mammal is enough like the human brain to warrant comparison. Obtain a sheep brain, protective skin cream or disposable gloves, dissecting pan, and instruments, and bring them to your laboratory bench.

1. Before beginning the dissection, turn your sheep brain so that you are viewing its left lateral aspect. Compare the various areas of the sheep brain (cerebrum, brain stem, cerebellum) to the photo of the human brain in Figure 10. Relatively speaking, which of these structures is obviously much larger in the human brain?

_____

2. Place the intact sheep brain ventral surface down on the dissecting pan and observe the dura mater. Feel its consistency and note its toughness. Cut through the dura mater along the line of the longitudinal fissure (which separates the cerebral hemispheres) to enter the superior sagittal sinus. Gently force the cerebral hemispheres apart laterally to expose the corpus callosum deep to the longitudinal fissure.

3. Carefully remove the dura mater and examine the superior surface of the brain. Notice that, like the human brain, its surface is thrown into convolutions (fissures and gyri). Locate the arachnoid mater, which appears on the brain surface as a delicate "cottony" material spanning the fissures. In contrast, the innermost meninx, the pia mater, closely follows the cerebral contours.

Ventral Structures

Figure 11a and c shows the important features of the ventral surface of the brain. Turn the brain so that its ventral surface is uppermost.

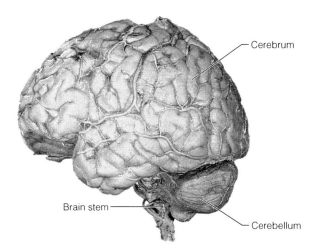

Figure 10   Photo of lateral aspect of the human brain.

1. Look for the clublike olfactory bulbs anteriorly, on the inferior surface of the frontal lobes of the cerebral hemispheres. Axons of olfactory neurons run from the nasal mucosa through the perforated cribriform plate of the ethmoid bone to synapse with the olfactory bulbs.

How does the size of these olfactory bulbs compare with those of humans?

_____

Is the sense of smell more important as a protective and a food-getting sense in sheep or in humans?

_____

2. The optic nerve (II) carries sensory impulses from the retina of the eye. Thus this cranial nerve is involved in the sense of vision. Identify the optic nerves, optic chiasma, and optic tracts.

3. Posterior to the optic chiasma, two structures protrude from the ventral aspect of the hypothalamus—the infundibulum (stalk of the pituitary gland) immediately posterior to the optic chiasma and the mammillary body. Notice that the sheep's mammillary body is a single rounded eminence. In humans it is a double structure.

4. Identify the cerebral peduncles on the ventral aspect of the midbrain, just posterior to the mammillary body of the hypothalamus. The cerebral peduncles are fiber tracts connecting the cerebrum and medulla. Identify the large oculomotor nerves (III), which arise from the ventral midbrain surface, and the tiny trochlear nerves (IV), which can be seen at the junction of the midbrain and pons. Both of these cranial nerves provide motor fibers to extrinsic muscles of the eyeball.

5. Move posteriorly from the midbrain to identify first the pons and then the medulla oblongata, both hindbrain structures composed primarily of ascending and descending fiber tracts.

6. Return to the junction of the pons and midbrain and proceed posteriorly to identify the following cranial nerves, all arising from the pons:

- Trigeminal nerves (V), which are involved in chewing and sensations of the head and face

- Abducens nerves (VI), which abduct the eye (and thus work in conjunction with cranial nerves III and IV)

- Facial nerves (VII), large nerves are involved in taste sensation, gland function (salivary and lacrimal glands), and facial expression

7. Continue posteriorly to identify:

- Vestibulocochlear nerves (VIII), purely sensory nerves that are involved with hearing and equilibrium

- Glossopharyngeal nerves (IX), which contain motor fibers innervating throat structures and sensory fibers transmitting taste stimuli (in conjunction with cranial nerve VII)

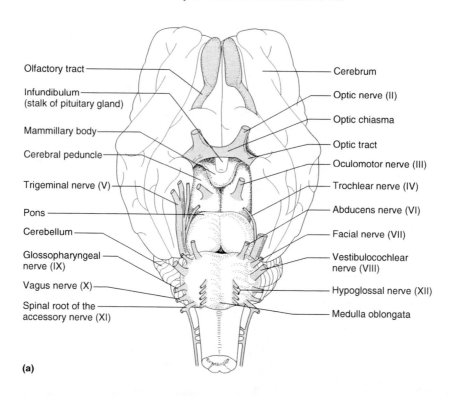

(a)

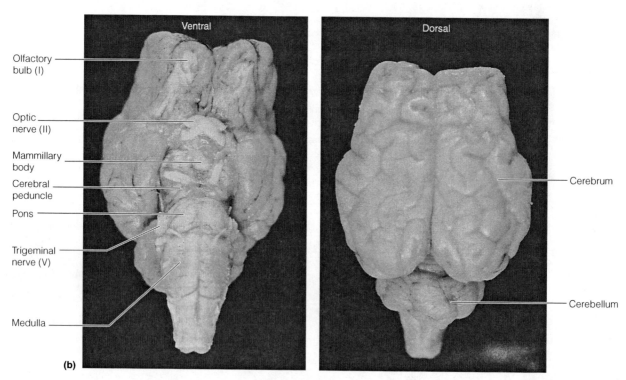

(b)

Figure 11 Intact sheep brain. (a) Diagrammatic ventral view. **(b)** Photographs showing ventral and dorsal views.

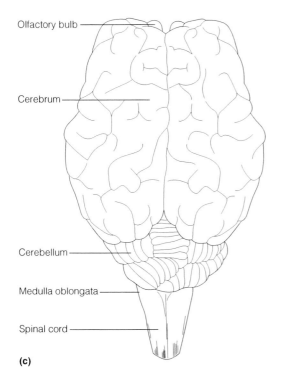

Olfactory bulb

Cerebrum

Cerebellum

Medulla oblongata

Spinal cord

(c)

Figure 11 (*continued*)   Intact sheep brain. (c)
Diagrammatic dorsal view.

• Vagus nerves (X), often called "wanderers," which serve many organs of the head, thorax, and abdominal cavity

• Accessory nerves (XI), which serve muscles of the neck, larynx, and shoulder; notice that the accessory nerves arise from both the medulla and the spinal cord

• Hypoglossal nerves (XII), which stimulate tongue and neck muscles

Dorsal Structures

1.   Refer to Figure 11b and c as a guide in identifying the following structures. Reidentify the now exposed cerebral hemispheres. How does the depth of the fissures in the sheep's cerebral hemispheres compare to that in the human brain?

_____

_____

2.   Carefully examine the cerebellum. Notice that, in contrast to the human cerebellum, it is not divided longitudinally, and that its fissures are oriented differently. What dural falx is missing that is present in humans?

_____

3.   Locate the three pairs of cerebellar peduncles, fiber tracts that connect the cerebellum to other brain structures, by lifting the cerebellum dorsally away from the brain stem. The most posterior pair, the inferior cerebellar peduncles, connect

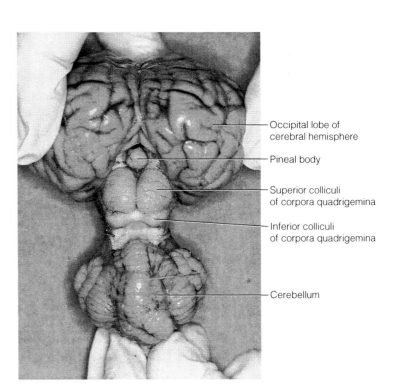

Occipital lobe of cerebral hemisphere

Pineal body

Superior colliculi of corpora quadrigemina

Inferior colliculi of corpora quadrigemina

Cerebellum

Figure 12   Means of exposing the dorsal midbrain structures of the sheep brain.

185

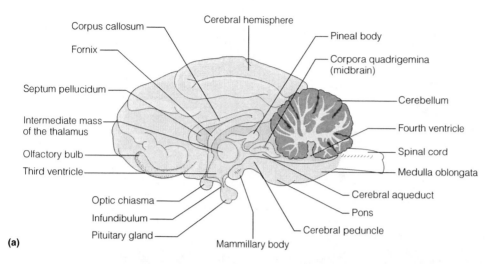

(a)

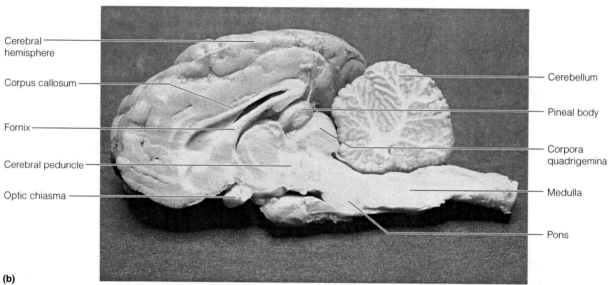

(b)

Figure 13 Sagittal section of the sheep brain showing internal structures. (a) Diagrammatic view. **(b)** Photograph.

the cerebellum to the medulla. The middle cerebellar peduncles attach the cerebellum to the pons, and the superior cerebellar peduncles run from the cerebellum to the midbrain.

4.   To expose the dorsal surface of the midbrain, gently spread the cerebrum and cerebellum apart, as shown in Figure 12. Identify the corpora quadrigemina, which appear as four rounded prominences on the dorsal midbrain surface. What is the function of the corpora quadrigemina?

_____

_____

Also locate the pineal body, which appears as a small oval protrusion in the midline just anterior to the corpora quadrigemina.

Internal Structures

1.   The internal structure of the brain can only be examined after further dissection. Place the brain ventral side down on the dissecting pan and make a cut completely through it in a superior to inferior direction. Cut through the longitudinal fissure, corpus callosum, and midline of the cerebellum. Refer to Figure 13 as you work.

2.   The thin nervous tissue membrane immediately ventral to the corpus callosum that separates the lateral ventricles is the septum pellucidum. Pierce this membrane and probe the lateral ventricle cavity. The fiber tract ventral to the septum pellucidum and anterior to the third ventricle is the fornix.

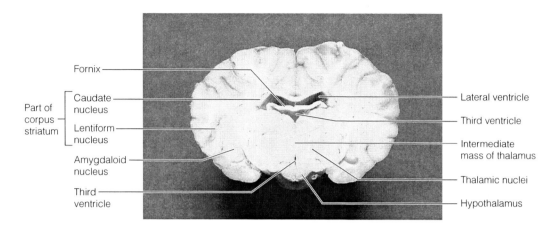

Fornix

Part of corpus striatum
- Caudate nucleus
- Lentiform nucleus

Amygdaloid nucleus

Third ventricle

Lateral ventricle

Third ventricle

Intermediate mass of thalamus

Thalamic nuclei

Hypothalamus

Figure 14 Frontal section of a sheep brain. Major structures revealed are the location of major basal nuclei in the interior, the thalamus, hypothalamus, and lateral and third ventricles.

How does the relative size of the fornix in this brain compare with the human fornix?

_____

_____

Why do you suppose this is so? (Hint: What is the function of this band of fibers?)

_____

_____

_____

3. Identify the thalamus, which forms the walls of the third ventricle and is located posterior and ventral to the fornix. The intermediate mass spanning the ventricular cavity appears as an oval protrusion of the thalamic wall. Anterior to the intermediate mass, locate the interventricular foramen, a canal connecting the lateral ventricle on the same side with the third ventricle.

4. The hypothalamus forms the floor of the third ventricle. Identify the optic chiasma, infundibulum, and mammillary body on its exterior surface. You can see the pineal body at the superoposterior end of the third ventricle, just beneath the junction of the corpus callosum and fornix.

5. Locate the midbrain by identifying the corpora quadrigemina that form its dorsal roof. Follow the cerebral aqueduct (the narrow canal connecting the third and fourth ventricles) through the midbrain tissue to the fourth ventricle. Identify the cerebral peduncles, which form its anterior walls.

6. Identify the pons and medulla, which lie anterior to the fourth ventricle. The medulla continues into the spinal cord without any obvious anatomical change, but the point at which the fourth ventricle narrows to a small canal is generally accepted as the beginning of the spinal cord.

7. Identify the cerebellum posterior to the fourth ventricle. Notice its internal treelike arrangement of white matter, the arbor vitae.

8. If time allows, obtain another sheep brain and section it along the frontal plane so that the cut passes through the infundibulum. Compare your specimen to the photograph in Figure 14, and attempt to identify all the structures shown in the figure.

9. Check with your instructor to determine if cow spinal cord sections (preserved) are available for the spinal cord studies. If not, save the small portion of the spinal cord from your brain specimen. Otherwise, dispose of all the organic debris in the appropriate laboratory containers and clean the dissecting instruments and tray before leaving the laboratory. ■

Illustrations: 1, 2, 4, 5, 7–9, 11, and 13: Precision Graphics. **Photographs:** 2b and c, and 4a: © Dr. Robert A. Chase. 3: © Benjamin/Cummings Publishing Company. Photo by Mark Nielsen, University of Utah. 6a–c and 10: From *A Stereoscopic Atlas of Human Anatomy*, by David L. Bassett. 11b and 12: © Benjamin/Cummings Publishing Company. Photo by Dr. Sharon Cummings, University of California, Davis. 13b and 14: © Elena Dorfman/Addison Wesley Longman.

Gross Anatomy of the Brain and Cranial Nerves

The Human Brain

1. Match the letters on the diagram of the human brain (right lateral view) to the appropriate terms listed at the left:

__H__ 1. frontal lobe

__B__ 2. parietal lobe

__J__ 3. temporal lobe

__C__ 4. precentral gyrus

__I__ 5. parieto-occipital sulcus

__G__ 6. postcentral gyrus

__A__ 7. lateral sulcus   __K__ 10. medulla

__F__ 8. central sulcus   __D__ 11. occipital lobe

__E__ 9. cerebellum   __L__ 12. pons

2. In which of the cerebral lobes would the following functional areas be found?

auditory area _____   olfactory area _____

primary motor area _____   visual area _____

primary sensory area _____   Broca's area _____

3. Which of the following structures are not part of the brain stem? (Circle the appropriate response or responses.)

cerebral hemispheres   pons   midbrain   cerebellum   medulla   diencephalon

4. Complete the following statements by writing the proper word or phrase on the corresponding blanks at the right.

A(n) __1__ is an elevated ridge of cerebral tissue. The convolutions seen in the cerebrum are important because they increase the __2__. Gray matter is composed of __3__. White matter is composed of __4__. A fiber tract that provides for communication between different parts of the same cerebral hemisphere is called a(n) __5__, whereas one that carries impulses to and from the cerebrum from and to lower CNS areas is called a(n) __6__ tract. The lentiform nucleus along with the amygdaloid and caudate nuclei are collectively called the __7__.

1. _____

2. _____

3. _____

4. _____

5. _____

6. _____

7. _____

5. Identify the structures on the following sagittal view of the human brain by matching the lettered areas to the proper terms at the left:

_____ 1. cerebellum

_____ 2. cerebral aqueduct

_____ 3. cerebral hemisphere

_____ 4. cerebral peduncle

_____ 5. choroid plexus

_____ 6. corpora quadrigemina

_____ 7. corpus callosum

_____ 8. fornix

_____ 9. fourth ventricle

_____ 10. hypothalamus

_____ 11. mammillary bodies

_____ 12. massa intermedia

_____ 13. medulla oblongata

_____ 14. optic chiasma

_____ 15. pineal body

_____ 16. pituitary gland

_____ 17. pons

_____ 18. septum pellucidum

_____ 19. thalamus

6. Using the letters from the diagram in item 5, match the appropriate structures with the descriptions given below:

_____ 1. site of regulation of body temperature and water balance; most important autonomic center

_____ 2. consciousness depends on the function of this part of the brain

_____ 3. located in the midbrain; contains reflex centers for vision and audition

_____ 4. responsible for regulation of posture and coordination of complex muscular movements

_____ 5. important synapse site for afferent fibers traveling to the sensory cortex

_____ 6. contains autonomic centers regulating blood pressure, heart rate, and respiratory rhythm, as well as coughing, sneezing, and swallowing centers

_____ 7. large commissure connecting the cerebral hemispheres

_____ 8. fiber tract involved with olfaction

_____ 9. connects the third and fourth ventricles

_____ 10. encloses the third ventricle

7. Embryologically, the brain arises from the rostral end of a tubelike structure that quickly becomes divided into three major regions. Groups of structures that develop from the embryonic brain are listed below. Designate the embryonic origin of each group as the hindbrain, midbrain, or forebrain.

_____ 1. the diencephalon, including the thalamus, optic chiasma, and hypothalamus

Review Sheet

_____ 2. the medulla, pons, and cerebellum

_____ 3. the cerebral hemispheres

8. What is the function of the basal nuclei? _____

_____

9. What is the corpus striatum, and how is it related to the fibers of the internal capsule? _____

_____

_____

10. A brain hemorrhage within the region of the right internal capsule results in paralysis of the left side of the body.

Explain why the left side (rather than the right side) is affected. _____

_____

11. Explain why trauma to the base of the brain is often much more dangerous than trauma to the frontal lobes. (*Hint:* Think about the relative functioning of the cerebral hemispheres and the brain stem structures. Which contain centers more vital to life?)

_____

_____

_____

12. In "split brain" experiments, the main commissure connecting the cerebral hemispheres is cut. First, name this commissure:

_____

Then, describe what results (in terms of behavior) can be anticipated in such experiments. (Use an appropriate reference if you need help with this one!)

_____

_____

_____

_____

Meninges of the Brain

Identify the meningeal (or associated) structures described below:

_____ 1. outermost meninx covering the brain; composed of tough fibrous connective tissue

_____ 2. innermost meninx covering the brain; delicate and highly vascular

_____ 3. structures instrumental in returning cerebrospinal fluid to the venous blood in the dural sinuses

_____ 4. structure that forms the cerebrospinal fluid

_____ 5. middle meninx; like a cobweb in structure

_____ 6. its outer layer forms the periosteum of the skull

_____ 7. a dural fold that attaches the cerebrum to the crista galli of the skull

_____ 8. a dural fold separating the cerebrum from the cerebellum

Cerebrospinal Fluid

Fill in the following flowchart by delineating the circulation of cerebrospinal fluid from its formation site (assume that this is one of the lateral ventricles) to the site of its reabsorption into the venous blood:

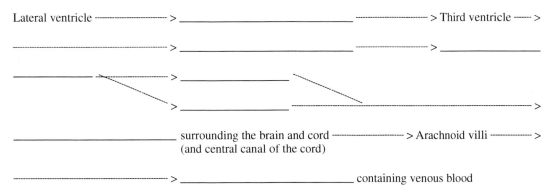

Lateral ventricle ------------------- > _____ ----------------- > Third ventricle ----- >

---------------------------------- > _____ --------------- > _____

_____ -----------> _____

----- > _____ --- >

_____ surrounding the brain and cord ---------------- > Arachnoid villi ----------- >
(and central canal of the cord)

------------------------------- > _____ containing venous blood

Now label appropriately the structures involved with circulation of CS fluid on the accompanying diagram. (These structures are identified by leader lines.)

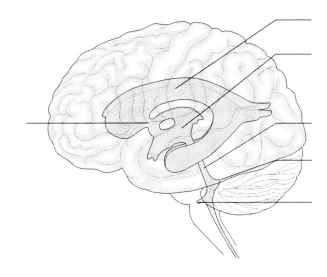

Cranial Nerves

1. Using the terms below, correctly identify all structures indicated by leader lines on the diagram below.

a. abducens nerve (VI)

b. accessory nerve (XI)

c. cerebellum

d. cerebral peduncle

e. decussation of the pyramids

f. facial nerve (VII)

g. frontal lobe of cerebral hemisphere

h. glossopharyngeal nerve (IX)

i. hypoglossal nerve (XII)

j. longitudinal fissure

k. mammillary body

l. medulla oblongata

m. oculomotor nerve (III)

n. olfactory bulb

o. olfactory tract

p. optic chiasma

q. optic nerve (II)

r. optic tract

s. pituitary gland

t. pons

u. spinal cord

v. temporal lobe of cerebral hemisphere

w. trigeminal nerve (V)

x. trochlear nerve (IV)

y. vagus nerve (X)

z. vestibulocochlear nerve (VIII)

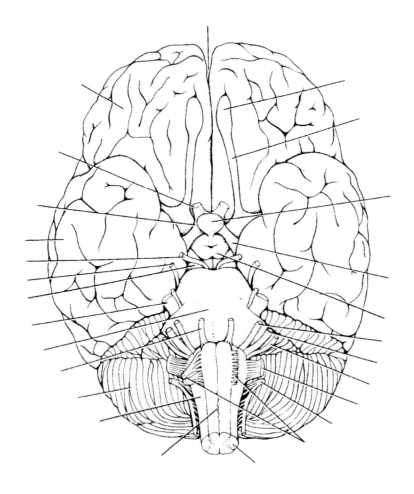

2. Provide the name and number of the cranial nerves involved in each of the following activities, sensations, or disorders:

_____ 1. shrugging the shoulders

_____ 2. smelling a flower

_____ 3. raising the eyelids; focusing the lens of the eye for accommodation; and pupillary constriction

_____ 4. slows the heart; increases the mobility of the digestive tract

_____ 5. involved in Bell's palsy (facial paralysis)

_____ 6. chewing food

_____ 7. listening to music; seasickness

_____ 8. secretion of saliva; tasting well-seasoned food

_____ 9. involved in "rolling" the eyes (three nerves—provide numbers only)

_____ 10. feeling a toothache

_____ 11. reading *Mad* magazine

_____ 12. purely sensory in function (three nerves—provide numbers only)

Dissection of the Sheep Brain

1. In your own words, describe the relative hardness of the sheep brain tissue as observed when cutting into it.

_____

Because formalin hardens all tissue, what conclusions might you draw about the relative hardness and texture of living brain

tissue? _____

2. How does the relative size of the cerebral hemispheres compare in sheep and human brains? _____

_____

What is the significance? _____

_____

3. What is the significance of the fact that the olfactory bulbs are much larger in the sheep brain than in the human

brain? _____

_____

Spinal Cord, Spinal Nerves, and the Autonomic Nervous System

Objectives

1. To identify important anatomical areas on a spinal cord model or appropriate diagram of the spinal cord, and to indicate the neuron type found in these areas (where applicable).

2. To indicate two major areas where the spinal cord is enlarged, and to explain the reasons for this anatomical characteristic.

3. To define *conus medullaris, cauda equina,* and *filum terminale.*

4. To locate on a diagram the fiber tracts in the spinal cord and to state their functional importance.

5. To list two major functions of the spinal cord.

6. To name the meningeal coverings of the spinal cord and state their function.

7. To describe the origin, fiber composition, and distribution of the spinal nerves, differentiating between roots, the spinal nerve proper, and rami, and to discuss the result of transecting these structures.

8. To discuss the distribution of the dorsal rami and ventral rami of the spinal nerves.

9. To identify the four major nerve plexuses, the major nerves of each, and their distribution.

10. To identify the site of origin and the function of the sympathetic and parasympathetic divisions of the autonomic nervous system, and to state how the autonomic nervous system differs from the somatic nervous system.

Materials

- ❏ Spinal cord model (cross section)
- ❏ Laboratory charts of the spinal cord and spinal nerves and sympathetic chain
- ❏ Red and blue pencils
- ❏ Preserved cow spinal cord sections with meninges and nerve roots intact
- ❏ Dissecting tray and instruments
- ❏ Dissecting microscope
- ❏ Histologic slide of spinal cord (cross section)
- ❏ Protective skin cream or disposable gloves
- ❏ Compound microscope
- ❏ *The Human Nervous System: The Spinal Cord and Spinal Nerves* videotape*

 See Appendix D, Exercise 21 for links to A.D.A.M. Interactive Anatomy.

*Available to qualified adopters from Benjamin/Cummings

Anatomy of the Spinal Cord

The cylindrical **spinal cord,** a continuation of the brain stem, is an association and communication center. It plays a major role in spinal reflex activity and provides neural pathways to and from higher nervous centers. Enclosed within the vertebral canal of the spinal column, the spinal cord extends from the foramen magnum of the skull to the first or second lumbar vertebra, where it terminates in the cone-shaped **conus medullaris** (Figure 1). Like the brain, it is cushioned and protected by meninges. The dura mater and arachnoid meningeal coverings extend beyond the conus medullaris, approximately to the level of S_2, and the **filum terminale,** a fibrous extension of the pia mater, extends even farther (into the coccygeal canal) to attach to the posterior coccyx. *Denticulate ligaments,* saw-toothed shelves of pia mater, secure the spinal cord to the bony wall of the vertebral column all along its length (See Figure 1c).

The fact that the meninges, filled with cerebrospinal fluid, extend well beyond the end of the spinal cord provides an excellent site for removing cerebrospinal fluid for analysis (as when bacterial or viral infections of the spinal cord or its meningeal coverings are suspected) without endangering the delicate spinal cord. This procedure, called a *lumbar tap,* is usually performed below L_3. Additionally, "saddle block" or caudal anesthesia for childbirth is normally administered (injected) between L_3 and L_5.

In humans, 31 pairs of spinal nerves arise from the spinal cord and pass through intervertebral foramina to serve the body area at their approximate level of emergence. The cord is about the size of a thumb in circumference for most of its length, but there are obvious enlargements in the cervical and lumbar areas where the nerves serving the upper and lower limbs issue from the cord.

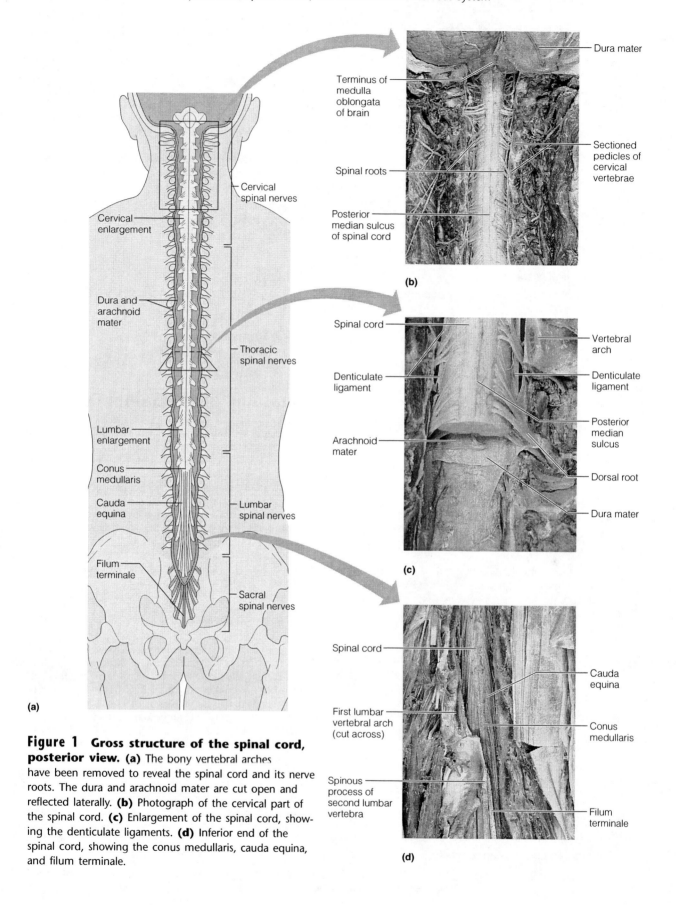

Figure 1 Gross structure of the spinal cord, posterior view. (a) The bony vertebral arches have been removed to reveal the spinal cord and its nerve roots. The dura and arachnoid mater are cut open and reflected laterally. (b) Photograph of the cervical part of the spinal cord. (c) Enlargement of the spinal cord, showing the denticulate ligaments. (d) Inferior end of the spinal cord, showing the conus medullaris, cauda equina, and filum terminale.

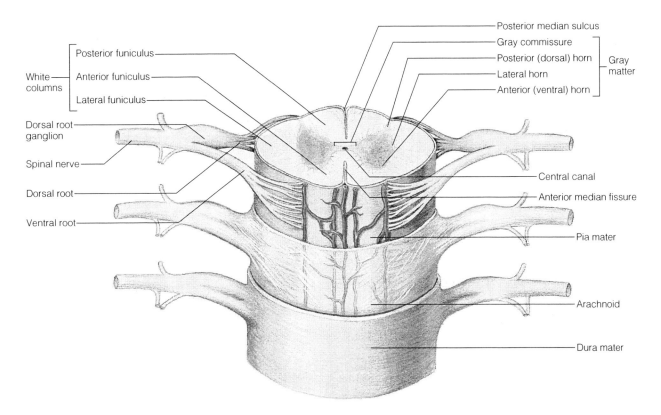

Figure 21.2 Anatomy of the human spinal cord (three-dimensional view).

Because the spinal cord does not extend to the end of the vertebral column, the spinal nerves emerging from the inferior end of the cord must travel through the vertebral canal for some distance before exiting at the appropriate intervertebral foramina. This collection of spinal nerves traversing the inferior end of the vertebral canal is called the **cauda equina** (Figure 1d) because of its similarity to a horse's tail (the literal translation of *cauda equina*).

A c t i v i t y :

Identifying Structures of the Spinal Cord

Obtain a model of a cross section of a spinal cord and identify its structures as they are described next. ■

Gray Matter

In cross section, the **gray matter** of the spinal cord looks like a butterfly or the letter H (Figure 2). The two posterior projections are called the **posterior,** or **dorsal, horns.** The two anterior projections are the **anterior,** or **ventral, horns.** The tips of the anterior horns are broader and less tapered than those of the posterior horns. In the thoracic and lumbar regions of the cord, there is also a lateral outpocketing of gray

matter on each side referred to as the **lateral horn.** The central area of gray matter connecting the two vertical regions is the **gray commissure.** The gray commissure surrounds the **central canal** of the cord, which contains cerebrospinal fluid.

Neurons with specific functions can be localized in the gray matter. The posterior horns, for instance, contain association neurons and sensory fibers that enter the cord from the body periphery via the **dorsal root.** The cell bodies of these sensory neurons are found in an enlarged area of the dorsal root called the **dorsal root ganglion.** The anterior horns contain cell bodies of motor neurons of the somatic nervous system (voluntary system), which send their axons out via the **ventral root** of the cord to enter the adjacent spinal nerve. The **spinal nerves** are formed from the fusion of the dorsal and ventral roots. The lateral horns, where present, contain nerve cell bodies of motor neurons of the autonomic nervous system (sympathetic division). Their axons also leave the cord via the ventral roots, along with those of the motor neurons of the anterior horns.

White Matter

The **white matter** of the spinal cord is nearly bisected by fissures (see Figure 2). The more open anterior fissure is the **anterior median fissure,** and the posterior one is the **posterior median sulcus.** The white matter is composed of myelinated fibers—some running to higher centers, some traveling

197

Ascending tracts

Descending tracts

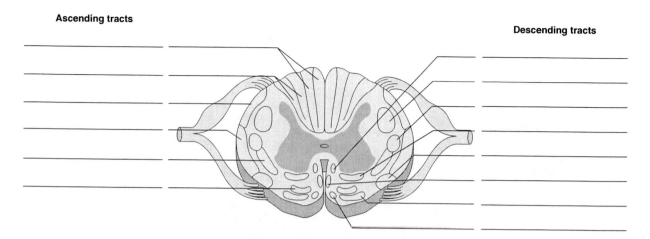

Figure 3   Cross section of the spinal cord showing the relative positioning of its major tracts.

from the brain to the cord, and some conducting impulses from one side of the cord to the other.

Because of the irregular shape of the gray matter, the white matter on each side of the cord can be divided into three primary regions or *white columns:* the **posterior, lateral,** and **anterior funiculi.** Each funiculus contains a number of fiber **tracts** composed of axons with the same origin, terminus, and function. Tracts conducting sensory impulses to the brain are called *ascending, or sensory, tracts;* those carrying impulses from the brain to the skeletal muscles are *descending,* or *motor, tracts.*

Because it serves as the transmission pathway between the brain and the body periphery, the spinal cord is an extremely important functional area. Even though it is protected by meninges and cerebrospinal fluid in the vertebral canal, it is highly vulnerable to traumatic injuries, such as might occur in an automobile accident.

When the cord is transected (or severely traumatized), both motor and sensory functions are lost in body areas normally served by that (and lower) regions of the spinal cord. Injury to certain spinal cord areas may even result in a permanent flaccid paralysis of both legs (paraplegia) or of all four limbs (quadriplegia). ■

A c t i v i t y :
Identifying Spinal Cord Tracts

With the help of your textbook or a laboratory chart showing the tracts of the spinal cord, label Figure 3 with the tract names that follow. Since each tract is represented on both sides of the cord, for clarity you can label the motor tracts on the right side of the diagram and the sensory tracts on the left side of the diagram. *Color ascending tracts blue and de-*

scending tracts red. Then fill in the functional importance of each tract beside its name below. As you work, try to be aware of how the naming of the tracts is related to their anatomical distribution.

Fasciculus gracilis _____

Fasciculus cuneatus _____

Posterior spinocerebellar _____

Anterior spinocerebellar _____

Lateral spinothalamic _____

Anterior spinothalamic _____

Lateral corticospinal _____

Anterior corticospinal _____

Rubrospinal _____

Tectospinal _____

Vestibulospinal _____

Medial reticulospinal _____

Lateral reticulospinal _____

Olivospinal _____ ■

Dissection:
Spinal Cord

1. Obtain a dissecting tray and instruments, protective skin cream or disposable gloves, and a segment of preserved spinal cord. Identify the tough outer meninx (dura mater) and the weblike arachnoid mater.

What name is given to the third meninx, and where is it found?

_____

_____

Peel back the dura mater and observe the fibers making up the dorsal and ventral roots. If possible, identify a dorsal root ganglion.

2. Cut a thin cross section of the cord and identify the anterior and posterior horns of the gray matter with the naked eye or with the aid of a dissecting microscope.

How can you be certain that you are correctly identifying the anterior and posterior horns?

_____

_____

Also identify the central canal, white matter, anterior median fissure, posterior median sulcus, and posterior, anterior, and lateral funiculi.

3. Obtain a prepared slide of the spinal cord (cross section) and a compound microscope. Refer to Figure 4 as you examine the slide carefully under low power. Observe the shape of the central canal.

Is it basically circular or oval? _____

Name the glial cell type that lines this canal. _____

What would you expect to find in this canal in the living animal?

_____

Can any neuron cell bodies be seen? _____

Where? _____

_____

What type of neurons would these most likely be—motor, association, or sensory?

_____

_____ ■

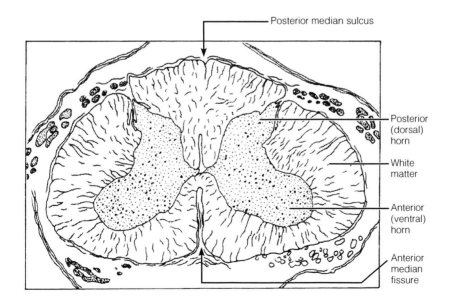

Figure 4 Cross section of the spinal cord. (See also Plate 8 in the Histology Atlas.)

Posterior median sulcus

Posterior (dorsal) horn

White matter

Anterior (ventral) horn

Anterior median fissure

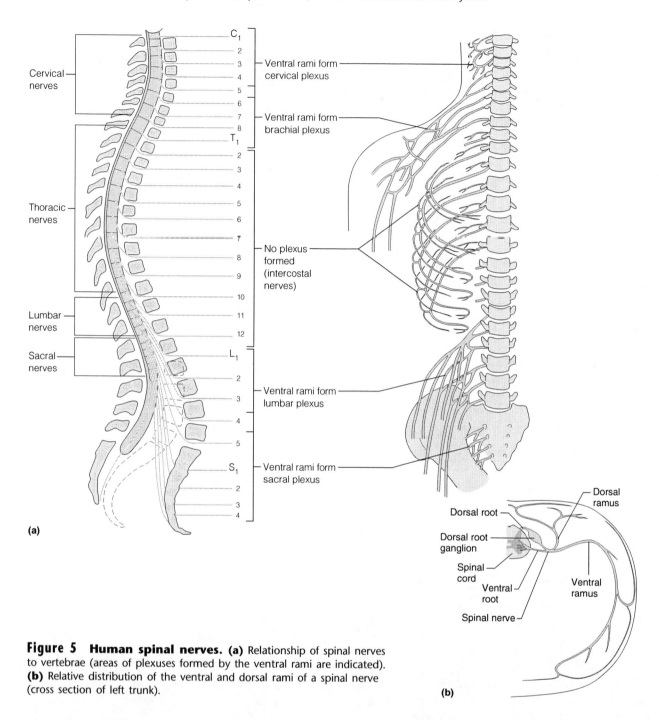

(a)

Cervical nerves

Thoracic nerves

Lumbar nerves

Sacral nerves

C_1
2
3
4
5
6
7
8
T_1
2
3
4
5
6
7
8
9
10
11
12
L_1
2
3
4
5
S_1
2
3
4

Ventral rami form cervical plexus

Ventral rami form brachial plexus

No plexus formed (intercostal nerves)

Ventral rami form lumbar plexus

Ventral rami form sacral plexus

Dorsal ramus

Dorsal root

Dorsal root ganglion

Spinal cord

Ventral root

Spinal nerve

Ventral ramus

(b)

Figure 5   Human spinal nerves. (a) Relationship of spinal nerves to vertebrae (areas of plexuses formed by the ventral rami are indicated). **(b)** Relative distribution of the ventral and dorsal rami of a spinal nerve (cross section of left trunk).

Spinal Nerves and Nerve Plexuses

The 31 pairs of human spinal nerves arise from the fusions of the ventral and dorsal roots of the spinal cord. Figure 5 shows how the nerves are named according to their point of issue. Because the ventral roots contain myelinated axons of motor neurons located in the cord and the dorsal roots carry sensory fibers entering the cord, all spinal nerves are **mixed nerves.** The first pair of spinal nerves leaves the vertebral canal between the base of the occiput and the atlas, but all the rest exit via the intervertebral foramina. The first through seventh pairs of cervical nerves emerge *above* the vertebra for which they are named. C_8 emerges between C_7 and T_1. (Notice that there are 7 cervical vertebrae, but 8 pairs of cervical nerves.) The remaining spinal nerve pairs emerge from the spinal cord *below* the same-numbered vertebra.

Almost immediately after emerging, each nerve divides into **dorsal** and **ventral rami.** (Thus each spinal nerve is only about 1 or 2 cm long.) The rami, like the spinal nerves, contain both motor and sensory fibers. The smaller dorsal rami serve the skin and musculature of the posterior body trunk at their approximate level of emergence. The ventral rami of spinal nerves T_2–T_{12} pass anteriorly as the **intercostal nerves** to supply the muscles of intercostal spaces, and the skin and muscles of the anterior and lateral trunk. The ventral rami of all other spinal nerves form complex networks of nerves called **plexuses.** These plexuses serve the motor and sensory needs of the muscles and skin of the limbs. The fibers of the ventral rami unite in the plexuses (with a few rami supplying fibers to more than one plexus). From the plexuses the fibers diverge again to form peripheral nerves, each of which contains fibers from more than one spinal nerve. The four major nerve plexuses and their chief peripheral nerves are described below and in Tables 1–3 and illustrated in Figures 6–8. Their names and site of origin should be committed to memory.

Cervical Plexus and the Neck

The **cervical plexus** (Figure 6 and Table 1) arises from the ventral rami of C_1 through C_5 to supply muscles of the shoulder and neck. The major motor branch of this plexus is the **phrenic nerve,** which arises from C_3–C_4 (plus some fibers from C_5) and passes into the thoracic cavity in front of the first rib to innervate the diaphragm. The primary danger of a broken neck is that the phrenic nerve may be severed, leading to paralysis of the diaphragm and cessation of breathing. A jingle to help you remember the rami (roots) forming the phrenic nerves is "C_3, C_4, C_5 keep the diaphragm alive."

Key:

▭ = Roots

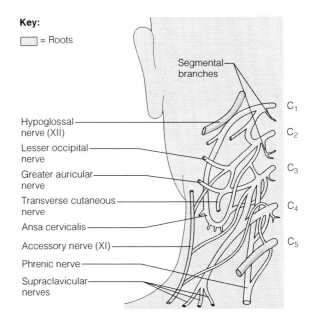

Figure 6   The cervical plexus. The nerves colored gray connect to the plexus but do not belong to it. (See Table 1.)

Table 1	Branches of the Cervical Plexus (See Figure 6)	

Nerves	Spinal Roots (Ventral Rami)	Structures Served
Cutaneous branches (superfical)		
Lesser occipital	C_2 (C_3)	Skin on posterolateral neck
Greater auricular	C_2, C_3	Skin of ear, skin over parotid gland
Transverse cutaneous	C_2, C_3	Skin on anterior and lateral aspect of neck
Supraclavicular (anterior, middle, and posterior)	C_3, C_4	Skin of shoulder and anterior chest
Motor branches (deep)		
Ansa cervicalis (superior and inferior roots)	C_1–C_3	Infrahyoid muscles of neck
Segmental and other muscular branches	C_1–C_5	Deep muscles of neck and portions of scalenes, levator scapulae, trapezius, and sternocleidomastoid muscles
Phrenic	C_3–C_5	Diaphragm (sole motor nerve supply)

Brachial Plexus and the Upper Limb

The **brachial plexus** is large and complex, arising from the ventral rami of C_5 through C_8 and T_1 (Table 2). The plexus, after being rearranged consecutively into *trunks, divisions,* and *cords,* finally becomes subdivided into five major *peripheral nerves* (Figure 7 and Plate F of the Human Anatomy Atlas).

The **axillary nerve,** which serves the muscles and skin of the shoulder, has the most limited distribution. The large **radial nerve** passes down the posterolateral surface of the arm and forearm, supplying all the extensor muscles of the arm, forearm, and hand and the skin along its course. The radial nerve is often injured in the axillary region by the pressure of a crutch or by hanging one's arm over the back of a chair. The **median nerve** passes down the anteromedial surface of the arm to supply most of the flexor muscles in the forearm and several muscles in the hand (plus the skin of the lateral surface of the palm of the hand).

- Hyperextend your wrist to identify the long, obvious tendon of your palmaris longus muscle, which crosses the exact midline of the anterior wrist. Your median nerve lies immediately deep to that tendon, and the radial nerve lies just *lateral* to it.

The **musculocutaneous nerve** supplies the arm muscles that flex the forearm and the skin of the lateral surface of the forearm. The **ulnar nerve** travels down the posteromedial surface of the arm. It courses around the medial epicondyle of the humerus to supply the flexor carpi ulnaris, the ulnar head of the flexor digitorum profundus of the forearm, and all intrinsic muscles of the hand not served by the median nerve. It supplies the skin of the medial third of the hand, both the anterior and posterior surfaces. Trauma to the ulnar nerve, which often occurs when the elbow is hit, produces a smarting sensation commonly referred to as "hitting the funny bone."

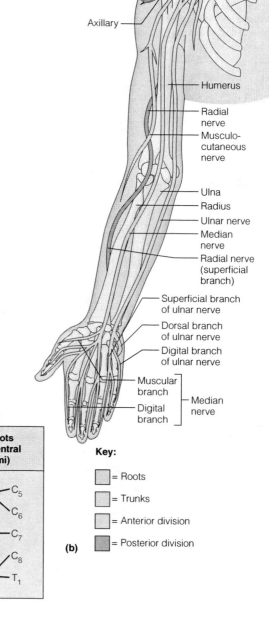

(b)

Key:

☐ = Roots

☐ = Trunks

☐ = Anterior division

■ = Posterior division

Major terminal branches (peripheral nerves)	Cords	Divisions	Trunks	Roots (ventral rami)
Musculocutaneous	Lateral	Anterior	Upper	C_5
Median		Posterior		C_6
Ulnar	Medial	Anterior	Middle	C_7
Radial		Posterior		C_8
Axillary	Posterior	Anterior / Posterior	Lower	T_1

(a)

Figure 7 Brachial plexus. (a) Flowchart of consecutive branches formed in the brachial plexus from the spinal roots (ventral rami) to the major nerves formed from the cords. **(b)** Distribution of the major peripheral nerves of the upper limb. (See Table 2. See also Plate E in the Human Anatomy Atlas.)

Table 2	Branches of the Brachial Plexus (See Figure 7)

Nerves	Cord and Spinal Roots (Ventral Rami)	Structures Served
Musculocutaneous	Lateral cord (C_5–C_7)	Muscular branches: flexor muscles in anterior arm (biceps brachii, brachialis, coracobrachialis) Cutaneous branches: skin on anterolateral forearm (extremely variable)
Median	By two branches, one from medial cord (C_8,T_1) and one from the lateral cord (C_5–C_7)	Muscular branches to flexor group of anterior forearm (palmaris longus, flexor carpi radialis, flexor digitorum superficialis, flexor pollicis longus, lateral half of flexor digitorum profundus, and pronator muscles); intrinsic muscles of lateral palm and first two fingers Cutaneous branches: skin of lateral two-thirds of hand, palm side and dorsum of fingers 2 and 3
Ulnar	Medial cord (C_8,T_1)	Muscular branches: flexor muscles in anterior forearm (flexor carpi ulnaris and medial half of flexor digitorum profundus); most intrinsic muscles of hand Cutaneous branches: skin of medial third of hand, both anterior and posterior aspects
Radial	Posterior cord (C_5–C_8, T_1)	Muscular branches: posterior muscles of arm, forearm, and hand (triceps brachii, anconeus, supinator, brachioradialis, extensors carpi radialis longus and brevis, extensor carpi ulnaris, and several muscles that extend the fingers) Cutaneous branches: skin of posterolateral surface of entire limb (except dorsum of fingers 2 and 3)
Axillary	Posterior cord (C_5,C_6)	Muscular branches: deltoid and teres minor muscles Cutaneous branches: some skin of shoulder region
Dorsal scapular	Branches of C_5 rami	Rhomboid muscles and levator scapulae
Long thoracic*	Branches of C_5–C_7 rami	Serratus anterior muscle
Subscapular*	Posterior cord; branches of C_5 and C_6 rami	Teres major and subscapular muscles
Suprascapular	Upper trunk (C_5,C_6)	Shoulder joint; supraspinatus and infraspinatus muscles
Pectoral (lateral and medial)*	Branches of lateral and medial cords (C_5–T_1)	Pectoralis major and minor muscles

* The long thoracic, subscapular, and pectoral nerves are not illustrated.

Severe injuries to the brachial plexus cause weakness or paralysis of the entire upper limb. Such injuries may occur when the upper limb is pulled hard and the plexus is stretched (as when a football tackler yanks the arm of the halfback), and by blows to the shoulder that force the humerus inferiorly (as when a cyclist is pitched headfirst off his motorcycle and grinds his shoulder into the pavement). ■

Lumbosacral Plexus and the Lower Limb

The **lumbosacral plexus,** which serves the pelvic region of the trunk and the lower limbs, is actually a complex of two plexuses, the lumbar plexus and the sacral plexus (see Figure 8). These plexuses interweave considerably and many fibers of the lumbar plexus contribute to the sacral plexus.

The Lumbar Plexus The **lumbar plexus** arises from ventral rami of L_1 through L_4 (and sometimes T_{12}). Its nerves serve the lower abdominopelvic region and the anterior thigh (Table 3). The largest nerve of this plexus is the **femoral nerve,** which passes beneath the inguinal ligament to innervate the anterior thigh muscles. The cutaneous branches of the femoral nerve (median and anterior femoral cutaneous and the saphenous nerves) supply the skin of the anteromedial surface of the entire lower limb.

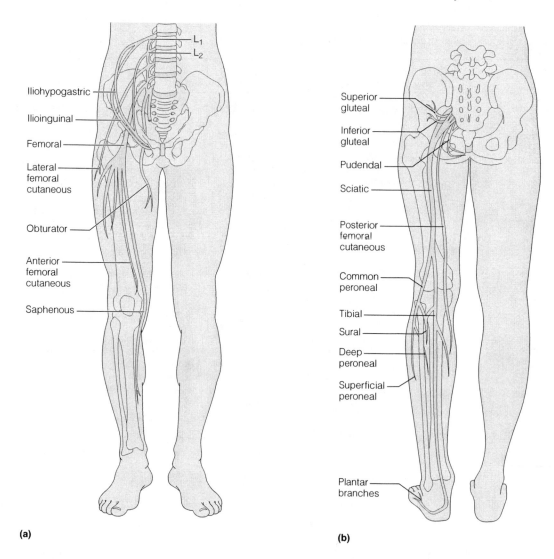

(a)

(b)

Figure 8 **Distribution of the major peripheral nerves of the lower limb.**
(a) Lumbar plexus. **(b)** Sacral plexus. See also Plates F, G, and H in the Human Anatomy Atlas.

The Sacral Plexus Arising from L_4 through S_4, the nerves of the **sacral plexus** supply the buttock, the posterior surface of the thigh, and virtually all sensory and motor fibers of the leg and foot (Table 3). The major peripheral nerve of this plexus is the **sciatic nerve,** the largest nerve in the body. The sciatic nerve leaves the pelvis through the greater sciatic notch and travels down the posterior thigh, serving its flexor muscles and skin. In the popliteal region, the sciatic nerve divides into the **common peroneal nerve** and the **tibial nerve,** which together supply the balance of the leg muscles and skin, both directly and via several branches.

Injury to the proximal part of the sciatic nerve, as might follow a fall or disc herniation, results in a number of lower limb impairments. *Sciatica* (si-at'ĭ-kah), characterized by stabbing pain radiating over the course of the sciatic nerve, is common. When the sciatic nerve is completely sev-

ered, the leg is nearly useless. The leg cannot be flexed and the foot drops into plantar flexion (dangles), a condition called *footdrop.* ■

Activity:

Identifying the Major Nerve Plexuses and Peripheral Nerves

Identify each of the four major nerve plexuses (and its major nerves) shown in Figures 6 to 8 on a large laboratory chart or model. Trace the courses of the nerves and relate those observations to the information provided in Tables 1 to 3. ■

Table 3 Branches of the Lumbosacral Plexus (See Figure 8)

Nerves	Spinal Roots (Ventral Rami)	Structures Served
The Lumbar Plexus		
Femoral	L_2–L_4	Skin of anterior and medial thigh via *anterior femoral cutaneous* branch; skin of medial leg and foot, hip and knee joints via *saphenous* branch; motor to anterior muscles (quadriceps and sartorius) of thigh; pectineus, iliacus
Obturator	L_2–L_4	Motor to adductor magnus (part), longus and brevis muscles, gracilis muscle of medial thigh, obturator externus; sensory for skin of medial thigh and for hip and knee joints
Lateral femoral cutaneous	L_2, L_3	Skin of lateral thigh; some sensory branches to peritoneum
Iliohypogastric	L_1	Skin of lower abdomen, lower back, hip; muscles of anterolateral abdominal wall (obliques and transversus) and pubic region
Ilioinguinal	L_1	Skin of external genitalia and proximal medial aspect of the thigh; inferior abdominal muscles
Genitofemoral	L_1, L_2	Skin of scrotum in males, of labia majora in females, and of anterior thigh inferior to middle portion of inguinal region; cremaster muscle in males
The Sacral Plexus		
Sciatic nerve	L_4, L_5, S_1–S_3	Composed of two nerves (tibial and common peroneal) in a common sheath that diverge just proximal to the knee
• Tibial (including sural branch and medial and lateral plantar branches)	L_4–S_3	Cutaneous branches: to skin of posterior surface of leg and sole of foot Motor branches: to muscles of back of thigh, leg, and foot (hamstrings [except short head of biceps femoris], posterior part of adductor magnus, triceps surae, tibialis posterior, popliteus, flexor digitorum longus, flexor hallucis longus, and intrinsic muscles of foot)
• Common peroneal (superficial and deep branches)	L_4–S_2	Cutaneous branches: to skin of anterior surface of leg and dorsum of foot Motor branches: to short head of biceps femoris of thigh, peroneal muscles of lateral compartment of leg, tibialis anterior, and extensor muscles of toes (extensor hallucis longus, extensors digitorum longus and brevis)
Superior gluteal	L_4, L_5, S_1	Motor branches: to gluteus medius and minimus and tensor fasciae latae
Inferior gluteal	L_5–S_2	Motor branches: to gluteus maximus
Posterior femoral cutaneous	S_1–S_3	Skin of buttock, posterior thigh, and popliteal region; length variable; may also innervate part of skin of calf and heel
Pudendal	S_2–S_4	Supplies most of skin and muscles of perineum (region encompassing external genitalia and anus); external anal sphincter

The Autonomic Nervous System

The **autonomic nervous system (ANS)** is the subdivision of the PNS that regulates body activities that are generally not under conscious control. It is composed of a special group of motor neurons serving cardiac muscle (the heart), smooth muscle (found in the walls of the visceral organs and blood vessels), and internal glands. Because these structures typically function without conscious control, this system is often referred to as the *involuntary nervous system.*

There is a basic anatomical difference between the motor pathways of the **somatic** (voluntary) **nervous system,** which

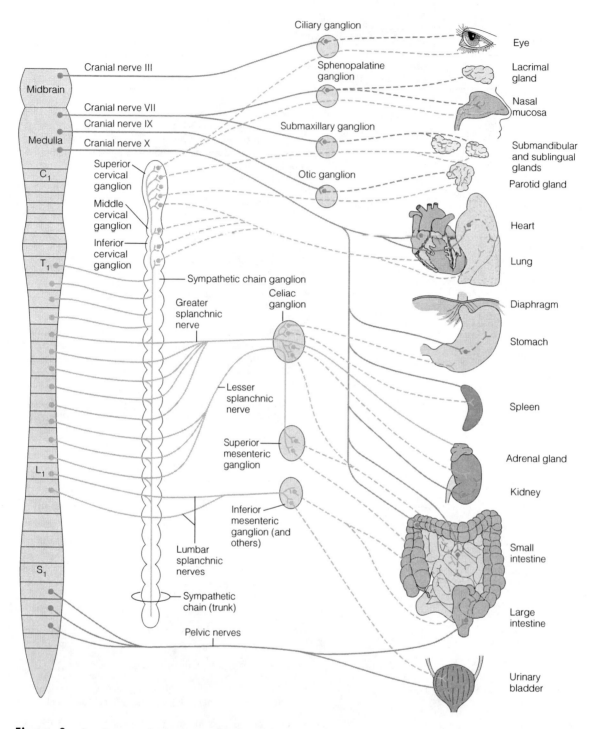

Figure 9 Anatomy of the autonomic nervous system. Parasympathetic fibers (craniosacral division) are shown, sympathetic fibers (thoracolumbar division). Solid lines represent preganglionic fibers; dashed lines indicate postganglionic fibers.

innervates the skeletal muscles, and those of the autonomic nervous system. In the somatic division, the cell bodies of the motor neurons reside in the CNS (spinal cord or brain), and their axons, sheathed in spinal nerves, extend all the way to the skeletal muscles they serve. However, the autonomic ner-

vous system consists of chains of two motor neurons. The first motor neuron of each pair, called the *preganglionic neuron*, resides in the brain or cord. Its axon leaves the CNS to synapse with the second motor neuron (*postganglionic neuron*), whose cell body is located in a ganglion outside the

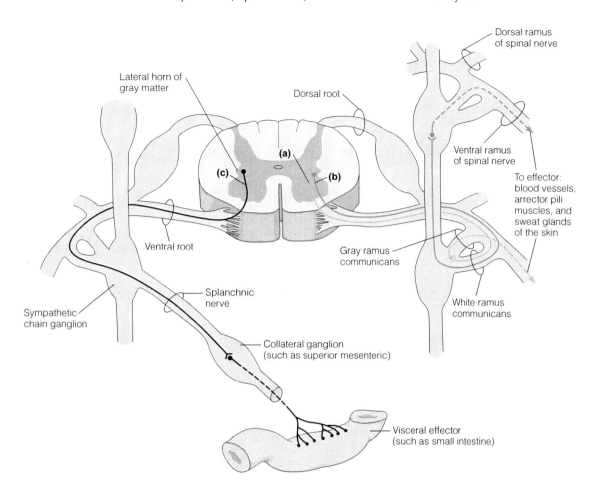

Figure 10 **Sympathetic pathways. (a)** Synapse in a sympathetic chain (paravertebral) ganglion at the same level. **(b)** Synapse in a sympathetic chain ganglion at a different level. **(c)** Synapse in a collateral (prevertebral) ganglion. Preganglionic neurons are shown with solid lines; postganglionic neurons are dashed lines.

CNS. The axon of the postganglionic neuron then extends to the organ it serves.

The autonomic nervous system has two major functional subdivisions (Figure 9). These, the sympathetic and parasympathetic divisions, serve most of the same organs, but generally cause opposing or antagonistic effects.

Parasympathetic Division

The preganglionic neurons of the **parasympathetic,** or **craniosacral,** division are located in brain nuclei of cranial nerves III, VII, IX, X and in the S_2 through S_4 level of the spinal cord. The axons of the preganglionic neurons of the cranial region travel in their respective cranial nerves to the *immediate area* of the head and neck organs to be stimulated. There they synapse with the postganglionic neuron in a **terminal,** or **intramural** (literally, "within the walls"), **ganglion.** The postganglionic neuron then sends out a very short axon to the organ it serves. In the sacral region, the preganglionic axons leave the ventral roots of the spinal cord and collectively form the **pelvic splanchnic nerves,** which travel to the pelvic cavity. In the pelvic cavity, the preganglionic ax-

ons synapse with the postganglionic neurons in ganglia located on or close to the organs served.

Sympathetic Division

The preganglionic neurons of the **sympathetic,** or **thoracolumbar,** division are in the lateral horns of the gray matter of the spinal cord from T_1 through L_2. The preganglionic axons leave the cord via the ventral root (in conjunction with the axons of the somatic motor neurons), enter the spinal nerve, and then travel briefly in the ventral ramus (Figure 10). From the ventral ramus, they pass through a small branch called the **white ramus communicans** to enter a **paravertebral ganglion** in the **sympathetic chain,** or **trunk,** which lies alongside the vertebral column (the literal meaning of *paravertebral*).

Having reached the ganglion, a preganglionic axon may take one of three main courses (see Figure 10). First, it may synapse with a postganglionic neuron in the sympathetic chain at that level. Second, the axon may travel upward or downward through the sympathetic chain to synapse with a postganglionic neuron in a paravertebral ganglion at another level. In either of these two instances, the postganglionic axons then reenter the ventral or dorsal ramus of a spinal nerve via a **gray ramus communicans** and travel in the ramus to innervate skin structures (sweat glands, arrector pili muscles attached to hair follicles, and the smooth muscles of blood vessel walls). Third, the axon may pass through the ganglion without synapsing and form part of the **splanchnic nerves,** which travel to the viscera to synapse with a postganglionic neuron in a **prevertebral** or **collateral ganglion.** The major prevertebral ganglia—the *celiac, superior mesenteric, inferior mesenteric,* and *hypogastric ganglia*—supply the abdominal and pelvic visceral organs. The postganglionic axon then leaves the ganglion and travels to a nearby visceral organ which it innervates.

Activity:
Locating the Sympathetic Chain

Locate the sympathetic chain on the spinal nerve chart. ■

Autonomic Functioning

As noted earlier, most body organs served by the autonomic nervous system receive fibers from both the sympathetic and parasympathetic divisions. The only exceptions are the structures of the skin (sweat glands and arrector pili muscles attached to the hair follicles), the pancreas and liver, the adrenal medulla, and essentially all blood vessels except those of the external genitalia, all of which receive sympathetic innervation only. When both divisions serve an organ, they have antagonistic effects. This is because their postganglionic axons release different neurotransmitters. The parasympathetic fibers, called **cholinergic fibers,** release acetylcholine; the sympathetic postganglionic fibers, called **adrenergic fibers,** release norepinephrine. (However, there are isolated examples of postganglionic sympathetic fibers, such as those serving blood vessels in the skeletal muscles, that release acetylcholine.) The preganglionic fibers of both divisions release acetylcholine.

The parasympathetic division is often referred to as the housekeeping, or "resting and digesting," system because it maintains the visceral organs in a state most suitable for normal functions and internal homeostasis; that is, it promotes normal digestion and elimination. In contrast, activation of the sympathetic division is referred to as the "fight or flight" response because it readies the body to cope with situations that threaten homeostasis. Under such emergency conditions, the sympathetic nervous system induces an increase in heart rate and blood pressure, dilates the bronchioles of the lungs, increases blood sugar levels, and promotes many other effects that help the individual cope with a stressor.

As we grow older, our sympathetic nervous system gradually becomes less and less efficient, particularly in causing vasoconstriction of blood vessels. When elderly people stand up quickly after sitting or lying down, they often become light-headed or faint. This is because the sympathetic nervous system is not able to react quickly enough to counteract the pull of gravity by activating the vasoconstrictor fibers. So, blood pools in the feet. This condition, **orthostatic hypotension,** is a type of low blood pressure resulting from changes in body position as described. Orthostatic hypotension can be prevented to some degree if *slow* changes in position are made. This gives the sympathetic nervous system a little more time to react and adjust. ■

Activity:
Comparing Sympathetic and Parasympathetic Effects

Several body organs are listed in the chart below. *Using your textbook as a reference,* list the effect of the sympathetic and parasympathetic divisions on each. ■

Organ or function	Parasympathetic effect	Sympathetic effect
Heart		
Bronchioles of lungs		
Digestive tract activity		
Urinary bladder		
Iris of the eye		
Blood vessels (most)		
Penis/clitoris		
Sweat glands		
Adrenal medulla		
Pancreas		

Illustrations: 2: Stephanie McCann. 3–7, 9, and 10: Precision Graphics. 8: Kristin Mount. **Photographs:** 1b–d: From *A Stereoscopic Atlas of Human Anatomy,* by David L. Bassett.

Spinal Cord, Spinal Nerves, and the Autonomic Nervous System

Anatomy of the Spinal Cord

1. Match the descriptions given below to the proper anatomical term:

    a. cauda equina   b. conus medullaris   c. filum terminale   d. foramen magnum

    _____ 1. most superior boundary of the spinal cord

    _____ 2. meningeal extension beyond the spinal cord terminus

    _____ 3. spinal cord terminus

    _____ 4. collection of spinal nerves traveling in the vertebral canal below the terminus of the spinal cord

2. Using the terms below, correctly identify on the diagram all structures provided with leader lines.

a. anterior (ventral) horn	f. dorsal root of spinal nerve	k. posterior (dorsal) horn
b. arachnoid mater	g. dura mater	l. spinal nerve
c. central canal	h. gray commissure	m. ventral ramus of spinal nerve
d. dorsal ramus of spinal nerve	i. lateral horn	n. ventral root of spinal nerve
e. dorsal root ganglion	j. pia mater	o. white matter

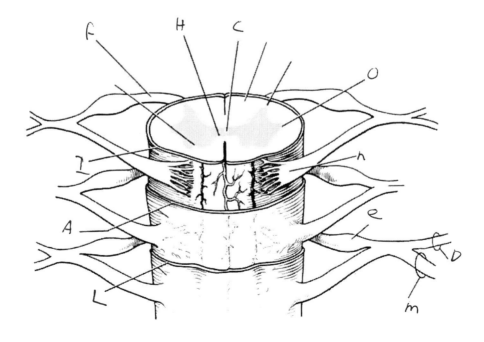

Review Sheet

3. Choose the proper answer from the following key to respond to the descriptions relating to spinal cord anatomy.

Key: a. afferent   b. efferent   c. both afferent and efferent   d. association

_____ 1. neuron type found in dorsal horn   _____ 4. fiber type in ventral root

_____ 2. neuron type found in ventral horn   _____ 5. fiber type in dorsal root

_____ 3. neuron type in dorsal root ganglion   _____ 6. fiber type in spinal nerve

4. Where in the vertebral column is a lumbar puncture generally done? _____

Why is this the site of choice? _____

_____

5. The spinal cord is enlarged in two regions, the _____ and the _____ regions.

What is the significance of these enlargements? _____

_____

6. How does the position of the gray and white matter differ in the spinal cord and the cerebral hemispheres?

_____

_____

7. Choose the name of the tract, from the following key, that might be damaged when the following conditions are observed. (More than one choice may apply.)

_____ 1. uncoordinated movement

_____ 2. lack of voluntary movement

_____ 3. tremors, jerky movements

_____ 4. diminished pain perception

_____ 5. diminished sense of touch

Key: a. fasciculus gracilis
      b. fasciculus cuneatus
      c. lateral corticospinal tract
      d. anterior corticospinal tract
      e. tectospinal tract
      f. rubrospinal tract
      g. lateral spinothalamic tract
      h. anterior spinothalamic tract
      i. posterior spinocerebellar tract
      j. vestibulospinal tract
      k. olivospinal tract
      l. anterior spinocerebellar tract

8. Use an appropriate reference to describe the functional significance of an upper motor neuron and a lower motor neuron:

upper motor neuron _____

_____

lower motor neuron _____

_____

Will contraction of a muscle occur if the lower motor neurons serving it have been destroyed? _____ If the upper motor

neurons serving it have been destroyed? _____ Using an appropriate reference, differentiate between flaccid and spastic

paralysis and note the possible causes of each. _____

Review Sheet

210

_____

_____

_____

_____

_____

Spinal Nerves and Nerve Plexuses

1. In the human, there are 31 pairs of spinal nerves named according to the region of the vertebral column from which they issue. The spinal nerves are named below; note, by number, the vertebral level at which they emerge:

   cervical nerves _____   sacral nerves _____

   lumbar nerves _____   thoracic nerves _____

2. The ventral rami of spinal nerves C_1 through T_1 and T_{12} through S_4 take part in forming _____,

   which serve the _____ of the body. The ventral rami of T_2 through T_{12} run

   between the ribs to serve the _____. The dorsal rami of the spinal nerves

   serve _____.

3. What would happen if the following structures were damaged or transected? (Use key choices for responses.)

   Key: a.   loss of motor function   b.   loss of sensory function   c.   loss of both motor and sensory function

   _____ 1.   dorsal root of a spinal nerve   _____ 3.   anterior ramus of a spinal nerve

   _____ 2.   ventral root of a spinal nerve

4. Define *plexus:* _____

   _____

5. Name the major nerves that serve the following body areas:

   _____ 1. head, neck, shoulders (name plexus only)

   _____ 2. diaphragm

   _____ 3. posterior thigh

   _____ 4. leg and foot (name two)

   _____ 5. most anterior forearm muscles

   _____ 6. arm muscles (name two)

   _____ 7. abdominal wall (name plexus only)

   _____ 8. anterior thigh

   _____ 9. medial side of the hand

Review Sheet

211

The Autonomic Nervous System

1. For the most part, sympathetic and parasympathetic fibers serve the same organs and structures. How can they exert antagonistic effects? (After all, nerve impulses are nerve impulses—aren't they?)

   _____

2. Name three structures that receive sympathetic but not parasympathetic innervation.

   _____

   _____

3. A pelvic splanchnic nerve contains (circle one):

   a. preganglionic sympathetic fibers   c. preganglionic parasympathetic fibers

   b. postganglionic sympathetic fibers   d. postganglionic parasympathetic fibers

4. The following chart states a number of conditions. Use a check mark to show which division of the autonomic nervous system is involved in each.

Sympathetic division	Condition	Parasympathetic division
	Secretes norepinephrine; adrenergic fibers	
	Secretes acetylcholine; cholinergic fibers	
	Long preganglionic axon; short postganglionic axon	
	Short preganglionic axon; long postganglionic axon	
	Arises from cranial and sacral nerves	
	Arises from spinal nerves T_1 through L_3	
	Normally in control	
	"Fight or flight" system	
	Has more specific control (Look it up!)	

5. You are alone in your home late in the evening, and you hear an unfamiliar sound in your backyard. List four physiologic events promoted by the sympathetic nervous system that would aid you in coping with this rather frightening situation:

   _____

   _____

   _____

   _____

6. Often after surgery, people are temporarily unable to urinate, and bowel sounds are absent. What division of the ANS is

   affected by the anesthesia? _____

Review Sheet

Human Reflex Physiology

The Reflex Arc

Reflexes are rapid, predictable, involuntary motor responses to stimuli; they are mediated over neural pathways called **reflex arcs.**

Reflexes can be categorized into one of two large groups: autonomic reflexes and somatic reflexes. **Autonomic (or visceral) reflexes** are mediated through the autonomic nervous system and are not subject to conscious control. These reflexes activate smooth muscles, cardiac muscle, and the glands of the body and they regulate body functions such as digestion, elimination, blood pressure, salivation, and sweating. **Somatic reflexes** include all those reflexes that involve stimulation of skeletal muscles by the somatic division of the nervous system. An example of such a reflex is the rapid withdrawal of a hand from a hot object.

Reflex testing is an important diagnostic tool for assessing the condition of the nervous system. Distorted, exaggerated, or absent reflex responses may indicate degeneration or pathology of portions of the nervous system, often before other signs are apparent.

If the spinal cord is damaged, the easily performed reflex tests can help pinpoint the area (level) of spinal cord injury. Motor nerves above the injured area may be unaffected, whereas those at or below the lesion site may be unable to participate in normal reflex activity. ■

Components of a Reflex Arc

All reflex arcs have five essential components (Figure 1):

1. The *receptor* reacts to a stimulus.

2. The *sensory neuron* conducts the afferent impulses to the CNS.

3. The *integration center* consists of one or more synapses in the CNS.

4. The *motor neuron* conducts the efferent impulses from the integration center to an effector.

5. The *effector,* muscle fibers or glands, responds to the efferent impulses by contracting or secreting a product, respectively.

Objectives

1. To define *reflex* and *reflex arc.*

2. To name, identify, and describe the function of each element of a reflex arc.

3. To indicate why reflex testing is an important part of every physical examination.

4. To describe and discuss several types of reflex activities as observed in the laboratory; to indicate the functional or clinical importance of each; and to categorize each as a somatic or autonomic reflex action.

5. To explain why cord-mediated reflexes are generally much faster than those involving input from the higher brain centers.

6. To investigate differences in reaction time of reflexes and unlearned responses.

Materials

- ❏ Reflex hammer
- ❏ Sharp pencils
- ❏ Cot (if available)
- ❏ Absorbent cotton (sterile)
- ❏ Tongue depressor
- ❏ Metric and 12-in. ruler
- ❏ Flashlight
- ❏ 100- or 250-ml beaker
- ❏ 10- or 25-ml graduated cylinder
- ❏ Lemon juice in dropper bottle
- ❏ Wide-range pH paper
- ❏ Large laboratory bucket containing freshly prepared 10% household bleach solution (for saliva-soiled glassware)
- ❏ Disposable autoclave bag
- ❏ Wash bottle containing 10% bleach solution

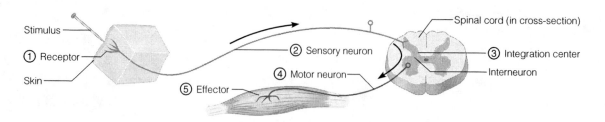

Figure 1 Simple reflex arcs. Components of all human reflex arcs: receptor, sensory neuron, integration center (one or more synapses in the CNS), motor neuron, and effector.

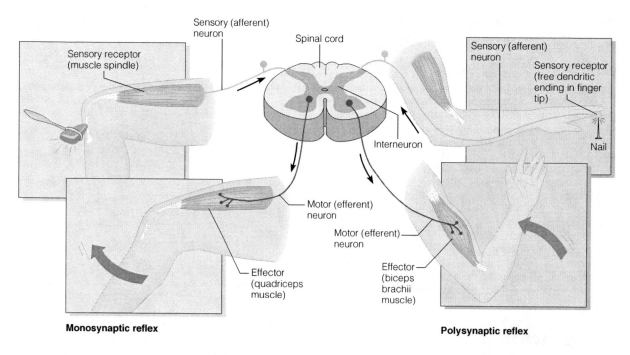

Monosynaptic reflex

Polysynaptic reflex

Figure 2 Monosynaptic and polysynaptic reflex arcs. The integration center is in the spinal cord, and in each example the receptor and effector are in the same limb.

The simple patellar or knee-jerk reflex shown in Figure 2a is an example of a simple, two-neuron, *monosynaptic* (literally, "one synapse") reflex arc. It will be demonstrated in the laboratory. However, most reflexes are more complex and *polysynaptic*, involving the participation of one or more association neurons in the reflex arc pathway. A three-neuron reflex arc (flexor reflex) is diagrammed in Figure 2b. Since delay or inhibition of the reflex may occur at the synapses, the more synapses encountered in a reflex pathway, the more time is required to effect the reflex.

Reflexes of many types may be considered programmed into the neural anatomy. Many *spinal reflexes* (reflexes that

are initiated and completed at the spinal cord level such as the flexor reflex) occur without the involvement of higher brain centers. These reflexes work equally well in decerebrate animals (those in which the brain has been destroyed), as long as the spinal cord is functional. Conversely, other reflexes require the involvement of functional brain tissue, since many different inputs must be evaluated before the appropriate reflex is determined. Superficial cord reflexes and pupillary responses to light are in this category. In addition, although many spinal reflexes do not require the involvement of higher centers, the brain is "advised" of spinal cord reflex activity and may alter it by facilitating or inhibiting the reflexes.

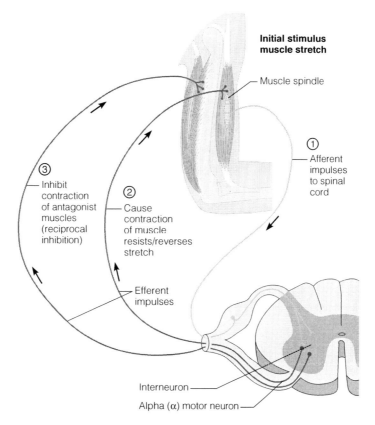

Figure 3 Events of the stretch reflex by which muscle stretch is damped. The events are shown in circular fashion. **(1)** Stretching of the muscle activates a muscle spindle. **(2)** Impulses transmitted by afferent fibers from muscle spindle to alpha motor neurons in the spinal cord result in activation of the stretched muscle, causing it to contract. **(3)** Impulses transmitted by afferent fibers from muscle spindle to interneurons in the spinal cord result in reciprocal inhibition of the antagonist muscle.

Somatic Reflexes

There are several types of somatic reflexes, including several that you will be eliciting during this laboratory session—the stretch, crossed extensor, superficial cord, corneal, and gag reflexes. Some require only spinal cord activity; others require brain involvement as well.

Spinal Reflexes

Stretch Reflexes **Stretch reflexes** are important postural reflexes, normally acting to maintain posture, balance, and locomotion. Stretch reflexes are initiated by tapping a tendon, which stretches the muscle the tendon is attached to. This stimulates the muscle spindles and causes reflex contraction of the stretched muscle or muscles, which resists further stretching. Even as the primary stretch reflex is occurring, impulses are being sent to other destinations as well. For example, branches of the afferent fibers (from the muscle spindles) also synapse with association neurons (interneurons) controlling the antagonist muscles (Figure 3). The inhibition of the antagonist muscles that follows, called *reciprocal inhibition,* causes them to relax and prevents them from resisting (or reversing) the contraction of the stretched muscle caused by the main reflex arc. Additionally, impulses are relayed to higher brain centers (largely via the dorsal white columns) to advise of muscle length, speed of shortening, and the like—information needed to maintain muscle tone and posture. Stretch reflexes tend to be hypoactive or absent in cases of peripheral nerve damage or ventral horn disease, and hyperactive in corticospinal tract lesions. They are absent in deep sedation and coma.

Activity:
Initiating Stretch Reflexes

1. Test the **patellar,** or knee-jerk, **reflex** by seating a subject on the laboratory bench with legs hanging free (or with knees crossed). Tap the patellar ligament sharply with the reflex hammer just below the knee to elicit the knee-jerk response, which assesses the L_2–L_4 level of the spinal cord (Figure 4). Test both knees and record your observations.

_____

_____

Which muscles contracted? _____

_____

What nerve is carrying the afferent and efferent impulses?

_____

2. Test the effect of mental distraction on the patellar reflex by having the subject add a column of three-digit numbers while you test the reflex again. Is the response greater than _or_ less than the first response?

_____

What are your conclusions about the effect of mental distraction on reflex activity?

_____

_____

3. Now test the effect of muscular activity occurring simultaneously in other areas of the body. Have the subject clasp the edge of the laboratory bench and vigorously attempt to pull it upward with both hands. At the same time, test the patellar reflex again. Is the response more or less vigorous than the first response?

_____

4. Fatigue also influences the reflex response. The subject should jog in position until she or he is very fatigued (**really fatigued**—no slackers). Test the patellar reflex again and record whether it is more or less vigorous than the first response.

_____

Would you say that nervous system activity _or_ muscle function is responsible for the changes you have just observed?

_____

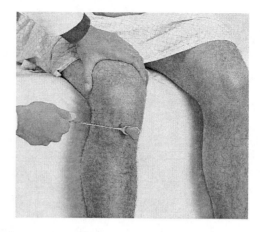

Figure 4 Testing the patellar reflex. The examiner supports the subject's knee so that the subject's muscles are relaxed, and then strikes the patellar ligament with the reflex hammer. The proper location may be ascertained by palpation of the patella.

Explain your reasoning. _____

_____

_____

5. The **Achilles,** or ankle-jerk, **reflex** assesses the first two sacral segments of the spinal cord. With your shoe removed and your foot dorsiflexed slightly to increase the tension of the gastrocnemius muscle, have your partner sharply tap your calcaneal (Achilles) tendon with the reflex hammer (Figure 5).

What is the result? _____

_____

Does the contraction of the gastrocnemius normally result in the activity you have observed?

_____ ∎

Crossed Extensor Reflex The **crossed extensor reflex** is more complex than the stretch reflex. It consists of a flexor, or withdrawal, reflex followed by extension of the opposite limb.

   This reflex is quite obvious when, for example, a stranger suddenly and strongly grips one's arm. The immediate response is to withdraw the clutched arm and push the in-

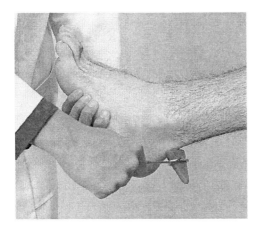

Figure 5 Testing the Achilles reflex. The examiner slightly dorsiflexes the subject's ankle by supporting the foot lightly in the hand, and then taps the Achilles tendon just above the ankle.

truder away with the other arm. The reflex is more difficult to demonstrate in a laboratory because it is anticipated, and under these conditions the extensor part of the reflex may be inhibited.

Activity:
Initiating the Crossed Extensor Reflex

The subject should sit with eyes closed and with the dorsum of one hand resting on the laboratory bench. Obtain a sharp pencil and suddenly prick the subject's index finger. What are the results?

_____

_____

_____

Did the extensor part of this reflex seem to be slow compared to the other reflexes you have observed?

_____

What are the reasons for this? _____

_____

_____

_____ ∎

The reflexes that have been demonstrated so far—the stretch and crossed extensor reflexes—are examples of reflexes in which the reflex pathway is initiated and completed at the spinal cord level.

Superficial Cord Reflexes The **superficial cord reflexes** (abdominal, cremaster, and plantar reflexes) result from pain and temperature changes. They are initiated by stimulation of receptors in the skin and mucosae. The superficial cord reflexes depend _both_ on functional upper-motor pathways and on the cord-level reflex arc. Since only the plantar reflex can be tested conveniently in a laboratory setting, we will use this as our example.

The **plantar reflex,** an important neurological test, is elicited by stimulating the cutaneous receptors in the sole of the foot. In adults, stimulation of these receptors causes the toes to flex and move closer together. Damage to the pyramidal (or corticospinal) tract, however, produces _Babinski's sign_, an abnormal response in which the toes flare and the great toe moves in an upward direction. (In newborn infants, Babinski's sign is seen due to incomplete myelination of the nervous system.)

Activity:
Initiating the Plantar Reflex

Have the subject remove a shoe and lie on the cot or laboratory bench with knees slightly bent and thighs rotated so that the lateral side of the foot rests on the cot. Alternatively, the subject may sit up and rest the lateral surface of the foot on a chair. Draw the handle of the reflex hammer firmly down the lateral side of the exposed sole from the heel to the base of the great toe (Figure 6).

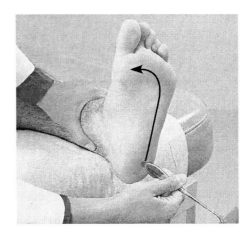

Figure 6 Testing the plantar reflex. Using a moderately sharp object, the examiner strokes the lateral border of the subject's sole, starting at the heel and continuing toward the big toe across the ball of the foot.

What is the response? _____

_____

Is this a normal plantar reflex or Babinski's sign?

_____ ■

Cranial Nerve Reflex Tests

In these experiments, you will be working with your lab partner to illustrate two somatic reflexes mediated by cranial nerves.

Corneal Reflex The **corneal reflex** is mediated through the trigeminal nerve (cranial nerve V). The absence of this reflex is an ominous sign because it often indicates damage to the brain stem resulting from compression of the brain or other trauma.

Activity:
Initiating the Corneal Reflex

Stand to one side of the subject; the subject should look away from you toward the opposite wall. Wait a few seconds and then quickly, *but gently,* touch the subject's cornea (on the side toward you) with a wisp of absorbent cotton. What is the reaction?

_____

What is the function of this reflex?

_____

_____

_____

Was the sensation that of touch *or* of pain?

_____

Why? _____

_____ ■

Gag Reflex The **gag reflex** tests the somatic motor responses of cranial nerves IX and X. When the oral mucosa on the side of the uvula is stroked, each side of the mucosa should rise, and the amount of elevation should be equal.*

---

* The uvula is the fleshy tab hanging from the roof of the mouth just above the root of the tongue.

Activity:
Initiating the Gag Reflex

For this experiment, select a subject who does not have a queasy stomach, because regurgitation is a possibility. Stroke the oral mucosa on each side of the subject's uvula with a tongue depressor. What happens?

_____

_____

⚠ Discard the used tongue depressor in the disposable autoclave bag before continuing. Do *not* lay it on the laboratory bench at any time. ■

Autonomic Reflexes

The autonomic reflexes include the pupillary, ciliospinal, and salivary reflexes, as well as a multitude of other reflexes. Work with your partner to demonstrate the four autonomic reflexes described next.

Pupillary Reflexes

There are several types of pupillary reflexes. The **pupillary light reflex** and the **consensual reflex** will be examined here. In both of these pupillary reflexes, the retina of the eye is the receptor, the optic nerve (cranial nerve II) contains the afferent fibers, the oculomotor nerve (cranial nerve III) is responsible for conducting efferent impulses to the eye, and the smooth muscle of the iris is the effector. Many central nervous system centers are involved in the integration of these responses. Absence of the normal pupillary reflexes is generally a late indication of severe trauma or deterioration of the vital brain stem tissue due to metabolic imbalance.

Activity:
Initiating Pupillary Reflexes

1. Conduct the reflex testing in an area where the lighting is relatively dim. Before beginning, obtain a metric ruler to measure and record the size of the subject's pupils as best you can.

Right pupil: _____ mm   Left pupil: _____ mm

2. Stand to the left of the subject to conduct the testing. The subject should shield his or her right eye by holding a hand vertically between the eye and the right side of the nose.

3. Shine a flashlight into the subject's left eye. What is the pupillary response?

_____

Measure the size of the left pupil: _____ mm

4. Observe the right pupil. Has the same type of change (called a *consensual response*) occurred in the right eye?

_____

Measure the size of the right pupil: _____ mm

The consensual response, or any reflex observed on one side of the body when the other side has been stimulated, is called a **contralateral response.** The pupillary light response, or any reflex occurring on the same side stimulated, is referred to as an **ipsilateral response.**

When a contralateral response occurs, what does this indicate about the pathways involved?

_____

_____

Was the sympathetic *or* the parasympathetic division of the autonomic nervous system active during the testing of these reflexes?

_____

What is the function of these pupillary responses?

_____

_____

_____ ■

Ciliospinal Reflex

The **ciliospinal reflex** is another example of reflex activity in which pupillary responses can be observed. This response may initially seem a little bizarre, especially in view of the consensual reflex just demonstrated.

A c t i v i t y :
Initiating the Ciliospinal Reflex

1. While observing the subject's eyes, gently stroke the skin (or just the hairs) on the left side of the back of the subject's neck, close to the hairline.

What is the reaction of the left pupil? _____

The reaction of the right pupil? _____

2. If you see no reaction, repeat the test using a gentle pinch in the same area.
    The response you should have noted—pupillary dilation—is consistent with the pupillary changes occurring when the sympathetic nervous system is stimulated. Such a response may also be elicited in a single pupil when more impulses from the sympathetic nervous system reach it for any

reason. For example, when the left side of the subject's neck was stimulated, sympathetic impulses to the left iris increased, resulting in the ipsilateral reaction of the left pupil.
    On the basis of your observations, would you say that the sympathetic innervation of the two irises is closely integrated?

_____Why or why not? _____

_____

_____ ■

Salivary Reflex

Unlike the other reflexes, in which the effectors were smooth or skeletal muscles, the effectors of the **salivary reflex** are glands. The salivary glands secrete varying amounts of saliva in response to reflex activation.

A c t i v i t y :
Initiating the Salivary Reflex

1. Obtain a small beaker, a graduated cylinder, lemon juice, and wide-range pH paper. After refraining from swallowing for 2 minutes, the subject is to expectorate (spit) the accumulated saliva into a small beaker. Using the graduated cylinder, measure the volume of the expectorated saliva and determine its pH.

Volume: _____ cc   pH:_____

2. Now place 2 or 3 drops of lemon juice on the subject's tongue. Allow the lemon juice to mix with the saliva for 5 to 10 seconds, and then determine the pH of the subject's saliva by touching a piece of pH paper to the tip of the tongue.

pH: _____

As before, the subject is to refrain from swallowing for 2 minutes. After the 2 minutes is up, again collect and measure the volume of the saliva and determine its pH.

Volume: _____ cc   pH:_____

3. How does the volume of saliva collected after the application of the lemon juice compare with the volume of the first saliva sample?

_____

How does the final saliva pH reading compare to the initial reading?

_____

To that obtained 10 seconds after the application of lemon juice?

_____

What division of the autonomic nervous system mediates the reflex release of saliva?

_____

⚠ Dispose of the saliva-containing beakers and the graduated cylinders in the laboratory bucket that contains bleach and put the used pH paper into the disposable autoclave bag. Wash the bench down with 10% bleach solution before continuing. ■

Reaction Time of Unlearned Responses

The time required for reaction to a stimulus depends on many factors—sensitivity of the receptors, velocity of nerve conduction, the number of neurons and synapses involved, and the speed of effector activation, to name just a few. The type of response to be elicited is also important. If the response involves a reflex arc, the synapses are facilitated and response time will be short. If, on the other hand, the response can be categorized as an unlearned response, then a far larger number of neural pathways and many types of higher intellectual activities—including choice and decision making—will be involved, and the time for response will be considerably lengthened.

There are various ways of testing reaction time of unlearned responses. The tests range in difficulty from simple to ultrasophisticated. Since the objective here is to demonstrate the major time difference between reflexes and unlearned responses, the simple approach will suffice.

Activity:
Testing Reaction Time for Unlearned Responses

1. Using a reflex hammer, elicit the patellar reflex in your partner. Note the relative reaction time needed for this reflex to occur.

2. Now test the reaction time for unlearned responses. The subject should hold a hand out, with the thumb and index finger extended. Hold a 12-in. ruler so that its end is exactly 1 in. above the subject's outstretched hand. The ruler should be in the vertical position with the numbers reading from the bottom up. When the ruler is dropped, the subject should be able to grasp it between thumb and index finger as it passes, without having to change position. Have the subject catch the ruler five times, varying the time between trials. The relative speed of reaction can be determined by reading the number on the ruler at the point of the subject's fingertips. (Thus if the number at the fingertips is 6 in., the subject was unable to catch the ruler until 7 in. of length had passed through his or her fingers; 6 in. of ruler length plus 1 in. to account for the distance of the ruler above the hand.) Record the number of inches that pass through the subject's fingertips for each trial:

Trial 1:_____ in.   Trial 4:_____ in.

Trial 2:_____ in.   Trial 5:_____ in.

Trial 3:_____ in.

3. Perform the test again, but this time say a simple word each time you release the ruler. Designate a specific word as a signal for the subject to catch the ruler. On all other words, the subject is to allow the ruler to pass through his fingers. Trials in which the subject erroneously catches the ruler are to be disregarded. Record the distance the ruler travels for five *successful* trials:

Trial 1:_____ in.   Trial 4:_____ in.

Trial 2:_____ in.   Trial 5:_____ in.

Trial 3:_____ in.

Did the addition of a specific word to the stimulus increase or decrease the reaction time?

_____

4. Perform the testing once again to investigate the subject's reaction to word association. As you drop the ruler, say a word—for example, *hot*. The subject is to respond with a word he or she associates with the stimulus word—for example, *cold*—catching the ruler while responding. If unable to make a word association, the subject must allow the ruler to pass through his or her fingers. Record the distance the ruler travels for five successful trials, as well as the number of times the ruler is not caught by the subject.

Trial 1:_____ in.   Trial 4:_____ in.

Trial 2:_____ in.   Trial 5:_____ in.

Trial 3:_____ in.

The number of times the subject was unable to catch the ruler:

_____

You should have noticed quite a large variation in reaction time in this series of trials. Why is this so?

_____

_____

_____

_____ ■

Illustrations: 1, 2, and 3: Precision Graphics. **Photographs:** 4, 5, and 6: © Benjamin/Cummings Publishing Company. Photo by Richard Tauber.

Human Reflex Physiology

The Reflex Arc

1. Define *reflex:* ___involuntary response to a stimulus_____

   _____

2. Name five essential components of a reflex arc: ___achilles_____, ___Patella_____,
   ___Biceps_____, ___triceps_____, and ___Plantar_____

3. In general, what is the importance of reflex testing in a routine physical examination? ___make sure that___
   ___a person has movement throughout_____

   _____

Somatic and Autonomic Reflexes

1. Use the key terms to complete the statements given below.

   Key: a. abdominal reflex   d. corneal reflex   g. patellar reflex
         b. Achilles jerk   e. crossed extensor reflex   h. plantar reflex
         c. ciliospinal reflex   f. gag reflex   i. pupillary light reflex

   Reflexes classified as somatic reflexes include a _____, _____, _____, _____, _____, _____, and _____.

   Of these, the simple stretch reflexes are _____ and _____, and the superficial cord reflexes are _____ and _____.

   Reflexes classified as autonomic reflexes include _____ and _____.

2. In what way do cord-mediated reflexes differ from those involving higher brain centers? _____

   _____

   Name two cord-mediated reflexes: _____ and _____

   _____

   Name two somatic reflexes in which the higher brain centers participate: _____

   and _____

3. Can the stretch reflex be elicited in a pithed animal? _____

   Explain your answer. _____

   _____

4. Trace the reflex arc, naming efferent and afferent nerves, receptors, effectors, and integration centers, for the following reflexes:

patellar reflex _____

_____

_____

Achilles reflex _____

_____

_____

5. Three factors that influence the rapidity and effectiveness of reflex arcs were investigated in conjunction with patellar reflex testing—mental distraction, effect of simultaneous muscle activity in another body area, and fatigue.

Which of these factors increases the excitatory level of the spinal cord? _____

Which factor decreases the excitatory level of the muscles? _____

When the subject was concentrating on an arithmetic problem, did the change noted in the patellar reflex indicate that brain

activity is necessary for the patellar reflex or only that it may modify it? _____

_____

6. Name the division of the autonomic nervous system responsible for each of the following reflexes:

ciliospinal reflex _____ salivary reflex _____

pupillary light reflex _____

7. The pupillary light reflex, the crossed extensor reflex, and the corneal reflex illustrate the purposeful nature of reflex activity. Describe the protective aspect of each:

pupillary light reflex _____

corneal reflex _____

crossed extensor reflex _____

_____

_____

_____

_____

8. Was the pupillary consensual response contralateral or ipsilateral? _____

Why would such a response be of significant value in this particular reflex? _____

_____

Review Sheet

222

9. Differentiate between the types of activities accomplished by somatic and autonomic reflexes. _____

_____

_____

_____

10. Several types of reflex activity were not investigated in this exercise. The most important of these are autonomic reflexes, which are difficult to illustrate in a laboratory situation. To rectify this omission, complete the following chart, using references as necessary.

Reflex	Organ involved	Receptors stimulated	Action
Micturition (urination)			
Hering-Breuer			
Defecation			
Carotid sinus			

Reaction Time of Unlearned Responses

1. Name at least three factors that may modify reaction time to a stimulus. _____

   _____

2. In general, how did the response time for the unlearned activity performed in the laboratory compare to that for the simple

   patellar reflex? _____

3. Did the response time without verbal stimuli decrease with practice? _____ Explain the reason for this.

   _____

4. Explain, in detail, why response time increased when the subject had to react to a word stimulus.

   _____

   _____

The Special Senses

❏ Dissectible eye model
❏ Chart of eye anatomy
❏ Preserved cow or sheep eye
❏ Dissecting tray and instruments
❏ Protective skin cream or disposable gloves
❏ Metric ruler
❏ Common straight pins
❏ Snellen eye chart (floor marked with chalk to indicate 20-ft distance from posted Snellen chart)
❏ Ishihara's color-blindness plates

F O R   H E A R I N G   A N D   E Q U I L I B R I U M

❏ Three-dimensional dissectible ear model and/or chart of ear anatomy
❏ Otoscope (if available)
❏ Alcohol swabs
❏ Prepared microscope slide of cochlea
❏ Absorbent cotton
❏ Pocket watch or clock that ticks
❏ 12-inch ruler
❏ Tuning forks (range of frequencies)
❏ Rubber mallet
❏ *Demonstration area:*
   Cochlea slide set up under a compound microscope for student observation

F O R   S M E L L   A N D   T A S T E

❏ Small mirror
❏ Paper towels
❏ Granulated sugar
❏ Cotton-tipped swabs
❏ Disposable autoclave bag

Text continues on next page

B E F O R E   Y O U   B E G I N

- Read the chapter on special senses in your textbook.
- Scan the exercise for the objectives you will be expected to accomplish during this laboratory session.
- Brush up on neuron structure.

In contrast to the small and widely distributed general receptors (touch, temperature, pressure, and pain), the **special sense receptors** are large, complex sensory organs (eyes and ears) or localized clusters of receptors (taste buds and olfactory epithelium). This chapter focuses on the functional anatomy of each of the special sense organs individually, but keep in mind that sensory inputs are overlapping.

Anatomy of the Eye

O B J E C T I V E   1 Describe the structure and function of the accessory visual structures.

External Anatomy and Accessory Structures

The adult human eye is a sphere some 2.5 cm (1 inch) in diameter. Only about one-sixth of the eye's anterior surface is observable (Figure 1); the remainder is protected by a cushion of fat and the walls of the bony orbit.

Anteriorly each eye is protected by the **eyelids.** (See Figure 1.) The medial and lateral junctions of the upper and lower eyelids are referred to as the **medial** and **lateral canthus** (respectively). A mucous membrane, the **conjunctiva,** lines the internal surface of the eyelids and continues over the anterior surface of the eyeball to the outer edge of the cornea where it fuses with the corneal epithelium. The conjunctiva secretes mucus, which lubricates the eyeball. Inflammation of the conjunctiva, often accompanied by redness of the eye, is called **conjunctivitis.**

The **eyelashes** project from the edge of each eyelid. **Ciliary glands,** modified sweat glands, lie between the eyelashes and help lubricate the eyeball. An inflammation of one of these glands is called a **sty.** The larger **tarsal glands,** located posterior to the eyelashes, secrete an oily substance.

(materials list, continued)

❏ Paper cups; paper plates

❏ Beaker containing 10% bleach solution

❏ Prepared dropper bottles of oil of cloves, oil of peppermint, and oil of wintergreen or corresponding flavors found in the condiment section of a supermarket

❏ Equal-sized food cubes of cheese, apple, dried prunes, banana, and hard-cooked egg white (These prepared foods should be in an opaque container; a foil-lined egg carton would work well.)

❏ Chipped ice

❏ Absorbent cotton

The **lacrimal apparatus** consists of the lacrimal gland and a system of ducts. The **lacrimal glands** lie superior and lateral to each eye. They continually release a dilute salt solution (tears) onto the anterior surface of the eyeball through several small ducts. The tears flush across the eyeball into the **lacrimal canaliculi** medially, then into the **lacrimal sac,** and finally into the **nasolacrimal duct,** which empties into the nasal cavity. Lacrimal fluid cleanses and protects the eye surface as it moistens and lubricates it.

Six **extrinsic eye muscles** attached to the exterior surface of each eyeball control eye movements. The names, positioning, and actions of these extrinsic muscles are noted in Figure 2.

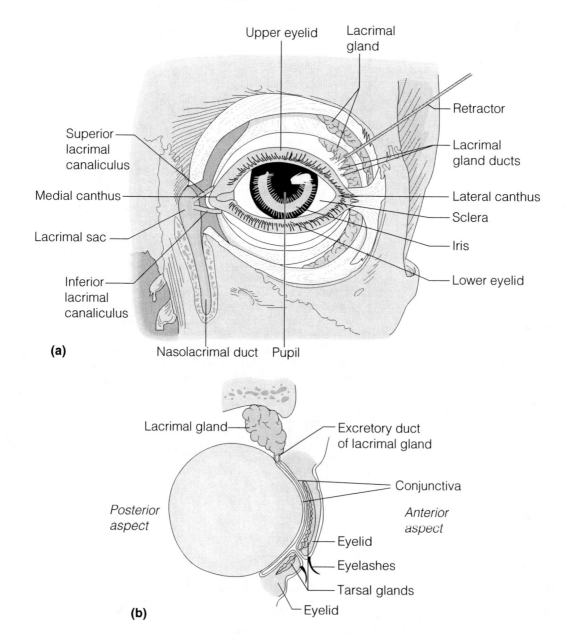

FIGURE 1 External anatomy of the eye and accessory structures. (a) Anterior view. **(b)** Sagittal section.

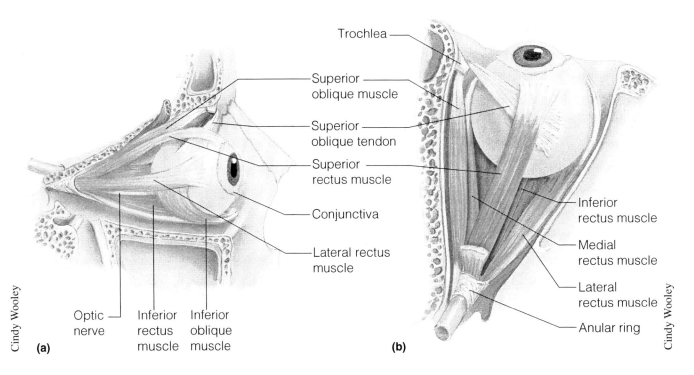

(c) Precision Graphics

Name	Controlling cranial nerve	Action
Lateral rectus	VI (abducens)	Moves eye laterally
Medial rectus	III (oculomotor)	Moves eye medially
Superior rectus	III (oculomotor)	Elevates eye or rolls it superiorly
Inferior rectus	III (oculomotor)	Depresses eye or rolls it inferiorly
Inferior oblique	III (oculomotor)	Elevates eye and turns it laterally
Superior oblique	IV (trochlear)	Depresses eye and turns it laterally

FIGURE 2 Extrinsic muscles of the eye. (a) Lateral view of the right eye. **(b)** Superior view of right eye. **(c)** Summary of actions of the extrinsic eye muscles, and cranial nerves that control them.

ACTIVITY 1

Identifying Accessory Eye Structures

Observe the eyes of another student, and identify as many accessory structures as possible. Ask the student to look to the left. What extrinsic eye muscles produce this action?

Right eye _____

Left eye _____

Ask your partner to look superiorly. What *two* extrinsic muscles of each eye can bring about this motion?

Right eye _____

Left eye _____

Internal Anatomy of the Eye

OBJECTIVE 2 Identify the internal structures of the eye when provided with a model, diagram, or preserved animal eye and list the functions of each.

The eye itself is a hollow sphere. Its wall is constructed of three **tunics,** or coats, and its interior is filled with *humors* that help to maintain its shape. The lens is supported upright in the eye's cavity and divides it into two chambers.

ACTIVITY 2

Identifying Internal Eye Structures

Obtain a dissectible eye model or observe a chart of eye anatomy to identify the structures described below. As you work, also refer to Figure 3.

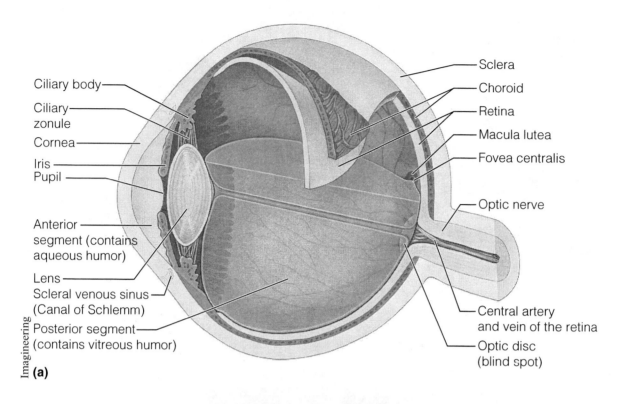

Imagineering

(a)

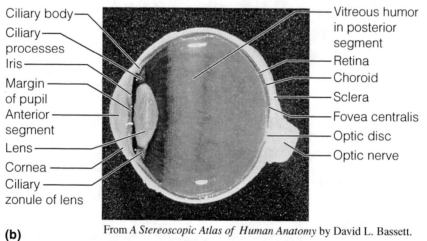

From *A Stereoscopic Atlas of Human Anatomy* by David L. Bassett.

(b)

FIGURE 3 Internal anatomy of the right eye (sagittal section). (a) Diagrammatic view. **(b)** Photograph of the human eye.

The outermost **fibrous tunic** of the eye is a protective layer composed of dense connective tissue. It has two obviously different regions: The opaque white **sclera,** seen anteriorly as the "white of the eye," forms the bulk of the fibrous tunic. Its central anterior portion is modified to form the transparent **cornea,** through which light enters the eye.

The middle tunic, called the **uvea,** is the **vascular tunic.** Its posterior part, the **choroid,** is blood-rich and contains a dark pigment that prevents light scattering within the eye. Anteriorly, the choroid is modified to form the **ciliary body,**

to which the lens is attached, and then the pigmented **iris.** The iris has a rounded opening, the **pupil,** through which light passes.

The iris is composed of circularly and radially arranged smooth muscle fibers and acts like the diaphragm of a camera to regulate the amount of light entering the eye. In close vision and bright light, the *circular muscles* of the iris contract, and the pupil constricts. In distant vision and in dim light, the *radial fibers* contract, enlarging (dilating) the pupil and allowing more light to enter the eye.

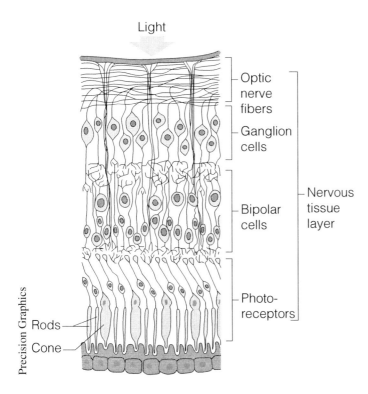

Light

— Optic nerve fibers

— Ganglion cells

— Nervous tissue layer

Bipolar cells

Photo-receptors

Rods

Cone

Precision Graphics

FIGURE 4 Microscopic anatomy of the retina.

The innermost **sensory tunic** of the eye is the delicate **retina.** This transparent **neural (nervous) layer** extends anteriorly only to the ciliary body. It contains the photoreceptors, **rods** and **cones,** which begin the chain of electrical events that pass from the photoreceptors to bipolar cells and then to the ganglion cells (Figure 4). When adequately stimulated, the ganglion cells generate nerve impulses that are ultimately transmitted to the optic cortex of the brain. Vision is the result. The photoreceptor cells are distributed over the entire neural retina, except where the optic nerve (the bundled axons of the ganglion cells) leaves the eyeball. This site is called the **optic disc,** or **blind spot** (see Figure 3). Lateral to each blind spot is the **macula lutea** (yellow spot), an area of high cone density. In its center is the **fovea centralis,** a minute pit about 0.5 mm in diameter, which contains only cones and is the area of greatest visual acuity. Focusing for discriminative vision occurs in the fovea centralis.

Light entering the eye is focused on the retina by the **lens,** which is held upright in the eye by a suspensory ligament called the **ciliary zonule** attached to the ciliary body. Activity of the ciliary muscle, which accounts for most of the ciliary body tissue, changes lens thickness to allow light to be properly focused on the retina.

The lens divides the eye into two segments. The **anterior segment** anterior to the lens contains a clear watery fluid called the **aqueous humor.** The **posterior segment** behind the lens is filled with the gel-like **vitreous humor,** or **vitreous body.** The aqueous humor is continually formed by the capillaries of the ciliary body. It helps to maintain the intraocular pressure of the eye and provides nutrients for the avascular lens and cornea. Aqueous humor is reabsorbed into

the **scleral venous sinus (canal of Schlemm),** a drainage duct located at the junction of the sclera and cornea. The vitreous humor reinforces the posterior part of the eyeball, and helps to keep the retina pressed firmly against the wall of the eyeball.

DISSECTION

The Cow (Sheep) Eye

1. Obtain a preserved cow or sheep eye, dissecting instruments, and a dissecting tray. Put on protective skin cream or disposable gloves if desired.

2. Examine the external surface of the eye, noticing the thick cushion of adipose tissue. Identify the optic nerve (cranial nerve II) as it leaves the eyeball, the cut remnants of the extrinsic eye muscles, the conjunctiva, the sclera, and the cornea. The normally transparent cornea is opalescent or opaque if the eye has been preserved. Refer to Figure 5 as you work.

3. Trim away most of the fat and connective tissue, but leave the optic nerve intact. Holding the eye with the cornea facing downward, carefully make an incision with a sharp scalpel into the sclera about ¼ inch above the cornea. The sclera of the preserved eyeball is *very* tough, so you will have to apply substantial pressure to penetrate it. But work gingerly because some of the fluid may squirt out of the eyeball when the sclera is pierced. Then, using scissors, cut around the circumference of the eyeball paralleling the corneal edge.

4. Carefully lift the anterior part of the eyeball away from the posterior portion. Conditions being proper, the vitreous body should remain with the posterior part of the eyeball. Move some of the vitreous humor aside to view the retina, which will resemble a wet, crumpled tissue. You will also see the following structure:

Pigmented choroid coat: Appears iridescent in the cow or sheep eye due to a special reflecting surface called the **tapetum lucidum.** This specialized surface reflects the light within the eye and is found in the eyes of animals that live under conditions of low-intensity light. It is not found in humans.

5. Examine the anterior part of the eye, and identify the following structures.

Ciliary body: Black pigmented body that appears in a halo encircling the lens.

Lens: Biconvex structure that is opaque in preserved specimens.

Ciliary zonule: A halo of delicate fibers attaching the lens to the ciliary body.

Carefully remove the lens, and identify the adjacent structures:

Iris: Anterior continuation of the ciliary body penetrated by the pupil.

Cornea: More convex anteriormost portion of the sclera; normally transparent but cloudy in preserved specimens.

6. Examine the posterior portion of the eyeball. Remove the vitreous humor, and identify the following structures:

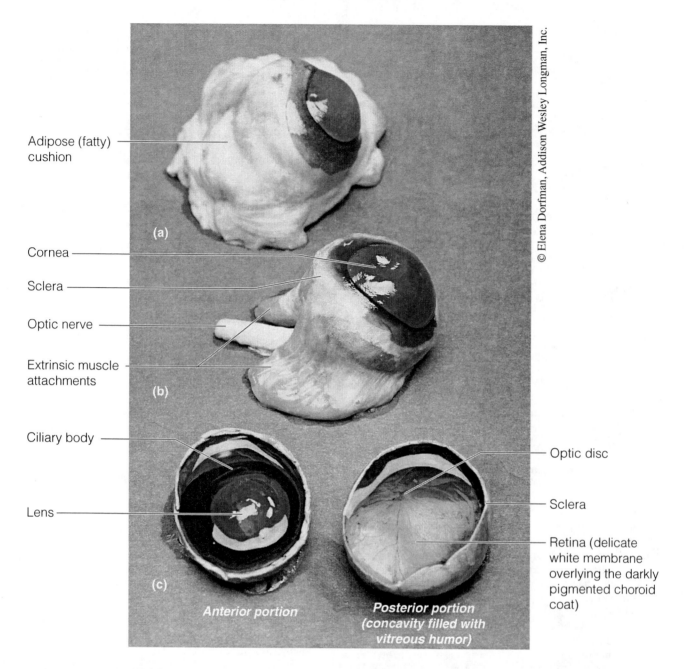

Adipose (fatty) cushion

Cornea

Sclera

Optic nerve

Extrinsic muscle attachments

Ciliary body

Lens

Optic disc

Sclera

Retina (delicate white membrane overlying the darkly pigmented choroid coat)

Anterior portion

Posterior portion (concavity filled with vitreous humor)

© Elena Dorfman, Addison Wesley Longman, Inc.

FIGURE 5 Anatomy of the cow eye. (a) Cow eye (entire) removed from orbit (notice the large amount of fat cushioning the eyeball). **(b)** Cow eye (entire) with fat removed to show the extrinsic muscle attachments and optic nerve. **(c)** Cow eye cut along the coronal plane to reveal internal structures.

Retina: The neural layer of the retina appears as a delicate white, probably crumpled membrane that separates easily from the pigmented choroid.

Notice its point of attachment. What is this point called?

_____ ▬

Visual Tests and Experiments

OBJECTIVE 3 Define *blind spot, refraction, hyperopia, myopia,* and *astigmatism,* and discuss image formation on the retina.

Demonstrating the Blind Spot

1. Hold Figure 6 about 18 inches from your eyes. Close your left eye, and focus your right eye on the X, which should be positioned so that it is directly in line with your right eye. Move the figure slowly toward your face, keeping your right eye focused on the X. When the dot focuses on the blind spot, which lacks photoreceptors, it will disappear.

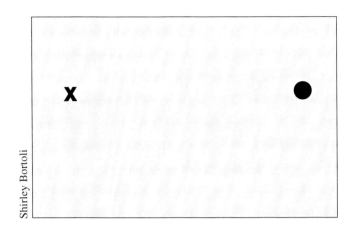

FIGURE 6 Blind spot test figure.

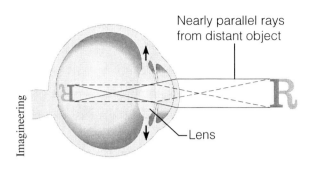

Nearly parallel rays from distant object

Lens

FIGURE 7 Refraction of light in the eye, resulting in the production of a real image on the retina.

2. Have your laboratory partner record in metric units the distance at which this occurs. The dot will reappear as the figure is moved closer. Distance at which the dot disappears:

Right eye _____

Repeat the test for the left eye. This time close the right eye and focus the left eye on the dot. Record the distance at which the X disappears:

Left eye _____

Refraction, Visual Acuity, and Astigmatism

When light passes from one substance to another with a different density, its velocity, or speed of transmission, changes, and the rays are bent, or **refracted.** Thus the light rays are refracted as they encounter the cornea, lens, and vitreous humor of the eye.

The bending power of the cornea and vitreous humor are constant. But the lens's refractive strength can be varied by changing its shape—that is, by making it more or less convex so that the light is properly converged and focused on the retina. The greater the lens convexity, or bulge, the more the light will be bent and the stronger the lens.

In general, light from a distant source (over 20 feet) approaches the eye as parallel rays, and no change in lens shape is necessary for it to focus properly on the retina. However, light from a close source tends to diverge, and the convexity of the lens must increase to make close vision possible. To achieve this, the ciliary muscle contracts, decreasing the tension of the suspensory ligament attached to the lens and allowing the elastic lens to "round up." The ability of the eye to focus specifically for close objects (less than 20 feet) is called **accommodation.** It should be noted that the image formed on the retina as a result of the light-bending activity of the lens (see Figure 7) is a **real image** (reversed from left to right, inverted, and smaller than the object).

The normal or **emmetropic eye** is able to accommodate properly. However, visual problems may result from (1) lenses that are too strong or too "lazy" (overconverging and underconverging, respectively); (2) structural problems, such as an eyeball that is too long or too short; or (3) a cornea or lens with improper curvatures.

Individuals in whom the image normally focuses in front of the retina have **myopia,** or "nearsightedness"; they can see close objects without difficulty, but distant objects are blurred or indistinct. Correction requires a concave lens, which causes the light reaching the eye to diverge.

If the image focuses behind the retina, the individual has **hyperopia,** or farsightedness. Such persons have no problems with distant vision but need glasses with convex lenses to boost the converging power of the lens for close vision.

Irregularities in the curvatures of the lens and/or the cornea lead to a blurred vision problem called **astigmatism.** Cylindrically ground lenses, which compensate for inequalities in the curvatures of the refracting surfaces, are prescribed to correct the condition.

The elasticity of the lens decreases dramatically with age, resulting in difficulty in focusing for close vision. This condition is called **presbyopia**—literally, "old vision." Lens elasticity can be tested by measuring the **near point of accommodation,** which is about 10 cm from the eye in young adults. It is closer in children and farther in old age.

ACTIVITY 4

Determining Near Point of Accommodation

To determine your near point of accommodation, hold a common straight pin at arm's length in front of one eye. Slowly move the pin toward that eye until the pin image becomes distorted. Have your lab partner use the metric ruler to measure the distance from your eye to the pin at this point, and record the distance below. Repeat the procedure for the other eye.

Near point for right eye _____

Near point for left eye _____

Visual acuity, or sharpness of vision, is generally tested with a Snellen eye chart, which consists of letters of various sizes

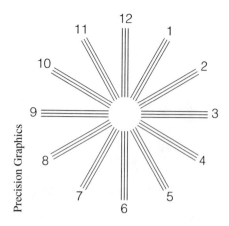

Precision Graphics

FIGURE 8 Astigmatism testing chart.

printed on a white card. The distance at which the normal eye can read a line of letters is printed at the end of that line.

ACTIVITY 5

Testing Visual Acuity

1. Have your partner stand 20 feet from the posted Snellen eye chart and cover one eye with a card or hand. As your partner reads each consecutive line aloud, check for accuracy. If this individual wears glasses, give the test twice—first with glasses off and then with glasses on.

2. Record the number of the line with the smallest-sized letters read. If it is 20/20, the person's vision for that eye is normal. If it is 20/40, or any ratio with a value less than one, he or she has less than the normal visual acuity. (Such an individual is myopic, so a person with 20/40 vision is seeing objects clearly at 20 feet that a person with normal vision sees clearly at 40 feet.) If the visual acuity ratio is greater than 1, vision is better than normal. Give your partner the number of the line corresponding to the smallest letters read, to record in step 4.

3. Repeat the process for the other eye.

4. Have your partner test and record your visual acuity. If you wear glasses, the test results *without* glasses should be recorded first.

Visual acuity, right eye _____

Visual acuity, left eye _____

ACTIVITY 6

Testing for Astigmatism

The astigmatism chart (Figure 8) tests for defects in the refracting surface of the lens and/or cornea.

   View the chart first with one eye and then with the other, focusing on the center of the chart. If all the radiating lines appear equally dark and distinct, your refracting surfaces are not distorted. If some of the lines are blurred or appear less dark than others, you have at least some degree of astigmatism.

Is astigmatism present in your left eye? _____

Right eye _____

Color Blindness

Ishihara's color-blindness plates are designed to test for deficiencies in the cones or color photoreceptor cells. There are three cone types—one type primarily absorbs the red wavelengths of visible light, another the blue wavelengths, and a third the green wavelengths. Nerve impulses reaching the brain from these different photoreceptor types are then interpreted (seen) as red, blue, and green, respectively. Interpretation of the intermediate colors of the visible light spectrum is a result of simultaneous input from more than one cone type.

ACTIVITY 7

Testing for Color Blindness

1. View the color plates in bright light or sunlight while holding them about 30 inches away and at right angles to your line of vision. Report to your laboratory partner what you see in each plate. Take no more than 3 seconds for each decision.

2. Your partner is to write down your responses and then check their accuracy with the correct answers provided in the color plate book. Is there any indication that you have some degree of color blindness?

_____ If so, what type? _____

_____

Repeat the procedure to test your partner's color vision.

Eye Reflexes

OBJECTIVE 4 Discuss the importance of the photopupillary and accommodation reflexes.

   Both intrinsic (internal) and extrinsic (external) muscles are necessary for proper eye function. The *intrinsic muscles,* controlled by the autonomic nervous system, are those of the ciliary body (which alters the lens curvature) and the radial and circular muscles of the iris (which control pupil size and thus regulate the amount of light entering the eye). The *extrinsic muscles* are the rectus and oblique muscles, which are attached to the outside of the eyeball (see Figure 2). These muscles control eye movement and make it possible to keep moving objects focused on the fovea centralis. They are also responsible for **convergence,** or medial eye movement, which is essential for near vision. When convergence occurs, both eyes are aimed at the near object viewed. The extrinsic eye muscles are controlled by the somatic nervous system.

ACTIVITY 8

Demonstrating Reflex Activity of Intrinsic and Extrinsic Eye Muscles

Activity of both the intrinsic and extrinsic muscle types is brought about by reflex actions that can be observed by conducting simple experiments. The *convergence reflex* mediated by the extrinsic eye muscles and the *accommodation reflex* mediated by the intrinsic eye muscles are described here. (The photopupillary reflex protects the delicate photoreceptor cells from damage due to excessive light and also involves the intrinsic muscles.)

Accommodation Pupillary Reflex

Have your partner gaze for approximately 1 minute at a distant object in the lab—*not* toward the windows or another light source. Observe your partner's pupils. Then hold some printed material 6 to 10 inches from his or her face, and direct him or her to focus on it.

How does pupil size change as your partner focuses on the printed material?

_____

Explain the value of this reflex.

_____

_____

Convergence Reflex

Repeat the previous experiment, this time noting the position of your partner's eyeballs both while he or she is gazing at the distant and at the close object (a pen or pencil). Do they change position as the object of focus is changed?

_____

In what way? _____

_____

Explain the importance of the convergence reflex.

_____

_____

_____ —

The Ear and Hearing and Balance

O B J E C T I V E 5 Identify the structures of the outer, middle, and inner ear by correctly labeling a diagram.

Gross Anatomy of the Ear

The ear, which contains sensory receptors for hearing and equilibrium, is divided into three major areas: the *outer ear,* the *middle ear,* and the *inner ear* (Figure 9). The outer and

middle ear structures serve the needs of the sense of hearing *only,* while inner ear structures function both in equilibrium and hearing reception.

ACTIVITY 9

Identifying Structures of the Ear

Obtain a dissectible ear model and identify the structures described below: Refer to Figure 9 as you work.

The **outer ear** is composed of the **auricle,** or **pinna,** and the **external acoustic meatus.** The pinna is the skin-covered cartilage encircling the auditory canal opening. The external auditory canal is a short, narrow chamber carved into the temporal bone. In its skin-lined walls are wax-secreting glands called **ceruminous glands.** The sound waves that enter the external auditory canal eventually hit the **tympanic membrane,** or **eardrum,** causing it to vibrate. The eardrum separates the outer from the middle ear.

The **middle ear** is a small air-filled chamber—the **tympanic cavity**—within the temporal bone. The cavity is spanned by three small bones, collectively called the **ossicles** (hammer, anvil, and stirrup),* which transmit the vibratory motion of the eardrum to the fluids of the inner ear via the **oval window.**

Connecting the middle ear chamber with the nasopharynx is the **pharyngotympanic (auditory) tube,** which can be opened temporarily to equalize the pressure of the middle ear cavity with external air pressure. This is an important function because the eardrum does not vibrate properly unless the pressure on both of its surfaces is the same.

The **inner ear** is a system of bony and rather tortuous chambers called the **osseous,** or **bony, labyrinth,** which is filled with a watery fluid called **perilymph.** Floating in the perilymph is the **membranous labyrinth,** a system filled with a more viscous fluid called **endolymph.** The three subdivisions of the bony labyrinth are the **cochlea,** the **vestibule,** and the **semicircular canals,** with the vestibule situated between the cochlea and semicircular canals.

ACTIVITY 10

Examining the Ear with an Otoscope (Optional)

1.   Obtain an otoscope and two alcohol swabs. Inspect your partner's ear canal and then select the speculum with the largest *diameter* (not length!) that will fit comfortably into his or her ear and permit good visibility. Clean the speculum thoroughly with an alcohol swab, and then attach it to the battery-containing otoscope handle. Before beginning, check that the otoscope light beam is strong. (If not, obtain another otoscope or new batteries.)

* The ossicles are often referred to by their Latin names, that is, **malleus, incus,** and **stapes,** respectively.

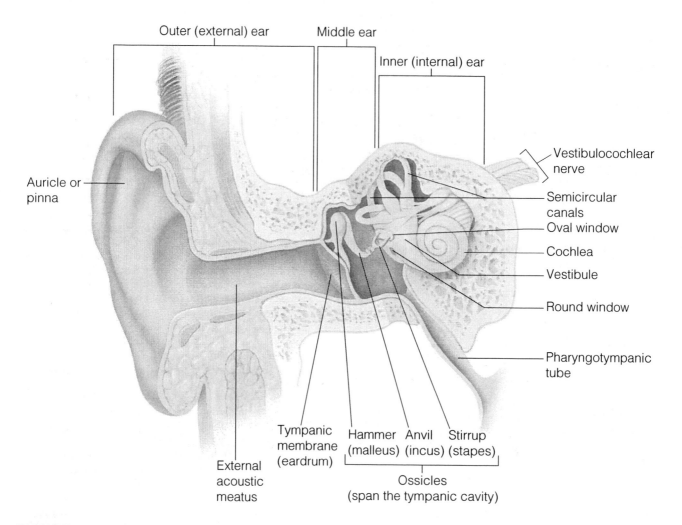

Outer (external) ear   Middle ear

Inner (internal) ear

Vestibulocochlear nerve

Semicircular canals

Oval window

Cochlea

Vestibule

Round window

Pharyngotympanic tube

Auricle or pinna

Tympanic membrane (eardrum)

Hammer (malleus) Anvil (incus) Stirrup (stapes)

External acoustic meatus

Ossicles
(span the tympanic cavity)

FIGURE 9 Anatomy of the ear.

2. When you are ready to begin the examination, hold the lighted otoscope securely between your thumb and forefinger (like a pencil), and rest the little finger of your otoscope-holding hand against your partner's head. This maneuver forms a brace that allows the speculum to move as your partner moves and prevents it from penetrating too deeply into the ear canal during the unexpected movements.

3. Grasp the ear pinna firmly and pull it up, back, and slightly laterally. If this causes your partner pain or discomfort, the external ear may be inflamed or infected. If this occurs, do not attempt to examine the ear canal.

4. Carefully insert the speculum of the otoscope into the external auditory canal in a downward and forward direction just far enough to permit examination of the tympanic membrane or eardrum. Note its shape, color, and vascular network. The healthy tympanic membrane is pearly white. During the examination, notice if there is any discharge or redness in the canal and identify earwax.

5. After the examination, thoroughly clean the speculum with the second alcohol swab before returning the otoscope to the supply area. ▪

Microscopic Anatomy of the Organ of Corti and the Mechanism of Hearing

O B J E C T I V E 6 Describe the anatomy of the organ of Corti and explain its role in hearing.

The snail-like cochlea (see Figures 9 and 10) contains the receptors for hearing. The cochlear membranous labyrinth, the **cochlear duct,** is a soft wormlike tube about 1½ inches long that winds through the turns of the cochlea and separates the perilymph-containing cochlear cavity into upper and lower chambers. The upper chamber abuts the oval window, which "seats" the foot plate of the stirrup located laterally in the tympanic cavity. The lower chamber is bounded by a membranous area called the **round window.** The cochlear duct, itself filled with endolymph, supports the

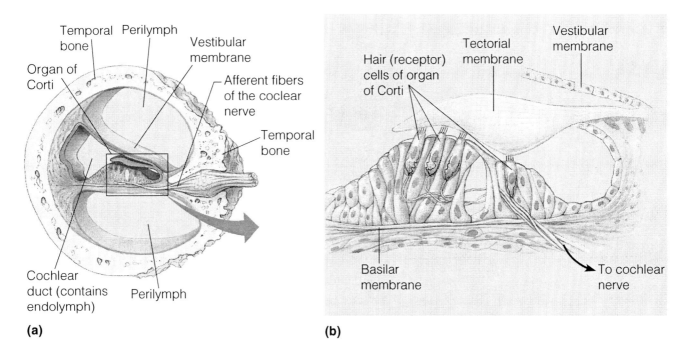

Temporal Perilymph
bone
Vestibular
membrane
Organ of
Corti
Afferent fibers
of the coclear
nerve

Temporal
bone

Cochlear
duct (contains
endolymph) Perilymph

(a)

Hair (receptor) Tectorial Vestibular
cells of organ membrane membrane
of Corti

Basilar To cochlear
membrane nerve

(b)

FIGURE 10 Anatomy of the cochlea. (a) A cross-sectional view of one turn of the cochlea, showing the relationship of the three chambers. The upper and lower chambers contain perilymph. The cochlear duct, which houses the organ of Corti, contains endolymph. **(b)** Detailed structure of the organ of Corti. The receptor cells (hair cells) rest on the basilar membrane.

organ of Corti, which contains the receptors for hearing and nerve endings of the cochlear division of the vestibulocochlear nerve (VIII).

The structure of the organ of Corti is shown in Figure 10b. The hair (auditory receptor) cells rest on the **basilar membrane,** which forms the floor of the cochlear duct, and their "hairs" (stereocilia) project into the gel-like **tectorial membrane** that overlies them. The roof of the cochlear duct is called the **vestibular membrane.**

Examining the Microscopic Structure of the Cochlea

Go to the demonstration area, and view the prepared microscope slide of the cochlea. Identify the areas described above and shown in Figure 10.

The mechanism of hearing begins as sound waves pass through the external auditory canal and through the middle ear into the inner ear, where the vibration eventually reaches the organ of Corti, which contains the receptors for hearing.

The traveling sound waves stimulate the hair cells of the organ of Corti where they peak. High-frequency waves (high-pitched sounds) peak close to the oval window and low-frequency waves (low-pitched sounds) peak farther up the basilar membrane near the apex of the cochlea. Once stimulated, the hair cells depolarize and begin the chain of

nervous impulses to the auditory centers of the temporal lobe cortex. This series of events results in the phenomenon we call hearing.

OBJECTIVE 7 Describe how one is able to localize sounds and to differentiate sensorineural from conduction deafness.

Conducting Laboratory Tests of Hearing

Perform the following hearing tests in a quiet area.

Acuity Test

Have your lab partner pack one ear with cotton and sit quietly with eyes closed. Obtain a ticking clock or pocket watch and hold it very close to his or her *unpacked* ear. Then slowly move it away from the ear until your partner signals that the ticking is no longer audible. Record the distance in inches at which ticking is inaudible.

Right ear _____ Left ear _____

Is the threshold of audibility sharp or indefinite?

_____

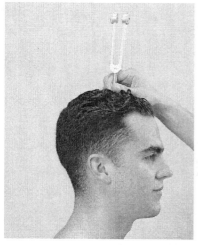 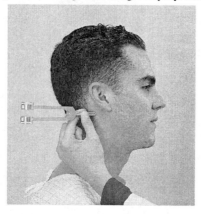 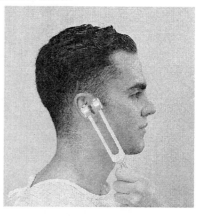

© Benjamin/Cummings Publishing Company. Photo by Richard Tauber.

(a) (b) (c)

FIGURE 11 The Weber and Rinne tuning fork tests. (a) The Weber test to evaluate whether the sound remains centralized (normal) or lateralizes to one side or the other (indicative of some degree of conductive or sensorineural deafness). **(b)** and **(c)** The Rinne test to compare bone conduction and air conduction.

Sound Localization

Ask your partner to close both eyes. Hold the pocket watch at an audible distance (about 6 inches) from his or her ear, and move it to various locations (front, back, sides, and above his or her head). Have your partner locate the position by pointing in each instance. Can the sound be localized equally well at all positions?

_____

If not, at what position(s) was the sound less easily located?

_____

_____

The ability to localize the source of a sound depends on two factors—the difference in the loudness of the sound reaching each ear and the time of arrival of the sound at each ear. How does this information help to explain your findings?

_____

_____

Weber Test to Determine Conductive and Sensorineural Deafness

Obtain a tuning fork and a rubber mallet. Strike the tuning fork with the rubber mallet and place the handle of the tuning fork medially on your partner's head (see Figure 11a). Is the tone equally loud in both ears, or is it louder in one ear?

_____

If it is equally loud in both ears, you have equal hearing or equal loss of hearing in both ears. If sensorineural deafness is present in one ear, the tone will be heard in the unaffected ear, but not in the ear with sensorineural deafness. If conduction deafness is present, the sound will be heard more strongly in the ear in which there is a hearing loss. Conduction deafness can be simulated by plugging one ear with cotton to interfere with the conduction of sound to the inner ear.

Rinne Test for Comparing Bone- and Air-Conduction Hearing

1. Strike the tuning fork, and place its handle on your partner's mastoid process (Figure 11b).

2. When your partner indicates that he or she can no longer hear the sound, hold the still-vibrating prongs close to his or her auditory canal (Figure 11c). If your partner hears the fork again (by air conduction) when it is moved to that position, hearing is not impaired. Record the test result as positive (+). (Record below in step 4.)

3. Repeat the test, but this time test air-conduction hearing first. After the tone is no longer heard by air conduction, hold the handle of the tuning fork on the bony mastoid process. If the subject hears the tone again by bone conduction after hearing by air conduction is lost, there is some conductive deafness and the result is recorded as negative (−).

4. Repeat the sequence for the opposite ear.

Right ear _____ Left ear _____

Does the subject hear better by bone or by air conduction?

_____

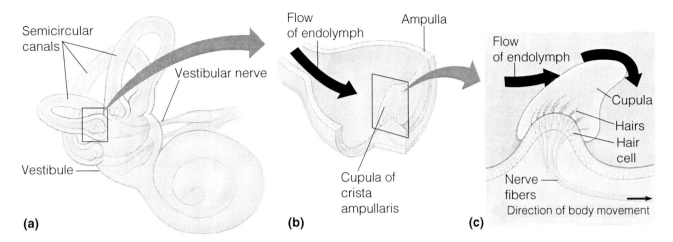

FIGURE 12 **Structure and function of the crista ampullaris. (a)** Arranged in the three spatial planes, the semicircular ducts in the semicircular canals each have a swelling called an *ampulla* at their base. **(b)** Each ampulla contains a crista ampullaris, a receptor that is essentially a cluster of hair cells with hairs projecting into a gelatinous cap called the *cupula*. **(c)** When head position changes in an angular direction, inertia causes the endolymph in the semicircular ducts to lag behind, pushing the cupula and bending the hair cells in the opposite direction. The bending results in increased impulse transmission in the sensory neurons. The mechanism adjusts quickly if rotation continues at a constant speed.

Anatomy of the Equilibrium Apparatus and Mechanisms of Equilibrium

O B J E C T I V E 8 Describe the anatomy of the equilibrium organs of the inner ear, and explain their relative roles in maintaining balance.

The equilibrium apparatus of the inner ear is in the vestibular and semicircular canal portions of the bony labyrinth. The vestibule contains the saclike **utricle** and **saccule,** and the semicircular chambers contain membranous **semicircular ducts.** Like the cochlear duct, these membranes (1) are suspended in perilymph within the bony chambers, (2) are filled with endolymph, and (3) contain receptor cells that are activated by the disturbance of their cilia.

The semicircular canals house *dynamic equilibrium* receptors. The canals are about ½ inch in circumference and are oriented in the three planes of space. At the base of each semicircular duct is an enlarged region, the **ampulla,** which contains a receptor region called a **crista ampullaris.** This receptor consists of a tuft of hair cells covered with a gelatinous cap, or **cupula** (Figure 12). These dynamic equilibrium receptors react to *changes* in angular motion rather than to motion itself, as described and illustrated in Figure 12b and c.

The membrane sacs within the vestibule contain **maculae,** *static equilibrium* receptors that respond to gravitational pull (thus providing information on which way is up or down) and to linear or straightforward changes in speed. The **otolithic membrane,** a gelatinous material containing small grains of calcium carbonate (**otoliths**), overrides the hair cells in each macula. As the head moves, the otoliths roll in response to changes in gravitational pull (Figure 13). As they bend different hair cells, they modify the rate of impulse transmission along the vestibular nerve.

The receptors of the semicircular canals and the vestibule rarely act independently. Also, the information these balance senses provide is enhanced by the proprioceptors and sight, as some of the following laboratory experiments demonstrate.

O B J E C T I V E 9 State the purpose of the Romberg test and describe the role of vision in maintaining equilibrium.

ACTIVITY 13

Conducting Laboratory Tests on Equilibrium

The functions of the semicircular canals and vestibule are not routinely tested in the laboratory, but the following simple tests should serve to illustrate normal equilibrium apparatus functioning.

Balance Test

Have your partner walk a straight line, placing one foot directly in front of the other.

Is he or she able to walk without noticeable wobbling from side to side?

_____

Did he or she experience any dizziness? _____

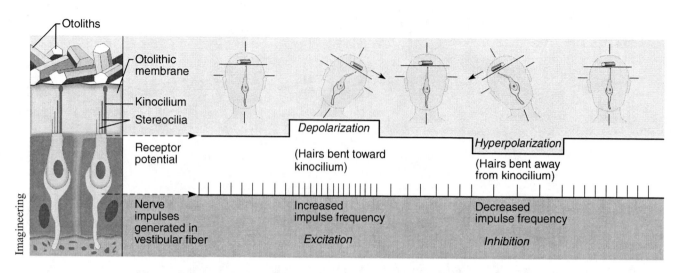

Otoliths

Otolithic membrane

Kinocilium

Stereocilia

Receptor potential

Depolarization

(Hairs bent toward kinocilium)

Hyperpolarization

(Hairs bent away from kinocilium)

Nerve impulses generated in vestibular fiber

Increased impulse frequency

Excitation

Decreased impulse frequency

Inhibition

Imagineering

FIGURE 13 The effect of gravitational pull on a macula receptor in the utricle. When movement of the otolithic membrane (direction by the arrow) bends the hair cells in the direction of the kinocilium, the vestibular fibers depolarize and generate action potentials more rapidly. When the hairs are bent in the direction away from the kinocilium, the nerve fibers send impulses at a reduced rate (i.e., below the resting rate of discharge).

The ability to walk with balance and without dizziness, unless subject to rotational forces, indicates normal function of the equilibrium apparatus.

Was nystagmus* present? _____

Romberg Test

The Romberg test determines the soundness of the dorsal white column of the spinal cord, which transmits impulses to the brain from the proprioceptors involved with posture.

1. Have your partner stand with his or her back to the blackboard.

2. Draw one line parallel to each side of your partner's body. He or she should stand erect, with feet together, eyes open and staring straight ahead for 2 minutes while you observe any movements. Did you see any gross swaying movements?

_____

3. Repeat the test. This time the subject's eyes should be closed. Note and record the degree of side-to-side movement.

_____

* **Nystagmus** is the involuntary rolling of the eyes in any direction or the trailing of the eyes slowly in one direction, followed by their rapid movement in the opposite direction. It is normal after rotation; abnormal otherwise. The direction of nystagmus is that of its quick phase on acceleration.

4. Repeat the test with the subject's eyes first open and then closed. This time, however, the subject should be positioned with his or her left shoulder toward, but not touching, the board so that you may observe and record the degree of front-to-back swaying.

_____

_____

Do you think the equilibrium apparatus of the inner ear was operating equally well in all these tests? _____

The proprioceptors? _____

Why was the observed degree of swaying greater when the eyes were closed?

_____

_____

What conclusions can you draw regarding the factors necessary for maintaining body equilibrium and balance?

_____

_____

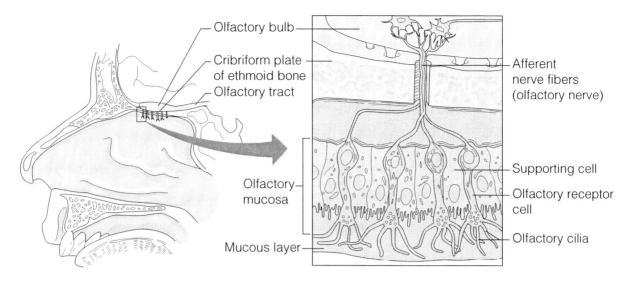

FIGURE 14 Location and cellular composition of olfactory epithelium.

Role of Vision in Maintaining Equilibrium

To further demonstrate the role of vision in maintaining equilibrium, perform the following experiment. (Ask your lab partner to record observations and act as a "spotter.") Stand erect, with your eyes open. Raise your left foot approximately 1 foot off the floor, and hold it there for 1 minute.

Record the observations: ——————————

——————————————————————

——————————————————————

Rest for 1 or 2 minutes; and then repeat the experiment with the same foot raised, but with your eyes closed.

Record the observations: ——————————

——————————————————————

——————————————————————

The Chemical Senses: Smell and Taste

The receptors for smell (olfaction) and taste (gustation) are classified as **chemoreceptors** because they respond to chemicals in solution.

Localization and Anatomy of the Olfactory and Taste Receptors

OBJECTIVE 10 Describe the location, structure, and function of the olfactory and taste receptors.

The **olfactory epithelium** (organ for the sense of smell) occupies an area of about 2.5 cm in the roof of each nasal cavity (Figure 14). The **olfactory receptor cells** are bipolar neurons whose **olfactory cilia** protrude from the epithelium. Axons emerging from their basal ends penetrate the cribriform plate of the ethmoid bone and proceed as the *olfactory nerves* to synapse in the olfactory bulbs lying on either side of the crista galli of the ethmoid bone. Impulses from neurons of the olfactory bulbs are then conveyed to the olfactory portion of the cortex.

The **taste buds,** specific receptors for the sense of taste, are widely distributed in the oral cavity. Most are located on the tongue (as described next). A few are found on the soft palate, pharynx, and inner surface of the cheeks.

The superior tongue surface is covered with small projections, or **papillae,** of three major types: sharp *filiform papillae* and the rounded *fungiform* and *circumvallate papillae*. The taste buds are located primarily on the sides of the circumvallate papillae (arranged in a V-formation on the posterior surface of the tongue) and on the more numerous fungiform papillae. The latter look rather like minute mushrooms and are widely distributed on the tongue. (See Figure 15.)

When taste is tested with pure chemical compounds, most taste sensations can be grouped into one of five basic qualities—sweet, salty, sour, bitter, and umami (u-mam'e; "delicious"), responsible for the steak and monosodium glutamate tastes.

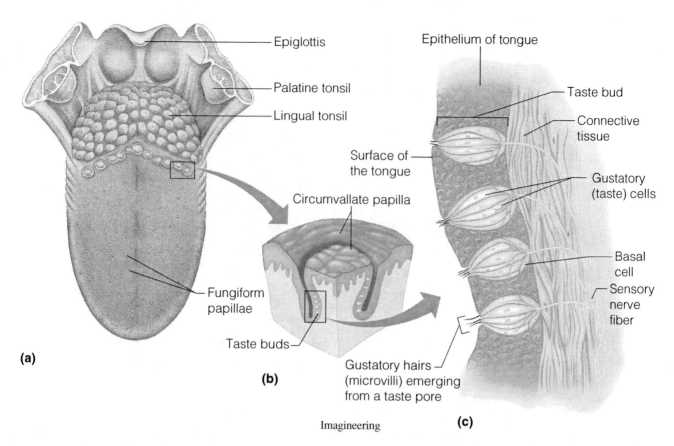

Epiglottis

Palatine tonsil

Lingual tonsil

Surface of
the tongue

Circumvallate papilla

Fungiform
papillae

Taste buds

(a)

(b)

Epithelium of tongue

Taste bud

Connective
tissue

Gustatory
(taste) cells

Basal
cell

Sensory
nerve
fiber

Gustatory hairs
(microvilli) emerging
from a taste pore

Imagineering

(c)

FIGURE 15 Location and structure of taste buds. (a) Taste buds on the tongue are associated with papillae, projections of the tongue mucosa. **(b)** A sectioned circumvallate papilla shows the position of the taste buds in its lateral walls. **(c)** An enlarged view of four taste buds.

Identification of Papillae on the Tongue

Use a mirror to examine your tongue. Can you pick out the various papillae types?

_____ If so, which? _____

_____ ▭

Each taste bud consists of a globular arrangement of two types of epithelial cells: the **gustatory,** or **taste, cells,** which are the actual receptor cells, and **supporting cells.** Basal cells at the bottom of each taste bud provide for new receptor cells. Several nerve fibers enter each taste bud and supply sensory nerve endings to each of the taste cells. The long microvilli of the receptor cells penetrate through an opening called the **taste pore.** When these microvilli, called **gustatory hairs,** are stimulated by specific chemicals in the solution, the taste cells depolarize. The afferent fibers from the taste buds to the gustatory cortex of the brain are carried in three cranial nerves: the _facial (VII), glossopharyngeal (IX),_ and _vagus (X) nerves._

Laboratory Experiments

Stimulating Taste Buds

1.   Obtain several paper towels and a disposable autoclave bag and bring them to your bench.

2.   With a paper towel, dry the superior surface of your tongue.

⚠   Immediately dispose of the paper towel in the auto-clave bag.

3.   Place a few sugar crystals on your dried tongue. Do _not_ close your mouth. Time how long it takes to taste the sugar.

_____ sec.

Why couldn't you taste the sugar immediately?

_____ ▭

CHART 1	Method of Identification			
Food	Texture only	Chewing with nostrils pinched	Chewing with nostrils open	Identification not made
Cheese				
Apple				
Banana				
Dried prunes				
Hard-cooked egg white				

Examining the Combined Effects of Smell, Texture, and Temperature on Taste

OBJECTIVE 11 List several factors that influence taste.

Effects of Smell and Texture

1. Ask the subject to sit with eyes closed and to pinch his or her nostrils shut.

2. Using a paper plate, obtain samples of the food items listed in Chart 1. At no time should the subject be allowed to see the foods being tested.

3. Use an out-of-sequence order of food testing. For each test, place a cube of food in the subject's mouth and ask him or her to identify the food by using the following sequence of activities:

• First, move the food around in the mouth with the tongue.

• Second, chew the food.

• Third, if a positive identification is not made with the first two techniques and the taste sense, ask the subject to release his or her pinched nostrils and to continue chewing with the nostrils open to see if a positive identification can be made.

Record the results on the chart by checking the appropriate column.

Was the sense of smell equally important in all cases?

_____

Where did it seem to be important and why?

_____

_____

Effect of Olfactory Stimulation

There is no question that what is commonly called taste depends heavily on the sense of smell, particularly in the case of strongly scented substances. The following experiments should illustrate this fact.

1. Obtain paper cups, vials of oil of wintergreen, peppermint, and cloves, and some fresh cotton-tipped swabs. Ask the subject to sit so that he or she cannot see which vial is being used and to dry the tongue and close the nostrils.

2. Apply a drop of one of the oils to the subject's tongue. Can he or she distinguish the flavor?

_____

_____

3. Have the subject open the nostrils, and record the change in sensation he or she reports.

_____

_____

4. Have the subject rinse the mouth well with water and dry the tongue.

5. Prepare two swabs, each with one of the two remaining oils.

6. Hold one swab under the subject's open nostrils, while touching the second swab to the tongue.

Record the reported sensations. _____

_____

_____

_____

! 7. Dispose of the used swabs and paper towels in the autoclave bag before continuing.

Which sense, taste or smell, appears to be more important in the proper identification of a strongly flavored volatile substance?

_____

Effect of Temperature

In addition to the effect that olfaction and food texture play in determining our taste sensations, the temperature of foods also helps determine whether we appreciate or even taste the food. To illustrate this, have your partner hold some chipped ice on the tongue for approximately a minute and then close his or her eyes. Immediately place any of the foods previously identified in his or her mouth and ask for an identification.

Results? _____

_____

_____

NAME_____

LAB TIME/DATE_____

Special Senses

The Eye and Vision: Anatomy

1. Several accessory eye structures contribute to the formation of tears and/or aid in lubrication of the eyeball. Match the described accessory structures with their secretion by choosing answers from the key.

    Key: conjunctiva   lacrimal glands   tarsal glands

    _____ 1.   mucus

    _____ 2.   oil

    _____ 3.   salt solution

2. The eyeball is wrapped in adipose tissue within the orbit. What is the function of the adipose tissue?

    _____

3. Why may it be necessary to blow one's nose after having a good cry? _____

    _____

4. What is a sty? _____

    _____

    Conjunctivitis? _____

    _____

5. What seven bones form the bony orbit? (Think! If you can't remember, check a skull or your textbook.)

    _____   _____   _____

    _____   _____   _____

    _____

6. Identify the lettered structures on the diagram by matching each letter with one of the terms to the right.

m anterior segment containing aqueous humor

F bipolar neurons

_____ canal of Schlemm

D ciliary body

O choroid

A cornea

n fovea centralis

G ganglion cells

I iris

K lens

_____ optic disc

P optic nerve

_____ photoreceptors

H pupil

_____ retina

h sclera

_____ suspensory ligaments

_____ vitreous body in posterior segment

Blowup of photosensitive retina

Notice the arrows drawn close to the left side of the iris in the diagram above. What do they indicate?

_____

_____

_____

7. Match the key responses with the descriptive statements that follow.

Key: aqueous humor   cornea   lens   sclera
         canal of Schlemm   fovea centralis   optic disc   suspensory ligament
         choroid   iris   retina   vitreous humor
         ciliary body

_____ 1. attaches the lens to the ciliary body

_____ 2. fluid filling the anterior segment of the eye

_____ 3. the blind spot

_____ 4. contains muscle that controls the size of the pupil

_____ 5. drains the aqueous humor from the eye

_____ 6. "sensory" tunic

_____ 7. substance occupying the posterior segment of the eyeball

_____ 8. forms most of the pigmented vascular tunic

_____ 9. tiny pit in the macula lutea; contains only cones

_____ 10. important light-bending structure of the eye; shape can be modified

_____ 11. anterior transparent part of the fibrous tunic

_____ 12. composed of tough, white, opaque, fibrous connective tissue

8. The intrinsic eye muscles are under the control of which of the following? (Circle the correct response.)

autonomic nervous system   somatic nervous system

Dissection of the Cow (Sheep) Eye

9. What modification of the choroid that is not present in humans is found in the cow eye? _____

_____

What is its function? _____

_____

10. Describe the appearance of the retina. _____

_____

At what point is it attached to the posterior aspect of the eyeball? _____

Visual Tests and Experiments

11. Use terms from the key to complete the statements concerning near and distance vision.

Key: contracted   decreased   increased   relaxed   taut   lax

During distance vision: The ciliary muscle is _____, the suspensory ligament is _____, the convexity of the lens is _____, and light refraction is _____. During close vision: The ciliary muscle is _____, the suspensory ligament is _____, lens convexity is _____, and light refraction is _____.

12. Explain why the part of the image hitting the blind spot is not seen. _____

13. Match the terms in column B with the descriptions in column A:

Column A		Column B
_____	1. light bending	accommodation
_____	2. ability to focus for close (under 20 ft) vision	astigmatism
_____	3. normal vision	convergence
_____	4. inability to focus well on close objects (farsightedness)	emmetropia
_____	5. nearsightedness	hyperopia
_____	6. blurred vision due to unequal curvatures of the lens or cornea	myopia
_____	7. medial movement of the eyes during focusing on close objects	refraction

14. Record your Snellen eye test results below:

Left eye (without glasses) _20/15_ (with glasses) _n/a_

Right eye (without glasses) _20/15_ (with glasses) _n/a_

Is your visual acuity normal, less than normal, or better than normal? _better_

Explain. _I see at 20 ft what others see at 15_

Explain why each eye is tested separately when using the Snellen eye chart. _eyes have diff. muscles and one can be worse than the other_

Explain 20/40 vision. _I see at 20 what others see at 40_

Explain 20/10 vision. _I see at 20 what others see at 10_

15. Define *astigmatism:* _____

16. Record the distance of your near point of accommodation as tested in the laboratory:

right eye _____ left eye _____

Is your near point within the normal range for your age? _____

17. How can you explain the fact that we see a great range of colors even though only three cone types exist?

_____

_____

18. In the experiment on the convergence reflex, what happened to the position of the eyeballs as the object was moved closer

to the subject's eyes? _____

What extrinsic eye muscles control the movement of the eyes during this reflex? _____

What is the value of this reflex? _____

_____

What would be the visual result of an inability of these muscles to function? _____

_____

19. Many college students struggling through mountainous reading assignments are told that they need glasses for "eyestrain." Why is it more of a strain on the extrinsic and intrinsic eye muscles to look at close objects than at far objects?

_____

_____

The Ear and Hearing and Balance: Anatomy

20. Select the terms from column B that apply to the column A descriptions. Some terms are used more than once.

Column A	Column B
_____, _____	auditory (pharyngotympanic) tube
_____ 1. collectively called the ossicles	anvil (incus)
_____, _____	cochlea
2. ear structures involved with balance	endolymph
_____ 3. transmits sound vibrations to the ossicles	external acoustic meatus
_____ 4. three circular passages, each in a different plane of space	hammer (malleus)
_____ 5. transmits the vibratory motion of the stirrup to the fluid in the inner ear	oval window
_____ 6. passage between the throat and the tympanic cavity	perilymph
_____ 7. fluid contained within the membranous labyrinth	pinna
	round window
	semicircular canals
	stirrup (stapes)
	tympanic membrane
	vestibule

21. Identify all indicated structures and ear regions that are provided with leader lines or brackets in the following diagram.

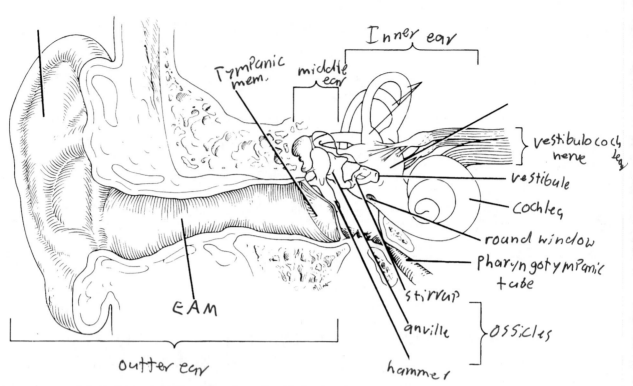

Inner ear

Tympanic mem.

middle ear

vestibulococh nerve

vestibule

cochlea

round window

Pharyngotympanic tube

stirrup

anville

ossicles

EAM

outter ear

hammer

22. Match the membranous labyrinth structures listed in column B with the descriptive statements in column A

Column A	Column B
_____ 1. contains the organ of Corti	ampulla
_____, _____ 2. sites of the maculae	basilar membrane
_____ 3. hair cells of organ of Corti rest on this membrane	cochlear duct
_____ 4. gel-like membrane overlying the hair cells of the organ of Corti	cochlear nerve
_____ 5. contains the cristae ampullaris	cupula
_____, _____,	otoliths
_____ 6. function in static equilibrium	semicircular ducts
_____, _____, _____,	tectorial membrane
_____ 7. function in dynamic equilibrium	vestibular nerve
_____ 8. carries auditory information to the brain	vestibular sacs
_____ 9. gelatinous cap overlying hair cells of the crista ampullaris	
_____ 10. grains of calcium carbonate in the maculae	

23. Describe how sounds of different frequency (pitch) are differentiated in the cochlea. _____

_____

_____

24. Explain the role of the endolymph of the semicircular canals in activating the receptors during angular motion.

_____

_____

_____

25. Explain the role of the otoliths in perception of static equilibrium (head position). _____

_____

_____

_____

Hearing and Balance Tests

26. Was the auditory acuity measurement made during the experiment the same or different for both ears?

_____ What factors might account for a difference in the acuity of the two ears?

_____

_____

27. During the sound localization experiment, in which position(s) was the sound least easily located?

_____

How can this observation be explained? _____

_____

28. When the tuning fork handle was pressed to your forehead during the Weber test, where did the sound seem to originate?

_____

Where did it seem to originate when one ear was plugged with cotton? _____

How do sound waves reach the cochlea when conduction deafness is present? _____

_____

29. The Rinne test evaluates an individual's ability to hear sounds conducted by air or bone. Which is typical of normal

hearing? _____

30. Define *nystagmus:* _____

_____

31. What is the usual reason for conducting the Romberg test? _____

_____

Was the degree of sway greater with the eyes open or closed? _____

Why? _____

_____

32. Normal balance, or equilibrium, depends on input from a number of sensory receptors. Name them.

_____

Chemical Senses: Localization and Anatomy of Olfactory and Taste Receptors

33. Describe the cellular makeup and the location of the olfactory epithelium. _____

_____

34. Name three sites where receptors for taste are found, and circle the predominant site:

_____, _____, and

_____

35. Describe the cellular makeup and arrangement of a taste bud. (Use a diagram, if helpful.)

_____

_____

Taste and Smell Experiments

36. Taste and smell receptors are both classified as _____ because they both respond to

_____

37. Why is it impossisble to taste substances with a dry tongue? _____

_____

38. Name three factors that influence our appreciation of foods. Substantiate each choice with an example from the laboratory experience.

1. _____ Substantiation _____

_____

_____

2. _____ Substantiation _____

_____

_____

3. _____ Substantiation _____

_____

_____

Expand on your explanation and choices by explaining why a cold, greasy hamburger is unappetizing to most people.

_____

_____

39. How palatable is food when you have a cold? _____

Explain. _____

_____

Special Senses: Olfaction and Taste

Objectives

1. To describe the location and cellular composition of the olfactory epithelium.
2. To describe the structure and function of the taste receptors.
3. To name the four basic qualities of taste sensation and list the chemical substances that elicit them.
4. To point out on a diagram of the tongue the predominant location of the basic types of taste receptors (salty, sweet, sour, bitter).
5. To explain the interdependence between the senses of smell and taste.
6. To name two factors other than olfaction that influence taste appreciation of foods.
7. To define *olfactory adaptation*.

Materials

- ❏ Prepared histologic slides: the tongue showing taste buds; nasal olfactory epithelium (longitudinal section)
- ❏ Compound microscope
- ❏ Small mirror
- ❏ Paper towels
- ❏ Granulated sugar
- ❏ Cotton-tipped swabs
- ❏ Disposable autoclave bag
- ❏ Paper cups; paper plates
- ❏ Prepared vials of 10% NaCl, 0.1% quinine or Epsom salt solution, 5% sucrose solution, and 1% acetic acid
- ❏ Beaker containing 10% bleach solution
- ❏ Prepared dropper bottles of oil of cloves, oil of peppermint, and oil of wintergreen or corresponding flavors found in the condiment section of a supermarket
- ❏ Equal-size food cubes of cheese, apple, raw potato, dried prunes, banana, raw carrot, and hard-cooked egg white (These prepared foods should be in an opaque container; a foil-lined egg carton would work well.)
- ❏ Chipped ice
- ❏ Absorbent cotton

The receptors for olfaction and taste are classified as **chemoreceptors** because they respond to chemicals or volatile substances in solution. Although four relatively specific types of taste receptors have been identified, the olfactory receptors are considered sensitive to a much wider range of chemical sensations. The sense of smell is the least understood of the special senses.

Localization and Anatomy of the Olfactory Receptors

The **olfactory epithelium** (organ of smell) occupies an area of about 2.5 cm in the roof of each nasal cavity (Figure 1a). Since the air entering the human nasal cavity must make a hairpin turn to enter the respiratory passages below, the nasal epithelium is in a rather poor position for performing its function. This is why sniffing, which brings more air into contact with the receptors, intensifies the sense of smell.

The specialized receptor cells in the olfactory epithelium are surrounded by **supporting cells,** nonsensory epithelial cells. The **olfactory receptor cells** are bipolar neurons whose **olfactory hairs** (actually cilia) extend outward from the epithelium. Axonal nerve fibers emerging from their basal ends penetrate the cribriform plate of the ethmoid bone and proceed as the *olfactory nerves* to synapse in the olfactory bulbs lying on either side of the crista galli of the ethmoid bone. Impulses from neurons of the olfactory bulbs are then conveyed to the olfactory portion of the cortex (uncus).

Activity:
Microscopic Examination of the Olfactory Epithelium

Obtain a longitudinal section of olfactory epithelium. Examine it closely, comparing it to Figure 1b. ■

From *Human Anatomy & Physiology Laboratory Manual*, **Main** Version, Fifth Edition, Elaine N. Marieb.

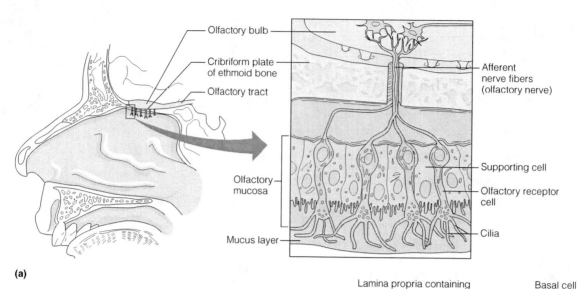

(a)

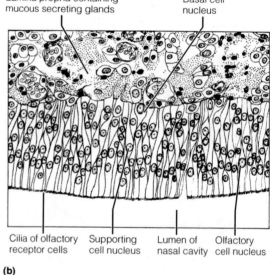

Lamina propria containing mucous secreting glands — Basal cell nucleus

Cilia of olfactory receptor cells — Supporting cell nucleus — Lumen of nasal cavity — Olfactory cell nucleus

(b)

Figure 1 Location and cellular composition of olfactory epithelium. (a) Diagrammatic representation. **(b)** Microscopic view. (See also Plate 17 in the Histology Atlas.)

Localization and Anatomy of Taste Buds

The **taste buds,** specific receptors for the sense of taste, are widely but not uniformly distributed in the oral cavity. Most are located on the dorsal surface of the tongue (as described next). A few are found on the soft palate, epiglottis, and inner surface of the cheeks.

The dorsal tongue surface is covered with small projections, or **papillae,** of three major types: sharp *filiform papillae* and the rounded *fungiform* and *circumvallate papillae.* The taste buds are located primarily on the sides of the circumvallate papillae (arranged in a V-formation on the posterior surface of the tongue) and on the more numerous fungiform papillae. The latter look rather like minute mushrooms and are widely distributed on the tongue. (See Figure 2.)

• Use a mirror to examine your tongue. Can you pick out the various papillae types?

_____ If so, which? _____

_____

Each taste bud consists largely of a globular arrangement of two types of modified epithelial cells: the **gustatory,** or **taste cells,** which are the actual receptor cells, and **supporting cells.** Several nerve fibers enter each taste bud and supply sensory nerve endings to each of the taste cells. The long microvilli of the receptor cells penetrate the epithelial surface through an opening called the **taste pore.** When these microvilli, called **gustatory hairs,** contact specific chemicals in the solution, the taste cells depolarize. The afferent fibers from the taste buds to the sensory cortex in the postcentral gyrus of the brain are carried in three cranial nerves: the *facial nerve (VII)* serves the anterior two-thirds of the tongue; the *glossopharyngeal nerve (IX)* serves the posterior third of the tongue; and the *vagus nerve (X)* carries a few fibers from the pharyngeal region.

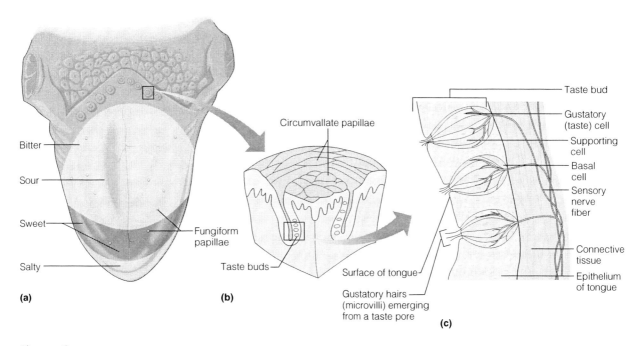

Figure 2 **Location and structure of taste buds.** **(a)** Taste buds on the tongue are associated with papillae, projections of the tongue mucosa. **(b)** A sectioned circumvallate papilla shows the position of the taste buds in its lateral walls. **(c)** An enlarged view of three taste buds. See also Plate 16 in the Histology Atlas.

Activity:
Microscopic Examination of Taste Buds

Obtain a microscope and a prepared slide of a tongue cross section. Use Figure 2b and Plate 16 in the Histology Atlas as guides to aid you in locating the taste buds on the tongue papillae. Make a detailed study of one taste bud. Identify the taste pore and gustatory hairs if observed. ■

Laboratory Experiments

Activity:
Stimulating Taste Buds

1. Obtain several paper towels and a disposable autoclave bag and bring them to your bench.

2. With a paper towel, dry the dorsal surface of your tongue.

⚠ Immediately dispose of the paper towel in the autoclave bag.

3. Place a few sugar crystals on your dried tongue. Do *not* close your mouth. Time how long it takes to taste the sugar.

_____ sec

Why couldn't you taste the sugar immediately?

_____ ■

Activity:
Plotting Taste Bud Distribution

When taste is tested with pure chemical compounds, most taste sensations can be grouped into one of four basic qualities—sweet, sour, bitter, or salty. Although all taste buds are believed to respond in some degree to all four classes of chemical stimuli, each type responds optimally to only one. This characteristic makes it possible to map the tongue to show the relative density of each type of taste bud.

The *sweet receptors* respond to a number of seemingly unrelated compounds such as sugars (fructose, sucrose, glucose), saccharine, and some amino acids. Some believe the common factor is the hydroxyl (OH^-) group. *Sour receptors* respond to hydrogen ions (H^+) or the acidity of the solution, *bitter receptors* to alkaloids, and *salty receptors* to metallic ions in solution.

1. Prepare to make a taste sensation map of your lab partner's tongue by obtaining the following: cotton-tipped swabs; one vial each of NaCl, quinine or Epsom salt solution, sucrose solution, and acetic acid; paper cups; and a flask of distilled or tap water.

2. Before each test, the subject should rinse his or her mouth thoroughly with water and lightly dry his or her tongue with a paper towel.

⚠ Dispose of used paper towels in the autoclave bag.

3. Generously moisten a swab with 5% sucrose solution and touch it to the center, back, tip, and sides of the dorsal surface of the subject's tongue.

4. Map, with O's on the tongue outline below, the location of the sweet receptors.

⚠ Put the used swab in the autoclave bag. Do not redip the swab into the sucrose solution.

5. Repeat the procedure with quinine (or Epsom salt solution) to map the location of the bitter receptors (use the symbol B), with NaCl to map the salt receptors (symbol +), and with acetic acid to map the sour receptors (symbol −).

⚠ *Use a fresh swab for each test,* and properly dispose of the swabs immediately after use.

What area of the tongue dorsum seems to lack taste receptors?

_____

How closely does your localization of the different taste receptors coincide with the information in your textbook?

_____

_____ ■

Activity:
Examining the Combined Effects of Smell, Texture, and Temperature on Taste

Effects of Smell and Texture

1. Ask the subject to sit with eyes closed and to pinch his or her nostrils shut.

2. Using a paper plate, obtain samples of the food items listed in the chart below. At no time should the subject be allowed to see the foods being tested.

3. Use an out-of-sequence order of food testing. For each test, place a cube of food in the subject's mouth and ask him or her to identify the food by using the following sequence of activities:

• First, manipulate the food with the tongue.

• Second, chew the food.

• Third, if a positive identification is not made with the first two techniques and the taste sense, ask the subject to release the pinched nostrils and to continue chewing with the nostrils open to determine if a positive identification can be made.

Record the results on the chart by checking the appropriate column.

Was the sense of smell equally important in all cases?

_____

Where did it seem to be important and why?

_____

_____ ■

Chart 1	Method of Identification			
Food	Texture only	Chewing with nostrils pinched	Chewing with nostrils open	Identification not made
Cheese	_____	_____	_____	_____
Apple	_____	_____	_____	_____
Raw potato	_____	_____	_____	_____
Banana	_____	_____	_____	_____
Dried prunes	_____	_____	_____	_____
Raw carrot	_____	_____	_____	_____
Hard-cooked egg white	_____	_____	_____	_____

Effect of Olfactory Stimulation

There is no question that what is commonly referred to as taste depends heavily on stimulation of the olfactory receptors, particularly in the case of strongly odoriferous substances. The following experiment should illustrate this fact.

1. Obtain vials of oil of wintergreen, peppermint, and cloves and some fresh cotton-tipped swabs. Ask the subject to sit so that he or she cannot see which vial is being used, and to dry the tongue and close the nostrils.

2. Apply a drop of one of the oils to the subject's tongue. Can he or she distinguish the flavor?

_____

3. Have the subject open the nostrils, and record the change in sensation he or she reports.

_____

4. Have the subject rinse the mouth well and dry the tongue.

5. Prepare two swabs, each with one of the two remaining oils.

6. Hold one swab under the subject's open nostrils, while touching the second swab to the tongue.

Record the reported sensations. _____

_____

_____

_____

7. ⚠ Dispose of the used swabs and paper towels in the autoclave bag before continuing.

Which sense, taste or smell, appears to be more important in the proper identification of a strongly flavored volatile substance?

_____

Effect of Temperature

In addition to the effect that olfaction and food texture play in determining our taste sensations, the temperature of foods also helps determine if the food is appreciated or even tasted. To illustrate this, have your partner hold some chipped ice on the tongue for approximately a minute and then close his or her eyes. Immediately place any of the foods previously identified in his or her mouth and ask for an identification.

Results? _____

_____

_____ ■

Activity:
Demonstrating Olfactory Adaptation

Obtain some absorbent cotton and two of the following oils (oil of wintergreen, peppermint, or cloves). Press one nostril shut. Hold the bottle of oil under the open nostril and exhale through the mouth. Record the time required for the odor to disappear (for olfactory adaptation to occur).

_____ sec

Repeat the procedure with the other nostril.

_____ sec

Immediately test another oil with the nostril that has just experienced olfactory adaptation. What are the results?

_____

_____

What conclusions can you draw? _____

_____

_____ ■

Illustrations: 1 and 2: Precision Graphics.

Special Senses: Olfaction and Taste

Localization and Anatomy of Taste Buds

1. Name three sites where receptors for taste are found, and circle the predominant site:

    _____ , _____ , and

    _____

2. Describe the cellular makeup and arrangement of a taste bud. (Use a diagram, if helpful.) _____

    _____

Localization and Anatomy of the Olfactory Receptors

1. Describe the cellular composition and the location of the olfactory epithelium. _____

    _____

    _____

2. How and why does sniffing improve your sense of smell? _____

    _____

Laboratory Experiments

1. Taste and smell receptors are both classified as _____, because they both

    respond to _____

2. Why is it impossible to taste substances with a dry tongue? _____

    _____

3. State the most important sites of the taste-specific receptors, as determined during the plotting exercise in the laboratory:

    salt _____   sour _____

    bitter _____   sweet _____

4. The basic taste sensations are elicited by specific chemical substances or groups. Name them:

    salt _____   sour _____

    bitter _____   sweet _____

Review Sheet

5. Name three factors that influence our appreciation of foods. Substantiate each choice with an example from the laboratory experience.

_____   Substantiation _____

_____

_____

_____   Substantiation _____

_____

_____

_____   Substantiation _____

_____

_____

Which of the factors chosen is most important? _____

Substantiate your choice with an example from everyday life. _____

_____

Expand on your explanation and choices by explaining why a cold, greasy hamburger is unappetizing to most people.

_____

_____

6. Babies tend to favor bland foods, whereas adults tend to like highly seasoned foods. What is the basis for this phenomenon?

_____

_____

7. How palatable is food when you have a cold? _____

Explain. _____

_____

8. What is the mechanism of olfactory adaptation? _____

_____

_____

In your opinion, is olfactory adaptation desirable? _____ Explain your answer.

_____

_____

Special Senses: Vision

Objectives

1. To describe the structure and function of the accessory visual structures.
2. To identify the structural components of the eye when provided with a model, an appropriate diagram, or a preserved sheep or cow eye, and list the function(s) of each.
3. To describe the cellular makeup of the retina.
4. To discuss the mechanism of image formation on the retina.
5. To trace the visual pathway to the optic cortex and indicate the effects of damage to various parts of this pathway.
6. To define the following terms:

refraction	*myopia*
accommodation	*hyperopia*
convergence	*cataract*
astigmatism	*glaucoma*
emmetropia	*conjunctivitis*

7. To discuss the importance of the pupillary and convergence reflexes.
8. To explain the difference between rods and cones with respect to visual perception and retinal localization.
9. To state the importance of an ophthalmoscopic examination.

Materials

- ❏ Dissectible eye model
- ❏ Chart of eye anatomy
- ❏ Preserved cow or sheep eye
- ❏ Dissecting pan and instruments
- ❏ Protective skin cream or disposable gloves

- ❏ Histologic section of an eye showing retinal layers
- ❏ Compound microscope

- ❏ Common straight pins
- ❏ Snellen eye chart (floor marked with chalk to indicate 20-ft distance from posted Snellen chart)
- ❏ Ishihara's color-blindness plates

- ❏ 1-inch-diameter discs of colored paper (white, red, blue, green)
- ❏ White, red, blue, and green chalk
- ❏ Metric ruler; meter stick
- ❏ Test tubes
- ❏ Laboratory lamp or penlight
- ❏ Ophthalmoscope

See Appendix C, Exercise 24 for links to A.D.A.M. Interactive Anatomy.

Anatomy of the Eye

External Anatomy and Accessory Structures

The adult human eye is a sphere measuring about 2.5 cm (1 inch) in diameter. Only about one-sixth of the eye's anterior surface is observable (Figure 1); the remainder is enclosed and protected by a cushion of fat and the walls of the bony orbit.

The **lacrimal apparatus** consists of the **lacrimal gland, lacrimal canals, lacrimal sac,** and the **nasolacrimal duct.** The lacrimal glands are situated superior to the lateral aspect of each eye. They continually liberate a dilute salt solution (tears) that flows onto the anterior surface of the eyeball through several small ducts. The tears flush across the eyeball into the lacrimal canals medially, then into the lacrimal sac, and finally into the nasolacrimal duct, which empties into the nasal cavity. The lacrimal secretion also contains **lysozyme,** an antibacterial enzyme. Because it constantly flushes the eyeball, the lacrimal fluid cleanses and protects the eye surface as it moistens and lubricates it. As we age, our eyes tend to become dry due to decreased lacrimation, and thus are more vulnerable to bacterial invasion and irritation.

The anterior surface of each eye is protected by the **eyelids,** or **palpebrae.** (See Figure 1.) The medial and lateral junctions of the upper and lower eyelids are referred to as the **medial** and **lateral canthus** (respectively). The **caruncle,** a fleshy elevation at the medial canthus, produces a whitish oily secretion. A mucous membrane, the **conjunctiva,** lines the internal surface of the eyelids (as the *palpebral conjunctiva*) and continues over the anterior surface of the eyeball to its junction with the corneal epithelium (as the *ocular,* or *bulbar, conjunctiva*). The conjunctiva secretes mucus, which aids in lubricating the eyeball. Inflammation of the conjunctiva, often accompanied by redness of the eye, is called **conjunctivitis.**

From *Human Anatomy & Physiology Laboratory Manual*, Main Version, Fifth Edition, Elaine N. Marieb.

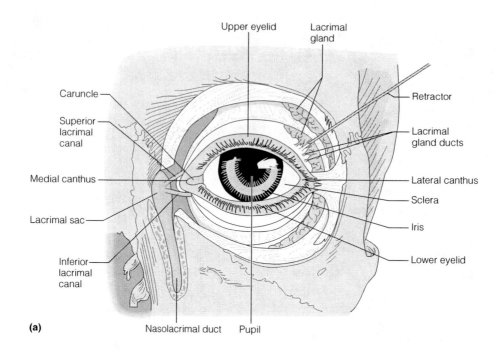

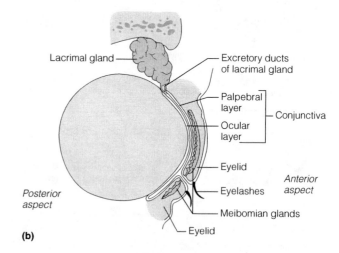

**Figure 1   External anatomy of
the eye and accessory structures.**
(a) Anterior view. (b) Sagittal section.

Projecting from the border of each eyelid is a row of short hairs, the **eyelashes.** The **ciliary glands,** modified sweat glands, lie between the eyelash hair follicles and help lubricate the eyeball. An inflammation of one of these glands is called a **sty.** Small sebaceous glands associated with the hair follicles and the larger **meibomian glands,** located posterior to the eyelashes, secrete an oily substance.

Six **extrinsic eye muscles** attached to the exterior surface of each eyeball control eye movement and make it possible for the eye to follow a moving object. The names and positioning of these extrinsic muscles are noted in Figure 2. Their actions are given in the chart accompanying that figure.

A c t i v i t y :
Identifying Accessory Eye Structures

Observe the eyes of another student and identify as many of the accessory structures as possible. Ask the student to look to the left. What extrinsic eye muscles are responsible for this action?

Right eye _____

Left eye _____ ■

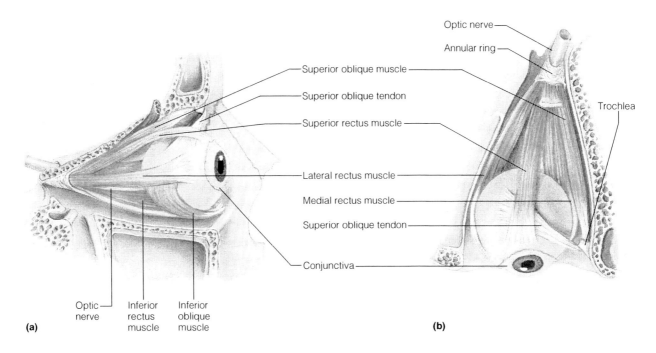

Figure 2 **Extrinsic muscles of the eye. (a)** Lateral view of the right eye. **(b)** Superior view of right eye. **(c)** Summary of actions of the extrinsic eye muscles, and cranial nerves that control them.

Internal Anatomy of the Eye

Anatomically, the wall of the eye is constructed of three tunics, or coats. The outermost **fibrous tunic** is a protective layer composed of dense avascular connective tissue. It has two obviously different regions: The opaque white **sclera** forms the bulk of the fibrous tunic and is observable anteriorly as the "white of the eye." Its anteriormost portion is modified structurally to form the transparent **cornea,** through which light enters the eye. (See Figure 3.)

The middle tunic, called the **uvea,** is the **vascular tunic.** Its posteriormost part, the **choroid,** is a richly vascular nutritive layer containing a dark pigment that prevents light scattering within the eye. Anteriorly, the choroid is modified to form the **ciliary body,** to which the lens is attached, and then

the pigmented **iris.** The iris is incomplete, resulting in a rounded opening, the **pupil,** through which light passes.

The iris is composed of circularly and radially arranged smooth muscle fibers and acts as a reflexively activated diaphragm to regulate the amount of light entering the eye. In close vision and bright light, the circular muscles of the iris contract, and the pupil constricts. In distant vision and in dim light, the radial fibers contract, enlarging (dilating) the pupil and allowing more light to enter the eye.

The innermost **sensory tunic** of the eye is the delicate, two-layered **retina.** The outer **pigmented epithelial layer** abuts and lines the entire uvea. The transparent inner **neural (nervous) layer** extends anteriorly only to the ciliary body. It contains the photoreceptors, **rods** and **cones,** which begin the chain of electrical events that ultimately result in the

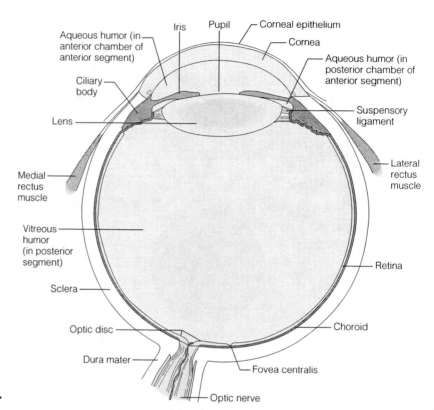

Figure 3 Internal anatomy of the eye (transverse section).

transduction of light energy into nerve impulses that are transmitted to the optic cortex of the brain. Vision is the result. The photoreceptor cells are distributed over the entire neural retina, except where the optic nerve leaves the eyeball. This site is called the **optic disc,** or blind spot. Lateral to each blind spot, and directly posterior to the lens, is an area called the **macula lutea** (yellow spot), an area of high cone density. In its center is the **fovea centralis,** a minute pit about ½ mm in diameter, which contains only cones and is the area of greatest visual acuity. Focusing for discriminative vision occurs in the fovea centralis.

Light entering the eye is focused on the retina by the **lens,** a flexible crystalline structure held vertically in the eye's interior by the **suspensory ligament** attached to the ciliary body. Activity of the ciliary muscle, which accounts for the bulk of ciliary body tissue, changes lens thickness to allow light to be properly focused on the retina.

In the elderly the lens becomes increasingly hard and opaque. **Cataracts,** which often result from this process, cause vision to become hazy or entirely obstructed. ∎

The lens divides the eye into two segments: the **anterior segment** anterior to the lens, which contains a clear watery fluid called the **aqueous humor,** and the **posterior segment** behind the lens, filled with a gel-like substance, the **vitreous humor,** or **vitreous body.** The anterior segment is further divided into anterior and **posterior chambers,** located before and after the iris, respectively. The aqueous humor is continually formed by the capillaries of the **ciliary processes** of the ciliary body. It helps to maintain the intraocular pressure of the eye and provides nutrients for the avascular lens and cornea. The aqueous humor is reabsorbed into the **scleral venous sinus (canal of Schlemm).** The vitreous humor provides the major internal reinforcement of the posterior part of the eyeball, and helps to keep the neural layer of the retina pressed firmly against the wall of the eyeball. It is formed *only* before birth.

Anything that interferes with drainage of the aqueous fluid increases intraocular pressure. When intraocular pressure reaches dangerously high levels, the retina and optic nerve are compressed, resulting in pain and possible blindness, a condition called **glaucoma.** ∎

Activity:
Identifying Internal Structures of the Eye

Obtain a dissectible eye model and identify its internal structures described above. As you work, also refer to Figure 3. ∎

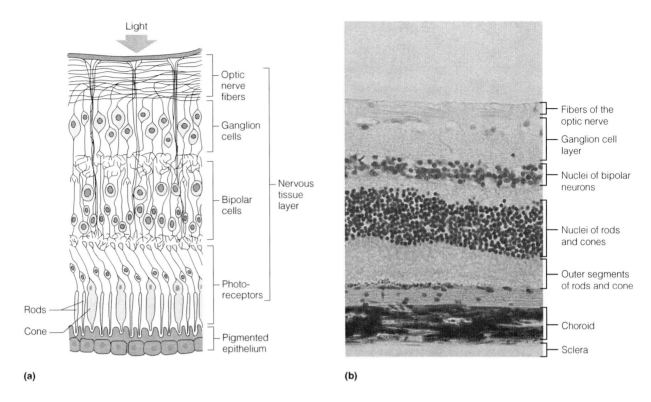

Light

— Optic nerve fibers

— Ganglion cells

— Nervous tissue layer

— Bipolar cells

— Photo-receptors

Rods —

Cone —

— Pigmented epithelium

(a)

— Fibers of the optic nerve

— Ganglion cell layer

— Nuclei of bipolar neurons

— Nuclei of rods and cones

— Outer segments of rods and cone

— Choroid

— Sclera

(b)

Figure 4   Microscopic anatomy of the cellular layers of the retina.
(a) Diagrammatic view. **(b)** Photomicrograph of the retina (1092X).

Microscopic Anatomy of the Retina

As described above, the retina consists of two main types of cells: a pigmented *epithelial* layer, which abuts the choroid, and an inner cell layer composed of *neurons,* which is in contact with the vitreous humor (Figure 4). The inner nervous layer is composed of three major neuronal populations. These are, from outer to inner aspect, the **photoreceptors** (rods and cones), the **bipolar cells,** and the **ganglion cells.**

The **rods** are the specialized receptors for dim light. Visual interpretation of their activity is in gray tones. The **cones** are color receptors that permit high levels of visual acuity, but they function only under conditions of high light intensity; thus, for example, no color vision is possible in moonlight. Only cones are found in the fovea centralis, and their number decreases as the retinal periphery is approached. By contrast, rods are most numerous in the periphery, and their density decreases as the macula is approached.

Light must pass through the ganglion cell layer and the bipolar neuron layer to reach and excite the rods and cones. As a result of a light stimulus, the photoreceptors undergo changes in their membrane potential that ultimately influence the bipolar neurons. These in turn stimulate the ganglion cells, whose axons leave the retina in the tight bundle of fibers known as the optic nerve. The retinal layer is thickest where the optic nerve attaches to the eyeball because an in-creasing number of ganglion cell axons converge at this point. It thins as it approaches the ciliary body.

Activity:
Studying the Microscopic Anatomy of the Retina

Obtain a histologic slide of a longitudinal section of the eye. Identify the retinal layers by comparing your view to Figure 4. ■

Visual Pathways to the Brain

The axons of the ganglion cells of the retina converge at the posterior aspect of the eyeball and exit from the eye as the optic nerve. At the **optic chiasma,** the fibers from the medial side of each eye cross over to the opposite side. The fiber tracts thus formed are called the **optic tracts.** Each optic tract contains fibers from the lateral side of the eye on the same side and from the medial side of the opposite eye.

The optic tract fibers synapse with neurons in the **lateral geniculate nucleus** of the thalamus, whose axons form the **optic radiation,** terminating in the **optic,** or **visual, cortex** in the occipital lobe of the brain. Here they synapse with the cortical cells, and visual interpretation occurs.

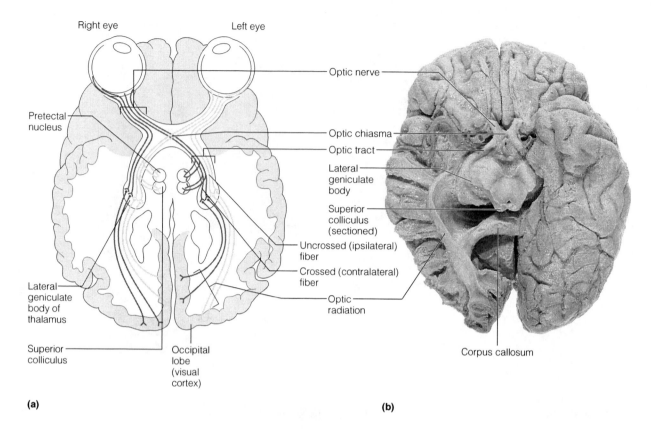

Right eye   Left eye

Optic nerve

Pretectal nucleus

Optic chiasma
Optic tract
Lateral geniculate body
Superior colliculus (sectioned)

Uncrossed (ipsilateral) fiber
Crossed (contralateral) fiber
Optic radiation

Lateral geniculate body of thalamus

Superior colliculus

Occipital lobe (visual cortex)

Corpus callosum

(a)

(b)

Figure 5   Visual pathway to the brain. (a) Diagram. (Note that fibers from the lateral portion of each retinal field do not cross at the optic chiasma.) **(b)** Photograph.

Activity:
Predicting the Effects of Visual Pathway Lesions

After examining Figure 5, determine what effects lesions in the following areas would have on vision:

In the right optic nerve _____

_____

Through the optic chiasma _____

_____

In the left optic tract _____

_____

In the right cerebral cortex (visual area) _____

_____

Dissection:
The Cow (Sheep) Eye

1.   Obtain a preserved cow or sheep eye, dissecting instruments, and a dissecting pan. Apply protective skin cream or don disposable gloves if desired.

2.   Examine the external surface of the eye, noting the thick cushion of adipose tissue. Identify the optic nerve (cranial nerve II) as it leaves the eyeball, the remnants of the extrinsic eye muscles, the conjunctiva, the sclera, and the cornea. The normally transparent cornea is opalescent or opaque if the eye has been preserved. Refer to Figure 6 as you work.

3.   Trim away most of the fat and connective tissue, but leave the optic nerve intact. Holding the eye with the cornea facing downward, carefully make an incision with a sharp scalpel into the sclera about ¼ inch above the cornea. (The sclera of the preserved eyeball is *very* tough so you will have to apply substantial pressure to penetrate it.) Using scissors, complete the incision around the circumference of the eyeball paralleling the corneal edge.

4.   Carefully lift the anterior part of the eyeball away from the posterior portion. Conditions being proper, the vitreous body should remain with the posterior part of the eyeball.

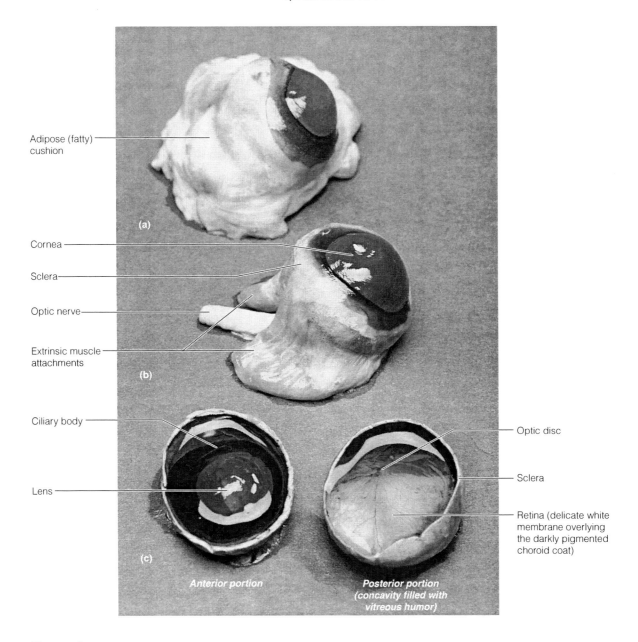

Figure 6   Anatomy of the cow eye. (a) Cow eye (entire) removed from orbit (notice the large amount of fat cushioning the eyeball). **(b)** Cow eye (entire) with fat removed to show the extrinsic muscle attachments and optic nerve. **(c)** Cow eye cut along the coronal plane to reveal internal structures.

5.   Examine the anterior part of the eye and identify the following structures:

Ciliary body: Black pigmented body that appears to be a halo encircling the lens.

Lens: Biconvex structure that is opaque in preserved specimens.

Suspensory ligament: A halo of delicate fibers attaching the lens to the ciliary body.

Carefully remove the lens and identify the adjacent structures:

Iris: Anterior continuation of the ciliary body penetrated by the pupil.

Cornea: More convex anteriormost portion of the sclera; normally transparent but cloudy in preserved specimens.

6.   Examine the posterior portion of the eyeball. Remove the vitreous humor, and identify the following structures:

Retina: The neural layer of the retina appears as a delicate white, probably crumpled membrane that separates easily from the pigmented choroid.

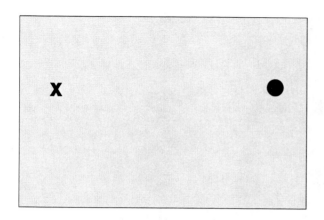

Figure 7 Blind spot test figure.

Note its point of attachment. What is this point called?

_____

Pigmented choroid coat: Appears iridescent in the cow or sheep eye owing to a special reflecting surface called the **tapetum lucidum.** This specialized surface reflects the light within the eye and is found in the eyes of animals that live under conditions of low-intensity light. It is not found in humans. ■

Visual Tests and Experiments
The Blind Spot

Activity:
Demonstrating the Blind Spot

1. Hold Figure 7 about 18 inches from your eyes. Close your left eye, and focus your right eye on the X, which should be positioned so that it is directly in line with your right eye. Move the figure slowly toward your face, keeping your right eye focused on the X. When the dot focuses on the blind spot, which lacks photoreceptors, it will disappear.

2. Have your laboratory partner record in metric units the distance at which this occurs. The dot will reappear as the figure is moved closer. Distance at which the dot disappears:

Right eye _____

Repeat the test for the left eye, this time closing the right eye and focusing the left eye on the dot. Record the distance at which the X disappears:

Left eye _____ ■

Afterimages

When light from an object strikes **rhodopsin,** the purple pigment contained in the rods of the retina, it triggers a photo-

chemical reaction that splits rhodopsin into its colorless precursor molecules (vitamin A and a protein called opsin). This event, called *bleaching of the pigment,* initiates a chain of events leading to impulse transmission along fibers of the optic nerve. Once bleaching has occurred in a rod, the photoreceptor pigment must be resynthesized before the rod can be restimulated. This takes a certain period of time. Both phenomena—that is, the stimulation of the photoreceptor cells and their subsequent inactive period—can be demonstrated indirectly in terms of positive and negative afterimages.

Activity:
Demonstrating Afterimages

1. Stare at a bright lightbulb for a few seconds, and then gently close your eyes for approximately 1 minute.

2. Record, in sequence of occurrence, what you "saw" after closing your eyes:

_____

_____

_____

The bright image of the lightbulb initially seen was a **positive afterimage** caused by the continued firing of the rods. The dark image of the lightbulb that subsequently appeared against a lighter background was the **negative afterimage,** an indication that the rhodopsin in the affected photoreceptor cells had been bleached. ■

Refraction, Visual Acuity, and Astigmatism

When light rays pass from one medium to another, their velocity, or speed of transmission, changes, and the rays are bent or **refracted.** Thus the light rays in the visual field are refracted as they encounter the cornea, lens, and vitreous humor of the eye.

The refractive index (bending power) of the cornea and vitreous humor are constant. But the lens's refractive index, or strength, can be varied by changing the lens's shape—that is, by making it more or less convex so that the light is properly converged and focused on the retina. The greater the lens convexity, or bulge, the more the light will be bent and the stronger the lens. Conversely, the less the lens convexity (the flatter it is), the less it bends the light.

In general, light from a distant source (over 20 feet) approaches the eye as parallel rays, and no change in lens convexity is necessary for it to focus properly on the retina. However, light from a close source tends to diverge, and the convexity of the lens must increase to make close vision possible. To achieve this, the ciliary muscle contracts, decreasing the tension on the suspensory ligament attached to the lens and allowing the elastic lens to "round up." Thus, a lens capable of bringing a *close* object into sharp focus is stronger (more convex) than a lens focusing on a more distant object. The ability of the eye to focus differentially for objects of near vision (less than 20 feet) is called **accommodation.** It should be noted that the image formed on the retina as a re-

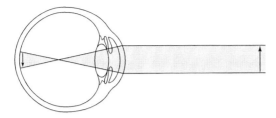

Figure 8 Refraction of light in the eye, resulting in the production of a real image on the retina.

sult of the refractory activity of the lens (see Figure 8) is a **real image** (reversed from left to right, inverted, and smaller than the object).

The normal or **emmetropic eye** is able to accommodate properly. However, visual problems may result from (1) lenses that are too strong or too "lazy" (overconverging and underconverging, respectively), (2) from structural problems such as an eyeball that is too long or too short to provide for proper focusing by the lens, or (3) a cornea or lens with improper curvatures.

Individuals in whom the image normally focuses in front of the retina are said to have **myopia,** or "near-sightedness" (Figure 9a); they can see close objects without difficulty, but distant objects are blurred or seen indistinctly. Correction requires a concave lens, which causes the light reaching the eye to diverge (Figure 9b).

If the image focuses behind the retina, the individual is said to have **hyperopia** or farsightedness. Such persons have no problems with distant vision but need glasses with convex lenses to augment the converging power of the lens for close vision (Figure 9c and d).

Irregularities in the curvatures of the lens and/or the cornea lead to a blurred vision problem called **astigmatism.** Cylindrically ground lenses, which compensate for inequalities in the curvatures of the refracting surfaces, are prescribed to correct the condition. ■

Near-Point Accommodation The elasticity of the lens decreases dramatically with age, resulting in difficulty in focusing for near or close vision. This condition is called **presbyopia**— literally, old vision. Lens elasticity can be tested by measuring the **near point of accommodation.** The near point of vision is about 10 cm from the eye in young adults. It is closer in children and farther in old age.

Activity:
Determining Near Point of Accommodation

To determine your near point of accommodation, hold a common straight pin at arm's length in front of one eye. Slowly move the pin toward that eye until the pin image becomes distorted. Have your lab partner measure the distance from your eye to the pin at this point, and record the distance below. Repeat the procedure for the other eye.

Near point for right eye _____

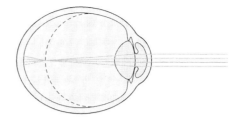

(a) Myopic eye (nearsighted)

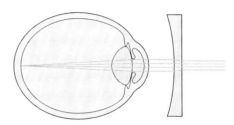

(b) Concave lens

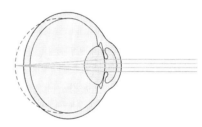

(c) Hyperopic eye (farsighted)

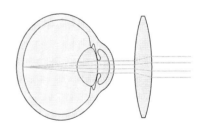

(d) Convex lens

Figure 9 Common refraction problems and their correction. In myopia: **(a)** light from a distant object focuses in front of the retina, and **(b)** correction involves the use of a concave lens that diverges the light before it enters the eye. In hyperopia: **(c)** light from a distant object focuses behind the retina, and **(d)** correction requires a convex lens that converges the light rays before they enter the eye.

Near point for left eye _____ ■

Visual Acuity **Visual acuity,** or sharpness of vision, is generally tested with a Snellen eye chart, which consists of letters of various sizes printed on a white card. This test is based on the fact that letters of a certain size can be seen clearly by

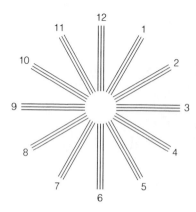

Figure 10 Astigmatism testing chart.

eyes with normal vision at a specific distance. The distance at which the normal, or emmetropic, eye can read a line of letters is printed at the end of that line.

Activity:
Testing Visual Acuity

1.   Have your partner stand 20 feet from the posted Snellen eye chart and cover one eye with a card or hand. As your partner reads each consecutive line aloud, check for accuracy. If this individual wears glasses, give the test twice—first with glasses off and then with glasses on.

2.   Record the number of the line with the smallest-sized letters read. If it is 20/20, the person's vision for that eye is normal. If it is 20/40, or any ratio with a value less than one, he or she has less than the normal visual acuity. (Such an individual is myopic.) If the visual acuity is 20/15, vision is better than normal, because this person can stand at 20 feet from the chart and read letters that are only discernible by the normal eye at 15 feet. Give your partner the number of the line corresponding to the smallest letters read, to record in step 4.

3.   Repeat the process for the other eye.

4.   Have your partner test and record your visual acuity. If you wear glasses, the test results *without* glasses should be recorded first.

Visual acuity, right eye _____

Visual acuity, left eye _____ ■

Activity:
Testing for Astigmatism

The astigmatism chart (Figure 10) is designed to test for defects in the refracting surface of the lens and/or cornea.

   View the chart first with one eye and then with the other, focusing on the center of the chart. If all the radiating lines appear equally dark and distinct, there is no distortion of your refracting surfaces. If some of the lines are blurred or appear less dark than others, at least some degree of astigmatism is present.

Is astigmatism present in your left eye? _____

Right eye? _____ ■

Color Blindness

Ishihara's color plates are designed to test for deficiencies in the cones or color photoreceptor cells. There are three cone types, each containing a different light-absorbing pigment. One type primarily absorbs the red wavelengths of the visible light spectrum, another the blue wavelengths, and a third the green wavelengths. Nerve impulses reaching the brain from these different photoreceptor types are then interpreted (seen) as red, blue, and green, respectively. Interpretation of the intermediate colors of the visible light spectrum is a result of overlapping input from more than one cone type.

Activity:
Testing for Color Blindness

1.   View the color plates in bright light or sunlight while holding them about 30 inches away and at right angles to your line of vision. Report to your laboratory partner what you see in each plate. Take no more than 3 seconds for each decision.

2.   Your partner is to write down your responses and then check their accuracy with the correct answers provided in the color plate book. Is there any indication that you have some degree of color blindness?

_____ If so, what type? _____

_____

Repeat the procedure to test your partner's color vision. ■

Relative Positioning of Rods and Cones on the Retina

The test subject for this demonstration should have shown no color vision problems during the test for color blindness. Students may work in pairs, or two students may perform the test for the entire class. White, red, blue, and green paper discs and chalk will be needed for this demonstration.

Activity:
Mapping the Rods and Cones

1.   Position the subject about 1 foot away from the blackboard.

2.   Make a small white chalk circle on the board immediately in front of the subject's right eye. Have the subject close the left eye and stare fixedly at the circle with the right eye throughout the test.

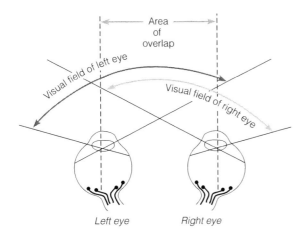

Figure 11 Overlapping of the visual fields.

3. To map the extent of the rod field, begin to move a white paper disc into the field of vision from various sides of the visual field (beginning at least 2 feet away from the white chalk circle) and plot with white chalk dots the points at which the disc first becomes visible to the test subject.

4. Repeat the procedure, using red, green, and blue paper discs and like-colored chalk to map the cone fields. Color (not object) identification is required.

5. After the test has been completed for all four discs, connect all dots of the same color. It should become apparent that each of the color fields has a different radius and that the rod and cone distribution on the retina is not uniform. (Normal fields have white outermost, followed by blue, red, and green as the fovea is approached.)

6. Record the rod and cone color field distribution observed in the laboratory review section using appropriately colored pencils. ■

Binocular Vision

Humans, cats, predatory birds, and most primates are endowed with **binocular** (two-eyed) **vision.** Although both eyes look in approximately the same direction, they see slightly different views. Their visual fields, each about 170 degrees, overlap to a considerable extent; thus there is two-eyed vision at the overlap area (Figure 11).

In contrast, the eyes of many animals (rabbits, pigeons, and others) are more on the sides of their head. Such animals see in two different directions and thus have a panoramic field of view and **panoramic vision.**

Although both types of vision have their good points, binocular vision provides three-dimensional vision and an accurate means of locating objects in space. The slight differ-

ences between the views seen by the two eyes are fused by the higher centers of the visual cortex to give us *depth perception.* Because of the manner in which the visual cortex resolves these two different views into a single image, it is sometimes referred to as the "cyclopean eye of the binocular animal."

A c t i v i t y :
Tests for Binocular Vision

1. To demonstrate that a slightly different view is seen by each eye, perform the following simple experiment.

Close your left eye. Hold a pencil at arm's length directly in front of your right eye. Position another pencil directly beneath it and then move the lower pencil about half the distance toward you. As you move the lower pencil, make sure it remains in the *same plane* as the stationary pencil, so that the two pencils continually form a straight line. Then, without moving the pencils, close your right eye and open your left eye. Notice that with only the right eye open, the moving pencil stays in the same plane as the fixed pencil, but that when viewed with the left eye, the moving pencil is displaced laterally away from the plane of the fixed pencil.

2. To demonstrate the importance of two-eyed binocular vision for depth perception, perform this second simple experiment.

Have your laboratory partner hold a test tube erect about arm's length in front of you. With both eyes open, quickly insert a pencil into the test tube. Remove the pencil, bring it back close to your body, close one eye, and quickly and without hesitation insert the pencil into the test tube. (Do not feel for the test tube with the pencil!) Repeat with the other eye closed.

Was it as easy to dunk the pencil with one eye closed as with both eyes open?

_____ ■

Eye Reflexes

Both intrinsic (internal) and extrinsic (external) muscles are necessary for proper eye functioning. The *intrinsic muscles,* controlled by the autonomic nervous system, are those of the ciliary body (which alters the lens curvature in focusing) and the radial and circular muscles of the iris (which control pupillary size and thus regulate the amount of light entering the eye). The *extrinsic muscles* are the rectus and oblique muscles, which are attached to the eyeball exterior (see Figure 1). These muscles control eye movement and make it possible to keep moving objects focused on the fovea centralis. They are also responsible for **convergence,** or medial eye movements, which is essential for near vision. When convergence occurs, both eyes are directed toward the near object viewed. The extrinsic eye muscles are controlled by the somatic nervous system.

Activity:
Demonstrating Reflex Activity of Intrinsic and Extrinsic Eye Muscles

Involuntary activity of both the intrinsic and extrinsic muscle types is brought about by reflex actions that can be observed in the following experiments.

Photopupillary Reflex

Sudden illumination of the retina by a bright light causes the pupil to constrict reflexively in direct proportion to the light intensity. This protective response prevents damage to the delicate photoreceptor cells.

Obtain a laboratory lamp or penlight. Have your laboratory partner sit with eyes closed and hands over his or her eyes. Turn on the light and position it so that it shines on the subject's right hand. After 1 minute, ask your partner to uncover and open the right eye. Quickly observe the pupil of that eye. What happens to the pupil?

_____

Shut off the light and ask your partner to uncover and open the opposite eye. What are your observations?

_____

_____

Accommodation Pupillary Reflex

Have your partner gaze for approximately 1 minute at a distant object in the lab—*not* toward the windows or another light source. Observe your partner's pupils. Then hold some printed material 6 to 10 inches from his or her face, and direct him or her to focus on it.

How does pupil size change as your partner focuses on the printed material?

_____

Explain the value of this reflex. _____

_____

_____

_____

Convergence Reflex

Repeat the previous experiment, this time using a pen or pencil as the close object to be focused on. Note the position of your partner's eyeballs both while he or she is gazing at the distant and at the close object. Do they change position as the object of focus is changed?

_____ In what way? _____

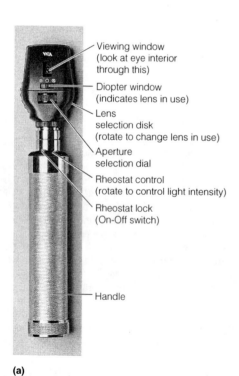

Viewing window (look at eye interior through this)

Diopter window (indicates lens in use)

Lens selection disk (rotate to change lens in use)

Aperture selection dial

Rheostat control (rotate to control light intensity)

Rheostat lock (On-Off switch)

Handle

(a)

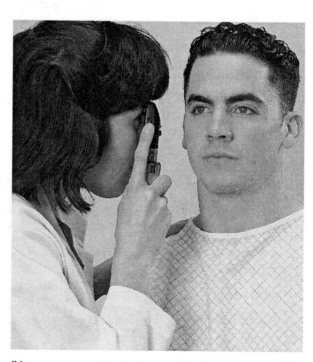

(b)

Figure 12 Structure and use of an ophthalmoscope. (a) Structure of an ophthalmoscope. **(b)** Proper position for examining the right eye with an ophthalmoscope.

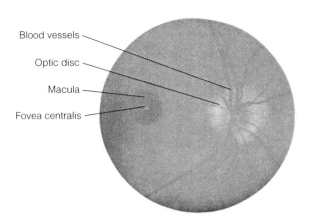

Blood vessels

Optic disc

Macula

Fovea centralis

Figure 13   Posterior portion of right retina.

Explain the importance of the convergence reflex.

＿＿＿＿＿＿＿＿＿＿＿＿＿＿＿＿＿＿＿

＿＿＿＿＿＿＿＿＿＿＿＿＿＿＿＿＿＿＿

＿＿＿＿＿＿＿＿＿＿＿＿＿＿＿＿＿ ∎

Ophthalmoscopic Examination of the Eye (Optional)

The ophthalmoscope is an instrument used to examine the *fundus,* or eyeball interior, to determine visually the condition of the retina, optic disc, and internal blood vessels. Certain pathologic conditions such as diabetes mellitus, arteriosclerosis, and degenerative changes of the optic nerve and retina can be detected by such an examination. The ophthalmoscope consists of a set of lenses mounted on a rotating disc (the **lens selection disc**), a light source regulated by a **rheostat control,** and a mirror that reflects the light so that the eye interior can be illuminated (Figure 12a).

The lens selection disc is positioned in a small slit in the mirror, and the examiner views the eye interior through this slit, appropriately called the **viewing window.** The focal length of each lens is indicated in diopters preceded by a + sign if the lens is convex and by a − sign if the lens is concave. When the zero (0) is seen in the **diopter window,** there is no lens positioned in the slit. The depth of focus for viewing the eye interior is changed by changing the lens.

The light is turned on by depressing the red **rheostat lock button** and then rotating the rheostat control in the clockwise direction. The aperture selection disc on the front of the instrument allows the nature of the light beam to be al-

tered. Generally, green light allows for clearest viewing of the blood vessels in the eye interior and is most comfortable for the subject.

Once you have examined the ophthalmoscope and have become familiar with it, you are ready to conduct an eye examination.

Activity:
Conducting an Ophthalmoscopic Examination

1. Conduct the examination in a dimly lit or darkened room with the subject comfortably seated and gazing straight ahead. To examine the right eye, sit face-to-face with the subject, hold the instrument in your right hand, and use your right eye to view the eye interior (Figure 12b). You may want to steady yourself by resting your left hand on the subject's head. To view the left eye, use your left eye, hold the instrument in your left hand, and steady yourself with your right hand.

2. Begin the examination with the 0 (no lens) in position. Grasp the instrument so that the lens disc may be rotated with the index finger. Holding the ophthalmoscope about 6 inches from the subject's eye, direct the light into the pupil at a slight angle—through the pupil edge rather than directly through its center. You will see a red circular area that is the illuminated eye interior.

3. Move in as close as possible to the subject's cornea (to within 2 in.) as you continue to observe the area. Steady your instrument-holding hand on the subject's cheek if necessary. If both your eye and that of the subject are normal, the fundus can be viewed clearly without further adjustment of the ophthalmoscope. If the fundus cannot be focused, slowly rotate the lens disc counterclockwise until the fundus can be clearly seen. When the ophthalmoscope is correctly set, the fundus of the right eye should appear as shown in Figure 13. (Note: If a positive [convex] lens is required and your eyes are normal, the subject has hyperopia. If a negative [concave] lens is necessary to view the fundus and your eyes are normal, the subject is myopic.)

When the examination is proceeding correctly, the subject can often see images of retinal vessels in his own eye that appear rather like cracked glass. If you are unable to achieve a sharp focus or to see the optic disc, move medially or laterally and begin again.

4. Examine the optic disc for color, elevation, and sharpness of outline, and observe the blood vessels radiating from near its center. Locate the macula, lateral to the optic disc. It is a darker area in which blood vessels are absent, and the fovea appears to be a slightly lighter area in its center. The macula is most easily seen when the subject looks directly into the light of the ophthalmoscope.

⚠ Do not examine the macula for longer than 1 second at a time.

5. When you have finished examining your partner's retina, shut off the ophthalmoscope. Change places with your partner (become the subject) and repeat steps 1–4. ∎

Illustrations: 1a and b: Wendy Hiller-Gee at BioMed Arts. 1c, 2–4, 10, and 11: Precision Graphics. 7–9: Shirley Bortoli.
Photographs: 5a and b: © Benjamin/Cummings Publishing Company. Photo by Stephen Spector, courtesy of Dr. Charles Thomas, Kansas University Medical Center. 6: © Elena Dorfman/Addison Wesley Longman. 12a and b: © Benjamin/Cummings Publishing Company. Photo by Richard Tauber. 13: © Don Wong, Science Source/Photo Researchers.

Special Senses: Vision

Anatomy of the Eye

1. Several accessory eye structures contribute to the formation of tears and/or aid in lubrication of the eyeball. Name three of these and then name the major secretory product of each. Indicate which has antibacterial properties by circling the correct secretory product. Students can choose any three of the following five answers.

Accessory structures	Product

2. The eyeball is wrapped in adipose tissue within the orbit. What is the function of the adipose tissue?

What seven bones form the bony orbit? (Think! If you can't remember, check a skull or your text.)

3. Why does one often have to blow one's nose after having a good cry? _____

4. Identify the extrinsic eye muscle predominantly responsible for the actions described below.

_____ 1. turns the eye laterally

_____ 2. turns the eye medially

_____ 3. turns the eye up and laterally

_____ 4. turns the eye inferiorly

_____ 5. turns the eye superiorly

_____ 6. turns the eye down and laterally

Review Sheet

5. What is a sty? _____

_____

Conjunctivitis? _____

6. Using the terms listed on the right, correctly identify all structures provided with leader lines in the diagram.

Blowup of photosensitive retina

Pigmented epithelium

a. anterior chamber

b. anterior segment containing aqueous humor

c. bipolar neurons

d. ciliary body and processes

e. ciliary muscle

f. choroid

g. cornea

h. dura mater

i. fovea centralis

j. ganglion cells

k. iris

l. lens

m. optic disc

n. optic nerve

o. photoreceptors

p. posterior chamber

q. retina

r. sclera

s. scleral venous sinus

t. suspensory ligaments

u. vitreous body in posterior segment

Notice the arrows drawn close to the left side of the iris in the diagram opposite. What do they indicate?

_____

_____

_____

7. Match the key responses with the descriptive statements that follow.

Key: a. aqueous humor   e. cornea   j. retina
        b. choroid   f. fovea centralis   k. sclera
        c. ciliary body   g. iris   l. scleral venous sinus
        d. ciliary processes of h. lens   m. suspensory ligament
            the ciliary body   i. optic disc   n. vitreous humor

_____ 1. attaches the lens to the ciliary body

_____ 2. fluid filling the anterior segment of the eye

_____ 3. the "white" of the eye

_____ 4. part of the retina that lacks photoreceptors

_____ 5. modification of the choroid that controls the shape of the crystalline lens

_____ 6. contains the ciliary muscle

_____ 7. drains the aqueous humor from the eye

_____ 8. tunic containing the rods and cones

_____ 9. substance occupying the posterior segment of the eyeball

_____ 10. forms the bulk of the heavily pigmented vascular tunic

_____, _____ 11. smooth muscle structures

_____ 12. area of critical focusing and discriminatory vision

_____ 13. form (by filtration) the aqueous humor

_____, _____, _____,

_____ 14. light-bending media of the eye

_____ 15. anterior continuation of the sclera—your "window on the world"

_____ 16. composed of tough, white, opaque, fibrous connective tissue

8. The iris is composed primarily of two smooth muscle layers, one arranged radially and the other circularly.

Which of these dilates the pupil? _____

9. You would expect the pupil to be dilated in which of the following circumstances? Circle the correct response(s).

a. in brightly lit surroundings   c. during focusing for near vision

b. in dimly lit surroundings   d. in observing distant objects

10. The intrinsic eye muscles are under the control of which of the following? (Circle the correct response.)

autonomic nervous system   somatic nervous system

Review Sheet

Microscopic Anatomy of the Retina

1. The two major layers of the retina are the epithelial and nervous layers. In the nervous layer, the neuron populations are arranged as follows from the epithelial layer to the vitreous humor. (Circle all proper responses.)

   bipolar cells, ganglion cells, photoreceptors   photoreceptors, ganglion cells, bipolar cells

   ganglion cells, bipolar cells, photoreceptors   photoreceptors, bipolar cells, ganglion cells

2. The axons of the _____ cells form the optic nerve, which exits from the eyeball.

3. Complete the following statements by writing either *rods* or *cones* on each blank:

   The dim light receptors are the _____. Only _____ are

   found in the fovea centralis, whereas mostly _____ are found in the periphery of the retina.

   _____ are the photoreceptors that operate best in bright light and allow for color vision.

Visual Pathways to the Brain

1. The visual pathway to the occipital lobe of the brain consists most simply of a chain of five neurons. Beginning with the photoreceptor cell of the retina, name them and note their location in the pathway.

   (1) _____   (4) _____

   (2) _____   (5) _____

   (3) _____   _____

2. Visual field tests are done to reveal destruction along the visual pathway from the retina to the optic region of the brain. Note where the lesion is likely to be in the following cases:

   Normal vision in left eye visual field; absence of vision in right eye visual field: _____

   Normal vision in both eyes for right half of the visual field; absence of vision in both eyes for left half of the visual

   field: _____

3. How is the right optic *tract* anatomically different from the right optic *nerve*? _____

   _____

   _____

   _____

Dissection of the Cow (Sheep) Eye

1. What modification of the choroid that is not present in humans is found in the cow eye? _____

   _____

   What is its function? _____

   _____

2. What is the anatomical appearance of the retina? _____

_____

At what point is it attached to the posterior aspect of the eyeball? _____

Visual Tests and Experiments

1. Match the terms in column B with the descriptions in column A:

Column A	Column B
_____ 1. light bending	a. accommodation
_____ 2. ability to focus for close (under 20 ft) vision	b. astigmatism
_____ 3. normal vision	c. convergence
_____ 4. inability to focus well on close objects (farsightedness)	d. emmetropia
_____ 5. nearsightedness	e. hyperopia
_____ 6. blurred vision due to unequal curvatures of the lens or cornea	f. myopia
_____ 7. medial movement of the eyes during focusing on close objects	g. refraction

2. Complete the following statements:

In farsightedness, the light is focused __1__ the retina. The lens required to treat myopia is a __2__ lens. The "near point" increases with age because the __3__ of the lens decreases as we get older. A convex lens, like that of the eye, produces an image that is upside down and reversed from left to right. Such an image is called a __4__ image.

1. _____

2. _____

3. _____

4. _____

3. Use terms from the key to complete the statements concerning near and distance vision.

Key: a. contracted   b. decreased   c. increased   d. relaxed   e. taut

During distance vision: The ciliary muscle is _____, the suspensory ligament is _____, the convexity of the lens

is _____, and light refraction is _____. During close vision: The ciliary muscle is _____, the suspensory ligament is

_____, lens convexity is _____, and light refraction is _____.

4. Explain why vision is lost when light hits the blind spot. _____

5. What is meant by the term *negative afterimage* and what does this phenomenon indicate? _____

_____

_____

_____

6. Record your Snellen eye test results below:

Left eye (without glasses) _____ (with glasses) _____

Right eye (without glasses) _____ (with glasses) _____

Is your visual acuity normal, less than normal, or better than normal? _____

Explain. _____

_____

Explain why each eye is tested separately when using the Snellen eye chart. _____

_____

Explain 20/40 vision. _____

_____

Explain 20/10 vision. _____

_____

7. Define *astigmatism:* _____

_____

How can it be corrected? _____

8. Record the distance of your near point of accommodation as tested in the laboratory:

right eye _____ left eye _____

Is your near point within the normal range for your age? _____

9. Define *presbyopia:* _____

_____

What causes it? _____

10. To which wavelengths of light do the three cone types of the retina respond maximally?

_____, _____, and _____

11. How can you explain the fact that we see a great range of colors even though only three cone types exist?

_____

_____

12. From what condition does color blindness result? _____

_____

13. Record the results of the demonstration of the relative positioning of rods and cones in the circle below (use appropriately colored pencils).

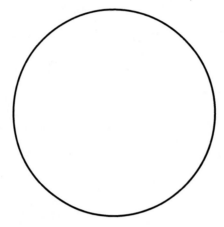

14. Explain the difference between binocular and panoramic vision. _____

_____

_____

_____

_____

What is the advantage of binocular vision? _____

What factor(s) are responsible for binocular vision? _____

_____

_____

15. In the experiment on the convergence reflex, what happened to the position of the eyeballs as the object was moved closer

to the subject's eyes? _____

What extrinsic eye muscles control the movement of the eyes during this reflex? _____

What is the value of this reflex? _____

_____

What would be the visual result of an inability of these muscles to function? _____

_____